# Texts in Computer Science

*Editors*
David Gries
Fred B. Schneider



For other titles published in this series, go to
http://www.springer.com/series/3191

Stefano Crespi Reghizzi

# Formal Languages and Compilation

Springer

Stefano Crespi Reghizzi
Politecnico di Milano
Italy
stefano.crespireghizzi@polimi.it

Series Editors:
David Gries
Department of Computer Science
415 Boyd Graduate Studies Research Center
The University of Georgia
Athens, GA 30602-7404, USA

Fred B. Schneider
Department of Computer Science
Upson Hall
Cornell University
Ithaca, NY 14853-7501, USA

ISBN 978-1-84882-049-4 e-ISBN 978-1-84882-050-0
DOI 10.1007/978-1-84882-050-0

British Library Cataloguing in Publication Data
A catalogue record for this book is available from the British Library

Library of Congress Control Number: 2008942386



Springer Science+Business Media
springer.com

**Reghizzi: Formal Languages and Compilation**



First Indian Reprint 2012

ISBN 978-81-322-0525-8



This edition is published by Springer (India) Private Limited, (a part of Springer Science+Business Media), Registered Office: 7th Floor, Vijaya Building, 17 Barakhamba Road, New Delhi – 110 001, India

Printed in India by Rashtriya Printers, Delhi.

# Preface

## State of books on compilers

The book collects and condenses the experience of years of teaching compiler courses and doing research on formal language theory, on compiler and language design, and to a lesser extent on natural language processing. In the turmoil of information technology developments, the subject of the book has kept the same fundamental principles over half a century, and its relevance for theory and practice is as important as in the early days.

This state of affairs of a topic, which is central to computer science and is based on consolidated principles, might lead us to believe that the accompanying textbooks are by now consolidated, much as the classical books on mathematics. In fact this is rather not true: there exist fine books on the mathematical aspects of language and automata theory, but the best books on translators are sort of encyclopaedias of algorithms, design methods, and practical know-how used in compiler design. Indeed a compiler is a microcosm, featuring a variety of aspects ranging from algorithmic wisdom to CPU and memory exploitation. As a consequence the textbooks have grown in size, and compete with respect to their coverage of the last developments on programming languages, processor architectures and clever mappings from the former to the latter.

## A basic textbook on compilation

To put things into order, in my opinion it is better to separate such complex topic into two parts, basic and advanced, which correspond with good approximation to the two subsystems of a compiler: the user language-specific front-end, and the machine language-specific back-end. The basic part is the subject of this book; it covers the principles and algorithms widely used for defining the syntax of languages and implementing simple translators. It does not include: the specific know-how needed for various classes of programming languages (imperative, functional, object oriented, etc.), the computer architecture-related aspects, and the optimization methods used to improve the machine code produced by the compiler.

In other textbooks the bias towards technological aspects, related to software and hardware architectures, has reduced the attention to the fundamental concepts of language specification and translation. This perhaps explains why such books do not exploit the improvements and simplifications made possible by decades of extensive use of syntax-directed methods, and still keep the irritating variants and repetitions, to be found in the historical papers which introduced the theory of translation. Moving from these premises, I decided to present in a simple minimalist way the essential principles and methods used in designing syntax-directed translators. Just a few examples: the coverage of the algorithms for processing regular expressions and finite automata is rather complete and condensed. The systematic discussion of ambiguous forms is intended to avoid pitfalls when designing grammars. The standard presentation of parsing algorithms has been improved, by unifying the concepts and notations used in different approaches, thus extending methods coverage with a reduced definitional apparatus. The concepts of syntactic translation are effectively linked to regular expressions, grammars and abstract automata, and pave the way to attribute grammars and syntax-directed translation. The book is not restricted to syntax. The sections on translation, semantic functions (attribute grammars), and static program analysis by data flow equations provide a more comprehensive understanding of the compilation process.

## Presentation

The text is illustrated by many small yet realistic and paradigmatic examples, to ease the understanding of the theory and the transfer to application. Many diagrams and figures enlighten the presentation. This book has been written by an engineer for future engineers and compiler or language designers: the choice of the theoretical properties is always driven by their utility and the conceptual economy they allow. Theoretical models of automata, transducers and formal grammars are extensively used, whenever practical motivation warrants. Formal properties are intuitively justified and illustrated by examples; proofs are outlined whenever possible, and reference is given to publications. Algorithms are described in a pseudo-code to avoid the disturbing details of a programming language, yet they are straightforward to convert to executable procedures. Links to further readings and published references are provided as footnotes.

## Intended audience

The main material can be taught in about 50 class hours to computer science or engineering students of the third year (graduate or upper division undergraduate), but of course cuts and selective specialization are possible. Actually the material is largely self-contained and is also suitable to self-learning. The first three chapters can be also used for introducing students (especially engineering ones) to the foundations of formal languages and automata, but other topics of theoretical computer science (such as computability and complexity) are not covered.

This book should be welcome by those willing to teach or to learn the essential concepts of syntax-directed compilation, without the need to rely on software tools and implementations. I believe that learning by doing is not always the best approach, and that early and excessive commitment to practical work may sometimes hinder the acquisition of the conceptual foundations. In the case of formal languages and data-flow analysis, the elegance and simplicity of the underlying theory allow students to acquire the fundamental paradigms of language structures, to avoid pitfalls such as ambiguity, and to adequately map structure to meaning. In this field, most relevant algorithms are simple enough to be practiced by paper and pencil. Of course, students should be encouraged to enroll in a parallel hands-on laboratory for experimenting syntax-directed methods and tools (like *flex* and *bison*) on realistic cases.

## Supplementary Web materials

Course slides and numerous problems with solutions (prepared by L. Breveglieri for the English language class) are available from the author Web site, hosted by Politecnico di Milano, http://www.dei.polimi.it/. Error indications and comments from readers are appreciated, and an errata-corrige will be setup on site.

## Aknowledgments

I remember and thank: Antonio Grasselli, who first fascinated me with a subject combining linguistic, mathematical and technological aspects; David Martin and Michel Melkanoff, my masters of "compilation" at UCLA; my colleagues Angelo Morzenti, Licia Sbattella, and especially Luca Breveglieri, for their critical revision; Alessandra Cherubini, Matteo Pradella, and Pierluigi San Pietro, research companions on formal languages and automata theory; my PhD students, former and present ones, and in particular, Giampaolo Agosta, Martino Sykora, and Simone Campanoni; ST Microelectronics, and especially Marco Cornero and Erven Rohou, for calling my attention to compilation technology for advanced microprocessors counteracting my theoretical drift.

*Stefano Crespi Reghizzi*
Milan, September 2008

# Contents

# Chapter 1
# Introduction

## 1.1 Intended Scope and Audience

The information technology revolution was made possible by the invention of electronic digital machines, but without programming languages their use would have been restricted to the few people able to write binary machine code. A programming language as a text contains features coming both from human languages and from mathematical logic. The translation from a programming language to machine code is known as *compilation*.[1] Language compilation is a very complex process, that would be impossible to master without systematic design methods. Such methods and their theoretical foundations are the argument of this book. They make up a consistent and largely consolidated body of concepts and algorithms, that are applied not just in compilers, but also in other fields. Automata theory is pervasively used in all branches of informatics to model situations or phenomena classifiable as time and space discrete systems. Formal grammars on the other hand originated in linguistic research and are widely applied in document processing in particular for the Web.

Coming to the prerequisites, the reader should have a good background in programming, but detailed knowledge of a specific programming language is not required, because our presentation of algorithms uses self-explanatory pseudo-code. The reader is expected to be familiar with basic mathematical theories and notations, namely set theory, algebra and logic. The above prerequisites are typically met by computer science/engineering or mathematic students with two or more years of university education.

The selection of topics and the presentation based on rigorous definitions and algorithms illustrated by many motivating examples should qualify the book for a university course, aiming to expose students to the importance of

[1] This term may sound strange; it originates in the early approach to the compilation of tables of correspondence between a command in the language and a series of machine operations.

good theories and of efficient algorithms for designing effective systems. In our experience about 50 hours of lecture suffice to cover the entire book.

The author's long experience in teaching the subject to different audiences, brings out the importance of combining theoretical concepts and examples. Moreover it is advisable that the students take advantage of well-known and documented software tools (such as classical *flex* and *bison*), to implement and experiment the main algorithm on realistic case studies.

With regard to the reach and limits, the book covers the essential concepts and methods needed to design simple translators based on the syntax-directed paradigm. It goes without saying that a real compiler for a programming language includes other technological aspects and know-how, in particular related to processor and computer architecture, which are not covered. Such know-how is essential for automatically translating a program to machine instructions and for transforming a program in order to make the best use of computational resources of a computer. The study of program transformation and optimization methods is a more advanced topic which follows the present introduction to compiler methods. The next section outlines the contents of the book.

## 1.2 Compiler Parts and Corresponding Concepts

There are two external interfaces to a compiler: the source language to be analyzed and translated, and the target language produced by the translator.

Chapter 2 describes the so-called syntactic methods that are generally adopted in order to provide a rigorous definition of the texts (or character strings) written in the source language. The methods to be presented are regular expressions, and context-free grammars. Both belong to formal language theory, a well-established chapter of theoretical computer science.

The first task of a compiler is to check the correctness of the source text, that is whether it complies with the syntactic definition of the source language by certain grammar rules. In order to perform the check, the algorithm scans the source text character by character and at the end it rejects or accepts the input depending on the result of the analysis. By a minimalist approach, such recognition algorithms can be conveniently described as mathematical machines or automata, in the tradition of the well-known Turing machine.

Chapter 3 covers finite automata, which are machines with a finite random access memory. They are the recognizers of the languages defined by regular expressions. Within compilation they are used for lexical analysis or scanning, to extract from the source text keywords, numbers, and in general the pieces of text corresponding to the lexical units or lexemes of the language.

Chapters 4 and 5 are devoted to the recognition problem for languages defined by context-free grammars. Recognition algorithms are first modelled as finite automata equipped with unbounded last-in-first-out memory or pushdown stack. For a compiler, the language recognizer is an essential component known as the syntax analyzer or parser. Its job is to check the syntactic correctness of a source text already subdivided into lexemes, and to construct a structural representation called a syntax tree.

The ultimate job of a compiler is to translate a source text to another language. The module responsible for completing the verification of the source language rules and for producing the translation is called the semantic analyzer. It operates on the structural representation produced by the parser.

The formal models of translation and the methods used to implement semantic analyzers are in Chapter 6, which describes two kinds of transformations. Pure syntactic translations are modelled by finite or pushdown transducers. Semantic translations are performed by functions or methods that operate on the syntax tree of the source text. Such translations will be specified by a practical extension to context-free grammars called attribute grammars. This approach, by combining the accuracy of formal syntax and the flexibility of programming, conveniently expresses analysis and translation of syntax trees.

To give a concrete idea of compilation, typical simple examples are included: the type consistency check between variables declared and used in a programming language, the translation of high-level statements to machine instructions, and semantic-directed parsing.

For sure compilers do much more than syntax-directed translation. Static program analysis is an important example, consisting in examining a program to determine, ahead of execution, some properties, or to detect errors not covered by semantic analysis. The purpose is to improve the robustness, reliability, and efficiency of the program. An example of error detection is the identification of uninitialized variables. For code improvement, an example is the elimination of useless assignment statements.

Chapter 6 terminates with an introduction to the static analysis of programs modelled by their flow graph, viewed as a finite automaton. Several interesting problems can be formalized and statically analyzed by a common approach based on flow equations, and their solution by iterative approximations converging to the least fixed point.

# Chapter 2
# Syntax

## 2.1 Introduction

### 2.1.1 *Artificial and Formal Languages*

Many centuries after the spontaneous emergence of natural language for human communication, mankind has purposively constructed other communication systems and languages, to be called artificial, intended for very specific tasks. A few artificial languages, like the logical propositions of Aristotle or the music sheet notation of Guittone d'Arezzo, are very ancient, but their number has exploded with the invention of computers. Many of them are intended for man-machine communication, to instruct a programmable machine to do some task: to perform a computation, to prepare a document, to search a database, to control a robot, and so on. Other languages serve as interfaces between devices, e.g.,, Postscript is a language produced by a text processor commanding a printer.

Any designed language is artificial by definition, but not all artificial languages are formalized: thus a programming language like Java is formalized, but Esperanto, although designed by man, is not.

For a language to be formalized (or formal), the form of sentences (or syntax) and their meaning (or semantics) must be precisely and algorithmically defined. In other words, it should be possible for a computer to check that sentences are grammatically correct, and to determine their meaning.

Meaning is a difficult and controversial notion. For our purposes, the meaning of a sentence can be taken to be the translation to another language which is known to the computer or the operator. For instance, the meaning of a Java program is its translation to the machine language of the computer executing the program.

In this book the term *formal language* is used in a narrower sense that excludes semantics. In the field of syntax, a formal language is a mathematical structure, defined on top of an alphabet, by means of certain axiomatic rules (formal grammar) or by using abstract machines such as the famous one due to A. Turing. The notions and methods of formal language are analogous to those used in number theory and in logic.

Thus formal language theory is only concerned with the form or syntax of sentences, not with meaning. A string (or text) is either valid or illegal, that is, it either belongs to the formal language or does not. Such theory makes a first important step towards the ultimate goal: the study of language translation and meaning, which will require additional methods.

### *2.1.2 Language Types*

A language in this book is a one-dimensional communication medium, made by sequences of symbolic elements of an alphabet, called terminal characters. Actually people often refer to language as other not textual communication media, which are more or less formalized by means of rules. Thus iconic languages focus on road traffic signs or video display icons. Musical language is concerned with sounds, rhythm, and harmony. Architects and designers of buildings and objects are interested in their spatial relations, which they describe as the language of design. Early child drawings are often considered as sentences of a pictorial language, which can be partially formalized in accordance with psychological theories. The formal approach to the syntax of this chapter has some interest for nontextual languages too.

Within computer science, the term language applies to a text made by a set of characters orderly written from, say, left to right. In addition the term is used to refer to other discrete structures, such as graphs, trees, or arrays of pixels describing a discrete picture. Formal language theories have been proposed and used to various degrees also for such nontextual languages[1].

Reverting to the main stream of textual languages, a frequent request directed to the specialist is to define and specify an artificial language. The specification may have several uses: as a language reference manual for future users, as an official standard definition, or as a contractual document for compiler designers to ensure consistency of specification and implementation.

It is not an easy task to write a complete and rigorous definition of a language. Clearly the exhaustive approach, to list all possible sentences or phrases, is unfeasible because the possibilities are infinite, since the length of sentences is usually unbounded. As a native language speaker, a programmer is not constrained by any strict limit on the length of phrases to be written. The problem to represent an infinite number of cases by a finite description can be addressed by an enumeration procedure, as in logic. When executed, the procedure generates longer and longer sentences, in an unending process if the language to be modelled is not finite.

---

[1] Just two examples and references: tree languages [21] and picture (or two dimensional) languages [23, 15].

This chapter presents a simple and established manner to express the rules of the enumeration procedure in the form of rules of a generative grammar (or syntax).

### 2.1.3 Chapter Outline

The chapter starts with the basic components of language theory: alphabet, string, and operations, such as concatenation and repetition, on strings and sets of strings.
The definition of the family of regular languages comes next.
Then the lists are introduced as a fundamental and pervasive syntax structure in all kinds of languages. From the exemplification of list variants, the idea of linguistic abstraction grows out naturally. This is a powerful reasoning tool to reduce the varieties of existing languages to a few paradigms.
After discussing the limits of regular languages, the chapter moves to context-free grammars. After the basic definitions the presentation focuses on structural properties, namely, equivalence, ambiguity, and recursion.
Exemplification continues with important linguistic paradigms such as: hierarchical lists, parenthesized structures, polish notations, and operator precedence expressions. Their combination produces the variety of forms to be found in artificial languages.
Then the classification of some common forms of ambiguity and corresponding remedies is offered as a practical guide for grammar designers.
Various transformations of rules (normal forms) are introduced, which should familiarize the reader with the modifications often needed for technical applications, to adjust a grammar without affecting the language it defines.
Returning to regular languages from the grammar perspective, the chapter evidences the greater descriptive capacity of context-free grammars.
The comparison of regular and context-free languages continues by considering the operations that may cause a language to exit or remain in one or the other family. Alphabetical transformations anticipate the operations studied in Chapter 6 as translations.
A discussion of unavoidable regularities found in very long strings, completes the theoretical picture.
The last section mentions the Chomsky classification of grammar types and exemplifies context-sensitive grammars, stressing the difficulty of this rarely used model.

## 2.2 Formal Language Theory

Formal language theory starts from the elementary notions of alphabet, string operations, and aggregate operations on sets of strings. By such operations complex languages can be obtained starting from simpler ones.

### *2.2.1 Alphabet and Language*

An *alphabet* is a finite set of elements called *terminal symbols* or *characters*. Let $\Sigma = \{a_1, a_2, \ldots, a_k\}$ be an alphabet with $k$ elements, i.e., its *cardinality* is $|\Sigma| = k$. A *string* (also called a *word*) is a sequence (i.e., an ordered set possibly with repetitions) of characters.

*Example 2.1.* Let $\Sigma = \{a, b\}$ be the alphabet. Some strings are: $aaba$, $aaa$, $abaa$, $b$.

A *language* is a set of strings on a specified alphabet.

*Example 2.2.* For the same alphabet $\Sigma = \{a, b\}$ three examples of languages follow:

$$L_1 = \{aa, aaa\}$$
$$L_2 = \{aba, aab\}$$
$$L_3 = \{ab, ba, aabb, abab, \ldots, aaabbb, \ldots\} = \text{set of strings having as many } a\text{'s as } b\text{'s}$$

Notice that a formal language viewed as a set has two layers: at the first level there is an unordered set of nonelementary elements, the strings. At the second level, each string is an ordered set of atomic elements, the terminal characters.

Given a language, a string belonging to it is called a *sentence* or *phrase*. Thus $bbaa \in L_3$ is a sentence of $L_3$, whereas $abb \notin L_3$ is an *incorrect* string.

The *cardinality* or size of a language is the number of sentences it contains. For instance, $|L_2| = |\{aba, aab\}| = 2$. If the cardinality is finite, the language is called *finite*, too. Otherwise, there is no finite bound on the number of sentences, and the language is termed *infinite*. To illustrate, $L_1$ and $L_2$ are finite, but $L_3$ is infinite.

One can observe a finite language is essentially a collection of words[2] sometimes called a *vocabulary*. A special finite language is the *empty* set or *language* $\emptyset$, which contains no sentence, $|\emptyset| = 0$. Usually, when a language contains just one element, the set braces are omitted writing e.g., $abb$ instead of $\{abb\}$.

---

[2] In mathematical writings the terms *word* and *string* are synonymous, in linguistics a word is a string having a meaning.

It is convenient to introduce the notation $|x|_b$ for the number of characters $b$ present in a string $x$. For instance:

$$|aab|_a = 2, \qquad |aba|_a = 2, \qquad |baa|_c = 0$$

The *length* $|x|$ of a string $x$ is the number of characters it contains, e.g.: $|ab| = 2$; $|abaa| = 4$.

Two strings

$$x = a_1 a_2 \ldots a_h \ , \quad y = b_1 b_2 \ldots b_k$$

are *equal* if $h = k$ and $a_i = b_i$, for every $i = 1, \ldots, h$. In words, examining the strings from left to right their respective characters coincide. Thus we obtain:

$$aba \neq baa, \qquad baa \neq ba$$

## String Operations

In order to manipulate strings it is convenient to introduce several operations. For strings

$$x = a_1 a_2 \ldots a_h \qquad y = b_1 b_2 \ldots b_k$$

*concatenation*[3] is defined as

$$x.y = a_1 a_2 \ldots a_h b_1 b_2 \ldots b_k$$

The dot may be dropped, writing $xy$ in place of $x.y$. This essential operation for formal languages plays the role addition has in number theory.

*Example 2.3.* For strings

$$x = \text{well} \ , \quad y = \text{in} \ , \quad z = \text{formed}$$

we obtain

$$xy = \text{wellin} \ , \quad yx = \text{inwell} \neq xy$$

$$(xy)z = \text{wellin.formed} = x(yz) = \text{well.informed} = \text{wellinformed}$$

Concatenation is clearly non-commutative, that is, the identity $xy \neq yx$ does not hold in general. The *associative* property holds:

$$(xy)z = x(yz)$$

This permits to write without parentheses the concatenation of three or more strings. The length of the result is the sum of the lengths of the concatenated strings:

$$|xy| = |x| + |y| \tag{2.1}$$

---

[3] Also termed *product* in mathematical works.

## Empty string

It is useful to introduce the concept of *empty* (or null) *string*, denoted by Greek epsilon $\varepsilon$, as the only string satisfying the identity

$$x\varepsilon = \varepsilon x = x$$

for every string $x$. From equality 2.1 it follows the empty string has length zero:

$$| \varepsilon | = 0$$

From an algebraic perspective, the empty string is the neutral element with respect to concatenation, because any string is unaffected by concatenating $\varepsilon$ to the left or right.
The empty string should not be confused with the empty set: in fact $\emptyset$ as a language contains no string, whereas the set $\{\varepsilon\}$ contains one, the empty string.

## Substrings

Let $x = uyv$ be the concatenation of some, possibly empty, strings $u, y, v$. Then $y$ is a *substring* of $x$; moreover, $u$ is a *prefix* of $x$, and $v$ is a *suffix* of $x$. A substring (prefix, suffix) is called *proper* if it does not coincide with string $x$.

Let $x$ be a string of length at least $k$, $|x| \geqslant k \geqslant 1$. The notation $Ini_k(x)$ denotes the prefix $u$ of $x$ having length $k$, to be termed the *initial* of length $k$.

*Example 2.4.* The string $x = aabacba$ contains the following components:

prefixes: $a, aa, aab, aaba, aabac, aabacb, aabacba$
suffixes: $a, ba, cba, acba, bacba, abacba, aabacba$
substrings: all prefixes and suffixes and the internal strings such as $a, ab, ba, bacb, \ldots$

Notice that $bc$ is not a substring of $x$, although both $b$ and $c$ occur in $x$. The initial of length two is $Ini_2(aabacba) = aa$.

## Mirror reflection

The characters of a string are usually read from left to right, but it is sometimes requested to reverse the order. The *reflection* of a string $x = a_1 a_2 ... a_h$ is the string $x^R = a_h a_{h-1} \ldots a_1$. For instance, it is

$$x = \text{roma} \qquad x^R = \text{amor}$$

The following identities are immediate:

$$(x^R)^R = x \qquad (xy)^R = y^R x^R \qquad \varepsilon^R = \varepsilon$$

**Repetitions**

When a string contains repetitions it is handy to have an operator denoting them. The *m-th power* ($m \geqslant 1$, integer) of a string $x$ is the concatenation of $x$ with itself $m - 1$ times:

$$x^m = \underbrace{xx \dots x}_{m \text{ times}}$$

By stipulation the zero power of any string is defined to be the empty string.

The complete definition is

$$\begin{cases} x^m = x^{m-1}x \,, \; m > 0 \\ x^0 = \varepsilon \end{cases}$$

Examples:

$$\begin{array}{llll} x = ab & x^0 = \varepsilon & x^1 = x = ab & x^2 = (ab)^2 = abab \\ y = a^2 = aa & y^3 = a^2a^2a^2 = a^6 & & \\ \varepsilon^0 = \varepsilon & \varepsilon^2 = \varepsilon & & \end{array}$$

When writing formulas, the string to be repeated must be parenthesized, if longer than one. Thus to express the 2nd power of $ab$, i.e., $abab$, one should write $(ab)^2$, not $ab^2$, which is the string $abb$.

Expressed differently, we assume the power operation takes *precedence* over concatenation. Similarly reflection takes precedence over concatenation: e.g., $ab^R$ returns $ab$, since $b^R = b$, while $(ab)^R = ba$.

### 2.2.2 Language Operations

It is straightforward to extend an operation, originally defined on strings, to an entire language: just apply the operation to all the sentences. By means of this general principle, previously defined string operations can be revisited, starting from those having one argument.

The reflection of a language $L$ is the set of strings that are the reflection of a sentence:

$$L^R = \{x \mid \underbrace{x = y^R \wedge y \in L}_{\text{characteristic predicate}} \}$$

Here the strings $x$ are specified by the property expressed in the so-called characteristic predicate.

Similarly the set of proper prefixes of a language $L$ is

$$\text{Prefixes}(L) = \{y \mid x = yz \wedge x \in L \wedge y \neq \varepsilon \wedge z \neq \varepsilon\}$$

*Example 2.5.* Prefix-free language
In some applications the loss of one or more final characters of a language sentence is required to produce an incorrect string. The motivation is that the compiler is then able to detect inadvertent truncation of a sentence.
A language is *prefix-free* if none of the proper prefixes of sentences is in the language; i.e., if the set Prefixes($L$) is disjoint from $L$.
Thus the language $L_1 = \{x \mid x = a^n b^n \wedge n \geqslant 1\}$ is prefix-free since every prefix takes the form $a^n b^m, n > m \geqslant 0$ and does not satisfy the characteristic predicate.

On the other hand, the language $L_2 = \{a^m b^n \mid m > n \geqslant 1\}$ contains $a^3 b^2$ as well as its prefix $a^3 b$.

Similarly, operations on two strings can be extended to two languages, by letting the first and second argument span the respective language, for instance *concatenation* of languages $L'$ and $L''$ is defined as

$$L'L'' = \{xy \mid x \in L' \wedge y \in L''\}$$

From this the extension of the $m$-th *power* operation on a language is straightforward:

$$L^m = L^{m-1}L\,,\ m > 0$$
$$L^0 = \{\varepsilon\}$$

Some special cases follow from previous definitions:

$$\emptyset^0 = \{\varepsilon\}$$
$$L.\emptyset = \emptyset.L = \emptyset$$
$$L.\{\varepsilon\} = \{\varepsilon\}.L = L$$

*Example 2.6.* Consider the languages

$$L_1 = \{a^i \mid i \geqslant 0, \text{even}\} = \{\varepsilon, aa, aaaa, \ldots\}$$

$$L_2 = \{b^j a \mid j \geqslant 1, \text{odd}\} = \{ba, bbba, \ldots\}$$

We obtain

$$L_1 L_2 = \{a^i.b^j a \mid (i \geqslant 0,\ \text{even}) \wedge (j \geqslant 1,\ \text{odd})\}$$
$$= \{\varepsilon ba, a^2 ba, a^4 ba, \ldots, \varepsilon b^3 a, a^2 b^3 a, a^4 b^3 a, \ldots\}$$

A common error when computing the power is to take $m$ times the *same* string. The result is a different set, included in the power:

$$\{x \mid x = y^m \wedge y \in L\} \subseteq L^m, \qquad m \geqslant 2$$

Thus for $L = \{a, b\}$ with $m = 2$ the left part is $\{aa, bb\}$ and the right part is $\{aa, ab, ba, bb\}$.

*Example 2.7.* Strings of finite length
The power operation allows a concise definition of the strings of length not exceeding some integer $k$. Consider the alphabet $\Sigma = \{a, b\}$. For $k = 3$ the language

$$\begin{aligned} L &= \{\varepsilon, a, b, aa, ab, ba, bb, aaa, aab, aba, abb, baa, bab, bba, bbb\} \\ &= \Sigma^0 \cup \Sigma^1 \cup \Sigma^2 \cup \Sigma^3 \end{aligned}$$

may also be defined as

$$L = \{\varepsilon, a, b\}^3$$

Notice that sentences shorter than $k$ are obtained using the empty string of the base language.
Slightly changing the example, the language $\{x \mid 1 \leqslant |x| \leqslant 3\}$ is defined, using concatenation and power, by the formula

$$L = \{a, b\}\{\varepsilon, a, b\}^2$$

### 2.2.3 Set Operations

Since a language is a set, the classical set operations, union ($\cup$), intersection ($\cap$), and difference ($\setminus$), apply to languages; set relations, inclusion ($\subseteq$), strict inclusion ($\subset$), and equality ($=$) apply as well.
Before introducing the complement of a language, the notion of *universal language* is needed: it is defined as the set of all strings of alphabet $\Sigma$, of any length, including zero.
Clearly the universal language is infinite and can be viewed as the union of all the powers of the alphabet:

$$L_{\text{universal}} = \Sigma^0 \cup \Sigma \cup \Sigma^2 \cup \ldots$$

The *complement* of a language $L$ of alphabet $\Sigma$, denoted by $\neg L$, is the set difference

$$\neg L = L_{\text{universal}} \setminus L$$

that is, the set of the strings of alphabet $\Sigma$ that are not in $L$. When the alphabet is understood, the universal language can be expressed as the complement of the empty language:

$$L_{\text{universal}} = \neg\emptyset$$

*Example 2.8.* The complement of a finite language is always infinite, for instance the set of strings of any length except two is

$$\neg(\{a,b\}^2) = \varepsilon \cup \{a,b\} \cup \{a,b\}^3 \cup \ldots$$

On the other hand, the complement of an infinite language may or may not be finite, as shown on one side by the complement of the universal language, on the other side by the complement of the set of even length strings with alphabet $\{a\}$:

$$L = \{a^{2n} \mid n \geqslant 0\} \qquad \neg L = \{a^{2n+1} \mid n \geqslant 0\}$$

Moving to set difference, consider alphabet $\Sigma = \{a, b, c\}$ and languages

$$L_1 = \{x \mid \quad |x|_a = |x|_b = |x|_c \geqslant 0\}$$

$$L_2 = \{x \mid \quad |x|_a = |x|_b \wedge |x|_c = 1\}$$

Then the differences are,

$$L_1 \setminus L_2 = \varepsilon \cup \{x \mid \quad |x|_a = |x|_b = |x|_c \geqslant 2\}$$

which represents the set of strings having the same number, excluding 1, of occurrences of letters $a, b, c$;

$$L_2 \setminus L_1 = \{x \mid \quad |x|_a = |x|_b \neq |x|_c = 1\}$$

the set of strings having one $c$ and the same number of occurrences of $a, b$, excluding 1.

### 2.2.4 Star and Cross

Most artificial and natural languages include sentences that can be lengthened at will, causing the number of sentences in the language to be unbounded. On the other hand, all the operations so far defined, with the exception of complement, do not allow to write a finite formula denoting an infinite language. In order to enable the definition of an infinite language, the next essential development extends the power operation to the limit.
The *star*[4] operation is defined as the union of all the powers of the base language:

$$L^* = \bigcup_{h=0\ldots\infty} L^h = L^0 \cup L^1 \cup L^2 \cup \ldots = \varepsilon \cup L \cup L^2 \cup \ldots$$

[4] Also known as Kleene's star and as closure by concatenation.

*Example 2.9.* For $L = \{ab, ba\}$

$$L^* = \{\varepsilon, ab, ba, abab, abba, baab, baba, ...\}$$

Every string of the star can be segmented into substrings which are sentences of the base language $L$.

Notice that starting with a finite base language, $L$, the "starred" language $L^*$ is infinite.

It may happen that the starred and base language are identical as in

$$L = \{a^{2n} \mid n \geqslant 0\} \qquad L^* = \{a^{2n} \mid n \geqslant 0\} \equiv L$$

An interesting special case is when the base is an alphabet $\Sigma$, then the star $\Sigma^*$ contains all the strings[5] obtained by concatenating terminal characters. This language is the same as the previous *universal language* of alphabet $\Sigma$.[6]

It is clear that any formal language is a subset of the universal language of the same alphabet; the relation

$$L \subseteq \Sigma^*$$

is often written to say that $L$ is a language of alphabet $\Sigma$.

Some useful properties of star:

$$\begin{array}{ll} L \subseteq L^* & \text{(monotonicity)} \\ \text{if } (x \in L^* \wedge y \in L^*) \text{ then } xy \in L^* & \text{(closure by concatenation)} \\ (L^*)^* = L^* & \text{(idempotence)} \\ (L^*)^R = (L^R)^* & \text{(commutativity of star and reflection)} \end{array}$$

*Example 2.10.* Idempotence

The monotonicity property affirms any language is included in its star. But for language $L_1 = \{a^{2n} \mid n \geqslant 0\}$ the equality ${L_1}^* = L_1$ follows from the idempotence property and the fact that $L_1$ can be equivalently defined by the starred formula $\{aa\}^*$.

For the empty language and empty string we have the identities

$$\emptyset^* = \{\varepsilon\} \qquad \{\varepsilon\}^* = \{\varepsilon\}$$

---

5 The length of a sentence in $\Sigma^*$ is unbounded but it may not be considered to be infinite. A specialized branch of this theory (see Perrin and Pin [41]) is devoted to so-called infinitary or omega-languages, which include also sentences of infinite length. They effectively model the situations when an eternal system can receive or produce messages of infinite length.

6 Another name for it is *free monoid*. In algebra a monoid is a structure provided with an associative composition law (concatenation) and a neutral element (empty string).

*Example 2.11.* Identifiers
Many artificial languages assign a name or identifier to each entity (variable, file, document, subprogram, object, etc.). A usual naming rule prescribes that an identifier should be a string with initial character in $\{A, B, \ldots, Z\}$ and containing any number of letters or digits $\{0, 1, \ldots, 9\}$, such as CICLO3A2. Using the alphabets

$$\Sigma_A = \{A, B, \ldots, Z\}, \qquad \Sigma_N = \{0, 1, \ldots, 9\}$$

the language of identifiers $I \subseteq (\Sigma_A \cup \Sigma_N)^*$ is

$$I = \Sigma_A(\Sigma_A \cup \Sigma_N)^*$$

To introduce a variance, prescribe that the length of identifiers should not exceed 5. Defining $\Sigma = \Sigma_A \cup \Sigma_N$, the language is

$$I_5 = \Sigma_A(\Sigma^0 \cup \Sigma^1 \cup \Sigma^2 \cup \Sigma^3 \cup \Sigma^4) = \Sigma_A(\varepsilon \cup \Sigma \cup \Sigma^2 \cup \Sigma^3 \cup \Sigma^4)$$

The formula expresses concatenation of language $\Sigma_A$, whose sentences are single characters, with the language constructed as the union of powers. A more elegant writing is

$$I_5 = \Sigma_A(\varepsilon \cup \Sigma)^4$$

Cross

A useful though dispensable operator, derived from star, is the *cross*[7]

$$L^+ = \bigcup_{h=1\ldots\infty} L^h = L \cup L^2 \cup \ldots$$

It differs from the star because the union is taken excluding power zero. The following relations hold:

$$L^+ \subseteq L^*$$
$$\varepsilon \in L^+ \text{ if and only if } \varepsilon \in L$$
$$L^+ = LL^* = L^*L$$

*Example 2.12.*

$$\{ab, bb\}^+ = \{ab, b^2, ab^3, b^2ab, abab, b^4, \ldots\}$$

$$\{\varepsilon, aa\}^+ = \{\varepsilon, a^2, a^4, \ldots\} = \{a^{2n} \mid n \geqslant 0\}$$

Not surprisingly a language can usually be defined by various formulas, that differ by their use of operators.

[7] Or nonreflective closure by concatenation.

*Example 2.13.* The strings four or more characters long may be defined by

- concatenating the strings of length four with arbitrary strings: $\Sigma^4\Sigma^*$;
- or by constructing the th power of the set of nonempty strings: $(\Sigma^+)^4$.

### 2.2.5 *Quotient*

Operations like concatenation, star, or union lengthen the strings or increase the cardinality of the set of strings they operate upon. Given two languages, the *(right) quotient* operation shortens the sentences of the first language by cutting a suffix, which is a sentence of the second language. The (right) quotient of $L'$ with respect to $L''$ is defined as

$$L = L'/_R\, L'' = \{y \mid \exists y, z \text{ such that } yz \in L' \wedge z \in L''\}$$

*Example 2.14.* Let

$$L' = \{a^{2n}b^{2n} \mid n > 0\}\,, \qquad L'' = \{b^{2n+1} \mid n \geqslant 0\}$$

The quotients are

$$L'/_R\, L'' = \{a^r b^s \mid (r \geqslant 2, \text{ even }) \wedge (1 \leqslant s < r, s \text{ odd })\} = \{a^2b, a^4b, a^4b^3, ....\}$$

$$L''/_R\, L' = \emptyset$$

A dual operation is the *left quotient* $L''/_L\ L'$ that shortens the sentences of the first language by cutting a prefix which is a sentence of the second language.

Other operations will be introduced later, in order to transform or translate a formal language by replacing the terminal characters with other characters or strings.

## 2.3 Regular Expressions and Languages

Theoretical investigation on formal languages has invented various categories of languages, in a way reminiscent of the classification of numerical domains introduced much earlier by number theory. Such categories are characterized by mathematical and algorithmic properties.

The first family of formal languages is called *regular* (or rational) and can be defined by an astonishing number of different approaches. Regular languages have been independently discovered in disparate scientific fields: the study of input signals driving a sequential circuit[8] to a certain state, the

[8] A digital component incorporating a memory.

lexicon of programming languages modelled by simple grammar rules, and the simplified analysis of neural behavior. Later such approaches have been complemented by a logical definition based on a restricted form of predicates.

To introduce the family, the first definition will be algebraic, using the union, concatenation, and star operations; then the family will be defined by certain simple grammar rules; last, Chapter 3 describes the algorithm for recognizing regular languages in the form of an abstract machine or automaton[9].

### 2.3.1 Definition of Regular Expression

A language of alphabet $\Sigma = \{a_1, a_2, \ldots, a_n\}$ is *regular* if it can be expressed by applying a finite number of times the operations of concatenation, union, and star, starting with the unitary languages[10] $\{a_1\}, \{a_2\}, \ldots, \{a_n\}$ or the empty language $\emptyset$.

More precisely a *regular expression* (r.e.) is a string $r$ containing the terminal characters of alphabet $\Sigma$ and the metasymbols[11]

. concatenation  $\cup$ union  $*$ star  $\emptyset$ empty set  ( )

in accordance with the following rules:

| | | |
|---|---|---|
| 1. $r = \emptyset$ | 3. $r = (s \cup t)$ | 5. $r = (s)^*$ |
| 2. $r = a, a \in \Sigma$ | 4. $r = (s.t)$ or $r = (st)$ | |

where $s$ and $t$ are r.e.

Parentheses may often be dropped by imposing the following precedence when applying operators: first star, then concatenation, and last union.

For improving expressivity, the symbols $\varepsilon$ (empty string) and cross may be used in an r.e., since they are derived from the three basic operations by the identities $\varepsilon = \emptyset^*$ and $s^+ = s(s)^*$.

It is customary to write the union cup '$\cup$' symbol as a vertical slash '|', called *alternative.*

Rules 1. to 5. compose the syntax of r.e., to be formalized later by means of a grammar (example 2.31, p. 32).

The meaning or denotation of an r.e. $r$ is a language $L_r$ over alphabet $\Sigma$, defined by the correspondence in Table 2.3.1.

---

9 The language family can also be defined by the form of the logical predicates characterizing language sentences, as e.g., in [52].

10 A unitary language contains one sentence.

11 In order to prevent confusion between terminals and metasymbols, the latter should not be in the alphabet. If not, metasymbols must be suitably recoded to make them distinguishable.

**Table 2.1** Language denoted by a regular expression.

| | *expression* $r$ | *language* $L_r$ |
|---|---|---|
| 1. | $\varepsilon$ | $\{\varepsilon\}$ |
| 2. | $a \in \Sigma$ | $\{a\}$ |
| 3. | $s \cup t$ or also $s \mid t$ | $L_s \cup L_t$ |
| 4. | $s.t$ or also $st$ | $L_s.L_t$ |
| 5. | $s^*$ | $L_s^*$ |

*Example 2.15.* Let $\Sigma = \{1\}$, where 1 may be viewed as a pulse or signal. The language denoted by expression

$$e = (111)^*$$

contains the sequences multiple of three

$$L_e = \{1^n \mid n \bmod 3 = 0\}$$

Notice that dropping the parentheses the language changes, due to the precedence of star over concatenation:

$$e_1 = 111^* = 11(1)^* \qquad L_{e_1} = \{1^n \mid n \geqslant 2\}$$

*Example 2.16.* Integers
Let $\Sigma = \{+, -, d\}$ where $d$ denotes any decimal digit $0, 1, \ldots, 9$. The expression

$$e = (+ \cup - \cup \varepsilon)dd^* \equiv (+ \mid - \mid \varepsilon)dd^*$$

produces the language

$$L_e = \{+, -, \varepsilon\}\{d\}\{d\}^*$$

of integers with or without a sign, such as $+353, -5, 969, +001$.

Actually the correspondence between r.e. and denoted language is so direct that it is customary to refer to the language $L_e$ by the r.e. $e$ itself.

A language is *regular* if it is denoted by a regular expression. The collection of all regular languages is called the *family REG* of *regular* languages.

Another simple family of languages is the collection of all *finite languages*, *FIN*. A language is in *FIN* if its cardinality is finite, as for instance the language of 32-bit binary numbers.

Comparing the *REG* and *FIN* families, it is easy to see that every finite language is regular, $FIN \subseteq REG$. In fact, a finite language is the union of finitely many strings $x_1, x_2, \ldots, x_k$, each one being the concatenation of finitely many characters, $x_i = a_1 a_2 \ldots a_{n_i}$. The structure of the r.e. producing a finite language is then a union of $k$ terms, made by concatenation of $n_i$

characters. But $REG$ includes nonfinite languages too, thus proving strict inclusion of the families, $FIN \subset REG$.

More language families will be introduced and compared with $REG$ later.

### 2.3.2 Derivation and Language

We formalize the mechanism by which an r.e. produces a string of the language. Supposing for now the given r.e. $e$ is fully parenthesized (except for atomic terms), we introduce the notion of *subexpression* (s.e.) in the next example:

$$e_0 = \left( \overbrace{\left( (a \cup (bb))^* \right)}^{e_1} \overbrace{\left( (c^+) \cup \underbrace{(a \cup (bb))}_{s} \right)}^{e_2} \right)$$

This r.e. is structured as concatenation of two parts $e_1$ and $e_2$, to be called subexpressions. In general an s.e. $f$ of an r.e. $e$ is a well-parenthesized substring immediately occurring inside the outermost parentheses. This means no other well-parenthesized substring of $e$ contains $f$. In the example, the substring labelled $s$ is not s.e. of $e_0$ but is s.e. of $e_2$.

When the r.e. is not fully parenthesized, in order to identify the subexpressions one has to insert (or to imagine) the missing parentheses, in agreement with operator precedence.

Notice that three or more terms, combined by union, need not to be pairwise parenthesized, because the operation is associative, as in:

$$(c^+ \cup a \cup (bb))$$

The same applies to three or more concatenated terms.

A union or repetition (star and cross) operator offers different choices for producing strings. By making a choice, one obtains an r.e. defining a less general language, which is included in the original one. We say an r.e. is a *choice* of another one in the following cases:

1. $e_k, 1 \leqslant k \leqslant m$, is a choice of the union $(e_1 \cup \ldots \cup e_k \cup \ldots \cup e_m)$
2. $e^m = \underbrace{e \ldots e}_{m \text{ times}}, m \geqslant 1$, is a choice of the expressions $e^*$, $e^+$
3. the empty string is a choice of $e^*$

Let $e'$ be an r.e.; an r.e. $e''$ can be derived from $e'$ by substituting some choice for $e'$. The corresponding relation called *derivation* between two regular expressions $e'$, $e''$ is defined next.

**Definition 2.17.** Derivation[12]
We say $e'$ *derives* $e''$ , written $e' \Rightarrow e''$ , if

$$e'' \text{ is a choice of } e'$$

or

$$e' = e_1 \dots e_k \dots e_m \text{ and } e'' = e_1 \dots e''_k \dots e_m$$
$$\text{where } e''_k \text{ is a choice of } e_k, 1 \leqslant k \leqslant m$$

A derivation can be applied two or more times in a row. We say $e_0$ derives $e_n$ in $n$ steps, written

$$e_0 \overset{n}{\Rightarrow} e_n$$

if

$$e_0 \Rightarrow e_1, \quad e_1 \Rightarrow e_2, \quad \dots, \quad e_{n-1} \Rightarrow e_n$$

The notation

$$e_0 \overset{+}{\Rightarrow} e_n$$

states that $e_0$ derives $e_n$ in some $n \geqslant 1$ steps. The case $n = 0$ corresponds to the identity $e_0 = e_n$ and says the derivation relation is reflective. We also write

$$e_0 \overset{*}{\Rightarrow} e_n \text{ for } \left(e_0 \overset{+}{\Rightarrow} e_n\right) \vee (e_0 = e_n)$$

*Example 2.18.* Immediate derivations:

$$a^* \cup b^+ \Rightarrow a^*, \qquad a^* \cup b^+ \Rightarrow b^+, \qquad (a^* \cup bb)^* \Rightarrow (a^* \cup bb)(a^* \cup bb)$$

Notice that the substrings of the r.e. considered must be chosen in order from external to internal, if one wants to produce all possible derivations. For instance, it would be unwise, starting from $e' = (a^* \cup bb)^*$, to choose $(a^2 \cup bb)^*$, because $a^*$ is not an s.e. of $e'$. Although 2 is a correct choice for the star, such premature choice would rule out the derivation of a valid sentence such as $a^2bba^3$.
Multi-step derivations:

$$a^* \cup b^+ \Rightarrow a^* \Rightarrow \varepsilon \text{ that is } a^* \cup b^+ \overset{2}{\Rightarrow} \varepsilon \text{ or also } a^* \cup b^+ \overset{+}{\Rightarrow} \varepsilon$$

$$a^* \cup b^+ \Rightarrow b^+ \Rightarrow bbb \text{ or also } (a^* \cup b^+) \overset{+}{\Rightarrow} bbb$$

Some expressions produced by derivation from an expression $r$ contain the metasymbols union, star, and cross; some others just terminal characters or the empty string (and maybe some redundant parentheses which can be cancelled). The latter expressions compose the language denoted by the r.e.

The *language defined by a regular expression* $r$ is

[12] Also called *implication*.

$$L_r = \{x \in \Sigma^* \mid r \stackrel{*}{\Rightarrow} x\}$$

Two r.e. are *equivalent* if they define the same language.

The coming example shows that different orders of derivation may produce the same sentence.

*Example 2.19.* Consider the derivations

1. $a^*(b \cup c \cup d)f^+ \Rightarrow aaa(b \cup c \cup d)f^+ \Rightarrow aaacf^+ \Rightarrow aaacf$
2. $a^*(b \cup c \cup d)f^+ \Rightarrow a^*cf^+ \Rightarrow aaacf^+ \Rightarrow aaacf$

Compare derivations 1. and 2. In 1. the first choice takes the leftmost s.e. ($a^*$), whereas in 2. another s.e. ($b \cup c \cup d$) is taken. Since the two steps are independent of each other, they can be applied in any order. By a further step, we obtain r.e. $aaacf^+$, and the last step produces sentence $aaacf$. The last step, being independent from the others, could be performed before, after, or in between.

The example has shown that many different but equivalent orders of choice making, derive the same sentence.

## Ambiguity of Regular Expressions

The next example conceptually differs from the preceding one with respect to the way different derivations produce the same sentence.

*Example 2.20.* Ambiguous regular expression

The language of alphabet $\{a, b\}$, characterized by the presence of at least one $a$, is defined by

$$(a \cup b)^* a (a \cup b)^*$$

where the compulsory presence of $a$ is evident. Now sentences containing two or more occurrences of $a$ can be obtained by multiple derivations, which differ with respect to the character identified with the compulsory one of the r.e. For instance, sentence $aa$ offers two possibilities:

$$(a \cup b)^* a (a \cup b)^* \Rightarrow (a \cup b) a (a \cup b)^* \Rightarrow aa(a \cup b)^* \Rightarrow aa\varepsilon = aa$$

$$(a \cup b)^* a (a \cup b)^* \Rightarrow \varepsilon a (a \cup b)^* \Rightarrow \varepsilon a (a \cup b) \Rightarrow \varepsilon aa = aa$$

This sentence (and the r.e. deriving it) is said to be ambiguous, because there are two structurally different derivations. On the other hand, sentence $ba$ is not ambiguous, because there exists only one set of choices, corresponding to derivation

$$(a \cup b)^* a (a \cup b)^* \Rightarrow (a \cup b) a (a \cup b)^* \Rightarrow ba(a \cup b)^* \Rightarrow ba\varepsilon = ba$$

In order to formalize the idea of ambiguity, it helps to number the letters of the r.e. $f$, obtaining a *numbered* r.e.:

$$f' = (a_1 \cup b_2)^* a_3 (a_4 \cup b_5)^*$$

which defines a regular language of alphabet $\{a_1, b_2, a_3, a_4, b_5\}$.

An r.e. $f$ is *ambiguous* if the language defined by the corresponding numbered r.e. $f'$ contains distinct strings $x, y$ such that they become identical when the numbers are erased[13]. For instance, strings $a_1 a_3$ and $a_3 a_4$ of language $f'$ prove ambiguity of $aa$.

Ambiguous definitions are a source of trouble in many settings. They should be avoided in general, although they may have the advantage of concision over unambiguous definitions. The concept of ambiguity will be thoroughly studied for grammars.

### 2.3.3 Other Operators

When regular expressions are used in practice, it may be convenient to add to the *basic operators* (union, concatenation, star) the derived operators power and cross.

For further expressivity other derived operators may be practical:

Repetition from $k$ to $n > k$ times: $[a]_k^n = a^k \cup a^{k+1} \cup \ldots \cup a^n$

Option: $[a] = (\varepsilon \cup a)$

Interval of ordered set: to represent any digit in the ordered set $0, 1, \ldots, 9$ the short notation is $(0 \ldots 9)$. Similarly the notation $(a \ldots z)$ and $(A \ldots Z)$ stand for the set of lower (respectively upper) case letters.

Sometimes, other set operations are also used: intersection, set difference, and complement. Expressions using such operators are called *extended r.e.*, although the name is not standard, and one has to specify the allowed operators.

*Example 2.21.* Extended r.e. with intersection

This operator provides a straightforward formulation of the fact that valid strings must simultaneously obey two conditions. To illustrate, let $\{a, b\}$ be the alphabet and assume a valid string must (1) contain substring $bb$ and (2) have even length. The former condition is imposed by r.e.

$$(a \mid b)^* bb (a \mid b)^*$$

the latter by r.e.

$$((a \mid b)^2)^*$$

and the language by the r.e. extended with intersection

$$((a \mid b)^* bb (a \mid b)^*) \cap ((a \mid b)^2)^*$$

13 Notice the empty string too may be ambiguous. Observe formulas $(ab)^* \mid \varepsilon$ and $(ab)^* \mid c^*$.

The same language can be defined by a basic r.e., without intersection, but the formula is more complicated. It says substring $bb$ can be surrounded by two strings of even length or by two strings of odd length:

$$((a \mid b)^2)^* bb((a \mid b)^2)^* \mid (a \mid b)((a \mid b)^2)^* bb(a \mid b)((a \mid b)^2)^*$$

Furthermore it is sometimes simpler to define the sentences of a language *ex negativo*, by stating a property they should not have.

*Example 2.22.* Extended r.e. with complement
Consider the set $L$ of strings of alphabet $\{a, b\}$ not containing $aa$ as substring. The complement of the language is

$$\neg L = \{x \in (a \mid b)^* \mid x \text{ contains substring } aa\}$$

easily defined by r.e. $(a \mid b)^* aa(a \mid b)^*$, whence the extended r.e.

$$L = \neg((a \mid b)^* aa(a \mid b)^*)$$

The definition by a basic r.e.

$$(ab \mid b)^*(a \mid \varepsilon)$$

is, subjectively, less readable.

Actually it is not by coincidence that both preceding examples admit also an r.e. without intersection or complement. A theoretical result to be presented in Chapter 3 states that an r.e. extended with complement and intersection produces always a regular language, which by definition can be defined by a nonextended r.e. as well.

### 2.3.4 Closure Properties of REG Family

Let *op* be an operator to be applied to one or two languages, to produce another language. A language family is *closed by operator op* if the language, obtained applying *op* to any languages of the family, is in the same family.

*Property 2.23.* The family *REG* of regular languages is closed by the operators concatenation, union, and star (therefore also by derived operators such as cross).

The property descends from the very definition of r.e. and of *REG* (p. 19). In spite of its theoretical connotation, the property has practical relevance: two regular languages can be combined using the above operations, at no risk of losing the nice features of the class of regular languages. This will have an important practical consequence, to permit compositional design of algorithms used to check if an input string is valid for a language. Furthermore we anticipate the $REG$ family is closed by intersection, complement, and reflection too, which will be proved later.

The next statement provides an alternative definition of family $REG$.

*Property 2.24.* The family $REG$ of regular languages is *the smallest* language family such that: (i) it contains all finite languages and (ii) it is closed by concatenation, union, and star.

The proof is simple. Suppose by contradiction a family exists $F \subset REG$, which is closed by the same operators and contains all finite languages. Consider any language $L_e$ defined by an r.e. $e$; the language is obtained by repeated applications of the operators present in $e$, starting with some finite languages consisting of single characters. It follows from the hypothesis that language $L(e)$ belongs also to family $F$, which then contains any regular language, contradicting the strict inclusion $F \subset REG$.

We anticipate other families exist which are closed by the same operators of property 2.23. Chief among them is the family $CF$ of context-free languages, to be introduced soon. From statement 2.24 follows a containment relation between the two families, $REG \subset CF$.

## 2.4 Linguistic Abstraction

If one recalls the programming languages he is familiar with, he may observe that, although superficially different in their use of keywords and separators, they are often quite similar at a deeper level. By shifting focus from concrete to abstract syntax we can reduce the bewildering variety of language constructs to a few essential structures. The verb "to abstract" means[14]

> consider a concept without thinking of a specific example.

Abstracting away from the actual characters representing a language construct we perform a linguistic abstraction. This is a language transformation that replaces the terminal characters of the concrete language with other ones taken from an abstract alphabet. Abstract characters should be simpler and suitable to represent similar constructs from different artificial languages.[15]

By this approach the abstract syntax structures of existing artificial languages are easily described as composition of few elementary paradigms, by means of standard language operations: union, iteration, substitution (later defined). Starting from the abstract language, a concrete or real language is

---

[14] From WordNet 2.1.

[15] The idea of language abstraction is inspired by research in linguistics aiming at discovering the underlying similarities of human languages, disregarding morphological and syntactic differences.

obtained by the reverse transformation, metaphorically called coating with syntax sugar.

Factoring a language into its abstract and concrete syntax pays off in several ways. When studying different languages it affords much conceptual economy. When designing compilers, abstraction helps for portability across different languages, if compiler functions are designed to process abstract, instead of concrete, language constructs. Thus parts of, say, a C compiler can be reused for similar languages like FORTRAN or Pascal.

The surprisingly few abstract paradigms in use, will be presented in this chapter, starting from the ones conveniently specified by regular expressions, the lists.

### 2.4.1 Abstract and Concrete Lists

An abstract *list* contains an unbounded number of elements $e$ of the same type. It is defined by r.e. $e^+$ or $e^*$, if elements can be missing.

An element for the moment should be viewed as a terminal character; but in later refinements, the element may become a string from another formal language: think e.g., of a list of numbers.

#### Lists with Separators and Opening/Closing Marks

In many concrete cases, adjacent elements must be separated by strings called *separators*, $s$ in abstract syntax. Thus in a list of numbers, a separator should delimit the end of a number and the beginning of the next one.

A *list with separators* is defined by r.e. $e(s\,e)^*$, saying the first element can be followed by zero or more pairs $se$. The equivalent definition $(e\,s)^*e$ differs by giving evidence to the last element.

In many concrete cases there is another requirement, intended for legibility or computer processing: to make the start and end of the list easily recognizable by prefixing and suffixing some special signs: in the abstract, the initial character or *opening mark* $i$, and the final character or *closing mark* $f$.

Lists with separators and opening/closing marks are defined as

$$ie(s\,e)^*f$$

*Example 2.25.* Some concrete lists

Lists are everywhere in languages, as shown by typical examples.

Instruction block: $begin\, instr_1; instr_2; \ldots instr_n end$

where *instr* possibly stands for assignment, go to, `if`-statement, `write`-statement, etc. Corresponding abstract and concrete terms are:

| *abstract alphabet* | *concrete alphabet* |
|---|---|
| $i$ | *begin* |
| $e$ | *instr* |
| $s$ | ; |
| $f$ | *end* |

Procedure parameters: as in

$$\underbrace{procedure\ WRITE(}_{i}\underbrace{par_1}_{e}\underbrace{,}_{s}\ par_2, \ldots, par_n\underbrace{)}_{f}$$

Should an empty parameter list be legal, as e.g., *procedure* $WRITE()$, the r.e. becomes $i[e(s\,e)^*]f$.

Array definition: $\underbrace{array\ MATRIX\ '['}_{i}\underbrace{int_1}_{e}\underbrace{,}_{s}\ int_2, \ldots, int_n\underbrace{']'}_{f}$

where each *int* is an interval such as 10...50.

## Substitution

The above examples illustrate the mapping from concrete to abstract symbols. Language designers find it useful to work by stepwise refinement, as done in any branch of engineering, when a complex system is divided into its components, atomic or otherwise. To this end, we introduce the new language operation of substitution, that replaces a terminal character of a language termed the *source*, with a sentence of another language called the *target*. As always $\Sigma$ is the source alphabet and $L \subseteq \Sigma^*$ the source language. Consider a sentence of $L$ containing one or more occurrences of a source character $b$:

$$x = a_1 a_2 \ldots a_n \qquad \text{where for some } i, a_i = b$$

Let $\Delta$ be another alphabet, called target, and $L_b \subseteq \Delta^*$ be the *image language* of $b$. The *substitution* of language $L_b$ for $b$ in string $x$ produces a set of strings, that is, a language of alphabet $(\Sigma \setminus \{b\}) \cup \Delta$, defined as

$$\{y \mid y = y_1 y_2 \ldots y_n \wedge (\text{ if } a_i \neq b \text{ then } y_i = a_i \text{ else } y_i \in L_b)\}$$

Notice all characters other than $b$ do not change. By the usual approach the substitution can be defined on the whole source language, by applying the operation to every source sentence.

*Example 2.26.* Example 2.25 continued
Resuming the case of a parameter list, the abstract syntax is

$$ie(se)^*f$$

and the substitutions to be applied are tabulated below:

| *abstract char.* | *imagine* |
|---|---|
| $i$ | $L_i =$ *procedure* ⟨procedure identifier⟩( |
| $e$ | $L_e =$ ⟨parameter identifier⟩ |
| $s$ | $L_s =$ , |
| $f$ | $L_f =$ ) |

For instance, the opening mark $i$ is replaced with a string of language $L_i$, where the procedure identifier has to agree with the rules of the technical language.
Clearly the target languages of the substitution depend on the syntax sugar of the concrete language intended for.
Notice the four substitutions are independent and can be applied in any order.

*Example 2.27.* Identifiers with underscore
In certain programming languages, long mnemonic identifier names can be constructed by appending alphanumeric strings separated by a low dash: thus $LOOP3\_OF\_35$ is a legal identifier. More precisely the first string must initiate with a letter, the others may contain letters and digits, and adjacent dashes are forbidden, as well as a trailing dash.
At first glance the language is a nonempty list of strings $s$, separated by a dash:

$$s(\_s)^*$$

However, the first string should be different from the others and may be taken to be the opening mark of a possibly empty list:

$$i(\_s)^*$$

Substituting to $i$ the language $(A \dots Z)(A \dots Z \mid 0 \dots 9)^*$, and to $s$ the language $(A \dots Z \mid 0 \dots 9)^+$, the final r.e. is obtained.

This is an overly simple instance of syntax design by abstraction and stepwise refinement, a method to be further developed now and after the introduction of grammars.
Other language transformations are studied in Chapter 6.

### Hierarchical or Precedence Lists

A recurrent construct is a list such that each element is in turn a list of a different type. The first list is attached to level 1, the second to level 2, and so on. The present abstract structure, called hierarchical list, is restricted to lists with a bounded number of levels. The case when levels are unbounded is studied later using grammars, under the name of nested structures.
A hierarchical list is also called a *list with precedences*, because a list at level $k$ bounds its elements more strongly than the list at level $k-1$; in other

words the elements at higher level must be assembled into a list, and each becomes an element at next lower level.
Each level may have opening/closing marks and separator; such delimiters are usually distinct level by level, in order to avoid confusion.
The structure of a $k \geqslant 2$ levels hierarchical list is

$$\begin{aligned} list_1 &= i_1 list_2 (s_1 list_2)^* f_1 \\ list_2 &= i_2 list_3 (s_2 list_3)^* f_2 \\ &\dots \\ list_k &= i_k e_k (s_k e_k)^* f_k \end{aligned}$$

Notice the last level alone may contain atomic elements. But a common variant permits at any level $k$ atomic elements $e_k$ to occur side by side with lists of level $k+1$. Some concrete examples follow.

*Example 2.28.* Two hierarchical lists

Block of print instructions: $begin\ instr_1; instr_2; \dots instr_n\ end$ where $instr$ is a print instruction, $WRITE(var_1, var_2, \dots, var_n)$, i.e., a list (from example 2.25). There are two levels:
Level 1: list of instructions $instr$, opened by $begin$, separated by semicolon and closed by $end$.
Level 2: list of variables $var$ separated by comma, with $i_2 = WRITE($ and $f_2 = )$.

Arithmetic expression not using parentheses: the precedence levels of operators determine how many levels there are in the list. For instance, the operators $\times, \div$ and $+, -$ are layered on two levels and the string

$$3 + \underbrace{5 \times 7 \times 4}_{\text{term}_1} - \underbrace{8 \times 2 \div 5}_{\text{term}_2} + 8 + 3$$

is a two-level list, with neither opening nor closing mark. At level one we find a list of terms ($e_1 =$ term) separated by the signs $+$ and $-$, i.e., by lower precedence operators. At level two we see a list of numbers, separated by higher precedence signs $\times, \div$.
One may go further and introduce a third level having the exponentiation sign "$**$" as separator.

Hierarchical structures are of course omnipresent in natural languages as well. Think of a list of nouns

father, mother, son, and daughter

Here we may observe a difference with respect to the abstract paradigm: the penultimate element has a distinct separator, possibly in order to warn the listener of an utterance that the list is approaching the end. Furthermore, items in the list may be enriched by second-level qualifiers, such as a list of adjectives.

In all sorts of documents and written media, hierarchical lists are extremely common. For instance, a book is a list of chapters, separated by white pages, between a front and back cover. A chapter is a list of sections; a section a list of paragraphs, and so on.

## 2.5 Context-Free Generative Grammars

We start the study of the context-free language family, which plays the central role in compilation. Initially invented by linguists for natural languages in the 1950s, context-free grammars have proved themselves extremely useful in computer science applications: all existing technical languages have been defined using such grammars. Moreover, since the early 1960s efficient algorithms have been found to analyze, recognize, and translate sentences of context-free languages. This chapter presents the relevant properties of context-free languages, illustrates their application by many typical cases, and lastly positions this formal model in the classical hierarchy of grammars and computational models due to Chomsky.

### *2.5.1 Limits of Regular Languages*

Regular expressions, though quite practical for describing list and related paradigms, falls short of the capacity needed to define other frequently occurring constructs. A case are the block structures (or nested parentheses) offered by many technical languages, schematized by

$$\textit{begin}\ \underbrace{\textit{begin}\ \underbrace{\textit{begin}\ldots\textit{end}}\ \underbrace{\textit{begin}\ldots\textit{end}}\ldots\ \textit{end}}\ \textit{end}$$

*Example 2.29.* Simple block structure
In brief, let $\{b, e\}$ be the alphabet, and consider a somewhat limited case of nested structures, such that all opening marks precede all closing marks. Clearly, opening/closing marks must have identical count:

$$L_1 = \{b^n e^n \mid n \geqslant 1\}$$

We argue this language cannot be defined by a regular expression, deferring the formal proof to a later section. In fact, since strings must have all $b$'s left of any $e$, either we write an overly general r.e. such as $b^+e^+$, which accepts illegal strings like $b^3e^5$; or we write a too restricted r.e. that exhaustively lists a finite sample of strings up to a bounded length. On the other hand, if we comply with the condition that the count of the two letters is the same by writing $(be)^+$, illegal strings like *bebe* creep in.

For defining this and other languages, regular or not, we move to the formal model of *generative* grammars.

### 2.5.2 Introduction to Context-Free Grammars

A generative *grammar* or *syntax*[16] is a set of simple rules that can be repeatedly applied in order to generate all and only the valid strings.

*Example 2.30.* Palindromes
The language to be defined

$$L = \{uu^R \mid u \in \{a, b\}^*\} = \{\varepsilon, aa, bb, abba, baab, \ldots, abbbba, \ldots\}$$

contains even-length strings having specular symmetry, called palindromes. The following grammar $G$ contains three rules:

$$pal \to \varepsilon \qquad pal \to a\ pal\ a \qquad pal \to b\ pal\ b$$

The arrow '→' is a metasymbol, exclusively used to separate the left from the right part of a rule.

To derive the strings, just replace symbol 'pal', termed *nonterminal*, with the right part of a rule, for instance:

$$pal \Rightarrow a\ pal\ a \Rightarrow ab\ pal\ ba \Rightarrow abb\ pal\ bba \Rightarrow \ldots$$

The derivation process can be chained and terminates when the last string obtained no longer contains a nonterminal symbol; at that moment the generation of the sentence is concluded. We complete the derivation:

$$abb\ pal\ bba \Rightarrow abb\varepsilon bba = abbbba$$

(Incidentally the language of palindromes is not regular.)

Next we enrich the example into a list of palindromes separated by commas, exemplified by sentence *abba, bbaabb, aa*. The grammar adds two list-generating rules to the previous ones:

$$\begin{array}{ll} list \to pal, list & pal \to \varepsilon \\ list \to pal & pal \to a\ pal\ a \\ & pal \to b\ pal\ b \end{array}$$

---

16 Sometimes the term *grammar* has a broader connotation than *syntax*, as when rules for computing the meaning of sentences are added to rules for enumerating them. When necessary, the intended meaning of the term will be made clear.

The first rule says: the concatenation of palindrome, comma, and list produces a (longer) list. The second says a list can be made of one palindrome.

Now there are two nonterminal symbols: *list* and *pal*; the former is termed *axiom* because it defines the designated language, the latter defines certain component substrings, also called *constituents* of the language, the palindromes.

*Example 2.31.* Metalanguage of regular expressions
A regular expression defining a language over a fixed terminal alphabet, say $\Sigma = \{a, b\}$, is a formula, that is, a string over the alphabet $\Sigma_{r.e.} = \{a, b, \cup, {}^*, \emptyset, (, )\}$; such strings can be viewed in turn as sentences of a language.
Following the definition of r.e. on p. 18, this language is generated by the following syntax $G_{r.e.}$:

$$\begin{array}{ll} 1.\ expr \to \emptyset & 4.\ expr \to (expr \cup expr) \\ 2.\ expr \to a & 5.\ expr \to (expr\ expr) \\ 3.\ expr \to b & 6.\ expr \to (expr)^* \end{array}$$

where numbering is only for reference. A derivation is

$$expr \Rightarrow_4 (expr \cup expr) \Rightarrow_5 ((expr\ expr) \cup expr) \Rightarrow_2 ((a\ expr) \cup expr) \Rightarrow_6$$
$$\Rightarrow ((a(expr)^*) \cup expr) \Rightarrow_4 ((a((expr \cup expr))^*) \cup expr) \Rightarrow_2$$
$$\Rightarrow ((a((a \cup expr))^*) \cup expr) \Rightarrow_3 ((a((a \cup b))^*) \cup expr) \Rightarrow_3 ((a((a \cup b))^*) \cup b) = e$$

Since the generated string can be interpreted as an r.e., it defines a second language of alphabet $\Sigma$:

$$L_e = \{a, b, aa, ab, aaa, aba, \ldots\}$$

the set of strings starting with letter $a$, plus string $b$.

A word of caution: this example displays two levels of languages, since the syntax defines certain strings to be understood as definitions of other languages. To avoid terminological confusion, we say the syntax stays at the *metalinguistic* level, that is, over the linguistic level; or that the syntax is a *metagrammar*.

To set the two levels apart, it helps to consider the alphabets: at meta-level the alphabet is $\Sigma_{r.e.} = \{a, b, \cup, {}^*, \emptyset, (, )\}$, whereas the final language has alphabet $\Sigma = \{a, b\}$, devoid of metasymbols.

An analogy with human language may also clarify the issue. A grammar of Russian can be written in, say, English. Then it contains both Cyrillic and Latin characters. Here English is the metalanguage and Russian the final language, which only contains Cyrillic characters.

Another illustration of language versus metalanguage is provided by XML, the metanotation used to define a variety of Web document types.

**Definition 2.32.** A *context-free* (*CF*) (or type 2 or BNF[17]) grammar $G$ is defined by four entities:

1. $V$, *nonterminal alphabet*, a set of symbols termed *nonterminals* (or metasymbols).
2. $\Sigma$, *terminal alphabet.*
3. $P$, a set of syntactic *rules* (or *productions*).
4. $S \in V$, a particular nonterminal termed *axiom.*

A rule of $P$ is an ordered pair $X \to \alpha$, with $X \in V$ and $\alpha \in (V \cup \Sigma)^*$.
Two or more rules

$$X \to \alpha_1, X \to \alpha_2, \ldots, X \to \alpha_n$$

with the same left part $X$ can be concisely grouped in

$$X \to \alpha_1 \mid \alpha_2 \mid \ldots \mid \alpha_n \qquad \text{or} \qquad X \to \alpha_1 \cup \alpha_2 \cup \ldots \cup \alpha_n$$

We say $\alpha_1, \alpha_2, \ldots, \alpha_n$ are the *alternatives* of $X$.

### 2.5.3 Conventional Grammar Representations

To prevent confusion, the metasymbols '$\to$', '$|$', '$\cup$', '$\varepsilon$' should not be used for terminal and nonterminal symbols; moreover, the terminal and nonterminal alphabets should be disjoint. In professional and scientific practice a few different styles are used to represent terminals and nonterminals, as specified in Table 2.2. The grammar of example 2.30 in the first style becomes:

$$< sentence > \to \varepsilon$$
$$< sentence > \to a < sentence > a$$
$$< sentence > \to b < sentence > b$$

Alternative rules may be grouped together:

$$< sentence > \to \varepsilon \mid a < sentence > a \mid b < sentence > b$$

If a technical grammar is large, of the order of some hundred rules, it should be written with care in order to facilitate searching for specific definitions, making changes, and cross referencing. Nonterminals should be identified by self-explanatory names and rules should be divided into sections and numbered for reference.

On the other hand, in very simple examples, the third style is more suitable,

---

17 Type 2 comes from Chomsky's classification. Backus Normal Form, or also Backus Naur Form, comes from the names of John Backus and Peter Naur, who pioneered the use of such grammars for programming language definition.

**Table 2.2** Different styles for writing grammars.

| *Nonterminals* | *Terminals* | *Examples* |
|---|---|---|
| words between angle brackets, for instance: $< sentence >$, $< list\,of\ sentences >$ | written as they are, without special marks | $< if\ sentence > \to$<br>$if < cond > then < sentence >$<br>$else < sentence >$ |
| words written as they are, without special marks; may not contain blank spaces, for instance: *sentence*, *list_of_sentences* | written in black, in italic or quoted, for instance:<br>**a then**<br>*'a' 'then'* | $if\_sentence \to$<br>**if** *cond* **then** *sentence* **else** *sentence*<br>or<br>$if\_sentence \to$<br>*'if' cond 'then' sentence 'else' sentence* |
| uppercase Latin letters; terminal and nonterminal alphabets disjoint | written as they are, without special marks | $F \to if\ C\ then\ D\ else\ D$ |

i.e., to have disjoint short symbols for terminals and nonterminals.
In this book, we often adopt for simplicity the following style:

- lowercase Latin letters near the beginning of the alphabet $\{a, b, \ldots\}$ for terminal characters;
- uppercase Latin letters $\{A, B, \ldots, Z\}$ for nonterminal symbols;
- lowercase Latin letters near the end of the alphabet $\{r, s, \ldots, z\}$ for strings over $\Sigma^*$ (i.e. including only terminals);
- lowercase Greek letters $\{\alpha, \beta, \ldots\}$ for strings over the combined alphabets $(V \cup \Sigma)^*$.

### Types of Rules

In grammar studies rules may be classified depending on their form, with the aim of making the study of language properties more immediate. For future reference we list in Table 2.3 some common types of rules along with their technical names. Each rule type is next schematized, with symbols adhering to the following stipulations: $a, b$ are terminals, $u, v, w$ denote possibly empty strings of terminals, $A, B, C$ are nonterminals, $\alpha, \beta$ denote possibly empty strings containing terminals and nonterminals; lastly $\sigma$ denotes a string of nonterminals.

The classification is based on the form of the right part RP of a rule, excepting the recursive classes that also consider the left part LP. We omit any part of a rule that is, irrelevant for the classification. Left- and right-

**Table 2.3** Classification of grammar rules.

| *Class* and *Description* | *Examples* |
|---|---|
| *terminal*: RP contains terminals or the empty string | $\rightarrow u \mid \epsilon$ |
| *empty (or null)*: RP is empty | $\rightarrow \epsilon$ |
| *initial*: LP is the axiom | $S \rightarrow$ |
| *recursive*: LP occurs in RP | $A \rightarrow \alpha\ A\ \beta$ |
| *left-recursive*: LP is prefix of RP | $A \rightarrow A\ \beta$ |
| *right-recursive*: LP is suffix of RP | $A \rightarrow \beta\ A$ |
| *left and right-recursive*: conjunction of two previous cases | $A \rightarrow A\beta A$ |
| *copy or categorization*: RP is a single nonterminal | $A \rightarrow B$ |
| *linear*: at most one nonterminal in RP | $\rightarrow u\ B\ v \mid w$ |
| *right-linear* (type 3): as linear but nonterminal is suffix | $\rightarrow u\ B \mid w$ |
| *left-linear* (type 3): as linear but nonterminal is prefix | $\rightarrow B\ v \mid w$ |
| *homogeneous normal*: $n$ nonterminals or just one terminal | $\rightarrow A_1 \ldots A_n \mid a$ |
| *Chomsky normal* (or homogeneous of degree 2): two nonterminals or just one terminal | $\rightarrow B\ C \mid a$ |
| *Greibach normal*: one terminal possibly followed by nonterminals | $\rightarrow a\ \sigma \mid b$ |
| *operator normal*: two nonterminals separated by a terminal (operator); more generally, strings devoid of adjacent nonterminals | $\rightarrow A\ a\ B$ |

linear forms are also known as *type 3* grammars from Chomsky classification. Most rule types will occur in the book; the remaining ones are listed for general reference.

We shall see that some of the grammar forms can be forced on any given grammar, leaving the language unchanged. Such forms are called *normal*.

### *2.5.4 Derivation and Language Generation*

We reconsider and formalize the notion of string derivation. Let $\beta = \delta A \eta$ be a string containing a nonterminal, where $\delta$ and $\eta$ are any, possibly empty strings. Let $A \rightarrow \alpha$ be a rule of $G$ and let $\gamma = \delta \alpha \eta$ be the string obtained replacing in $\beta$ nonterminal $A$ with the right part $\alpha$.

The relation between such two strings is called *derivation*. We say that $\beta$ *derives* $\gamma$ for grammar $G$, written

$$\beta \underset{G}{\Rightarrow} \gamma$$

or more simply $\beta \Rightarrow \gamma$ when the grammar name is understood. Rule $A \rightarrow \alpha$ is applied in such derivation and string $\alpha$ *reduces* to nonterminal $A$.

Consider now a chain of derivations of length $n \geqslant 0$:

$$\beta_0 \Rightarrow \beta_1 \Rightarrow \ldots \Rightarrow \beta_n$$

shortened to

$$\beta_0 \stackrel{n}{\Rightarrow} \beta_n$$

If $n = 0$, for every string $\beta$ we posit $\beta \stackrel{0}{\Rightarrow} \beta$, that is, the derivation relation is reflexive.

To express derivations of any length we write

$$\beta_0 \stackrel{*}{\Rightarrow} \beta_n \text{ (resp. } \beta_0 \stackrel{+}{\Rightarrow} \beta_n)$$

if the length of the chain is $n \geqslant 0$ (resp. $n \geqslant 1$).

The *language generated* or defined by a grammar $G$ *starting from nonterminal* $A$ is

$$L_A(G) = \{x \in \Sigma^* \mid A \stackrel{+}{\Rightarrow} x\}$$

It is the set of terminal strings deriving in one or more steps from $A$.
If the nonterminal is the axiom $S$, we have the *language generated by* $G$:

$$L(G) = L_S(G) = \{x \in \Sigma^* \mid S \stackrel{+}{\Rightarrow} x\}$$

In some cases we need to consider derivations producing strings still containing nonterminals. A *string form* generated by $G$ starting from nonterminal $A \in V$, is a string $\alpha \in (V \cup \Sigma)^*$ such that $A \stackrel{*}{\Rightarrow} \alpha$. In particular, if $A$ is the axiom, the string is termed *sentential form*. Clearly a sentence is a sentential form devoid of nonterminals.

*Example 2.33.* Book structure
The grammar defines the structure of a book, containing a front page ($f$) and a nonempty series (derived from nonterminal $A$) of chapters; each one starts with a title ($t$) and contains a nonempty series (derived from $B$) of lines ($l$).
Grammar $G_l$:

$$\begin{aligned} S &\to fA \\ A &\to AtB \mid tB \\ B &\to lB \mid l \end{aligned}$$

Some derivations are listed. From $A$ the string form $tBtB$ and the string $tlltl \in L_A(G_l)$; from the axiom $S$ sentential forms $fAtlB$, $ftBtB$ and sentence $ftltlll$.

The language generated from $B$ is $L_B(G_l) = l^+$; the language $L(G_l)$ generated by $G_l$ is defined by the r.e. $f(tl^+)^+$, showing the language is in the $REG$ family. In fact, this language is a case of an abstract hierarchical list.

A language is *context-free* if a context-free grammar exists that generates it. The family of context free languages is denoted by $CF$.
Two grammars $G$ and $G'$ are *equivalent* if they generate the same language, i.e., $L(G) = L(G')$.

*Example 2.34.* The next grammar $G_{l2}$ is clearly equivalent to $G_l$ of example 2.33:

$$\begin{aligned} S &\to fX \\ X &\to XtY \mid tY \\ Y &\to lY \quad \mid l \end{aligned}$$

since the only change affects the way nonterminals are identified. Also the following grammar $G_{l3}$

$$\begin{aligned} S &\to fA \\ A &\to AtB \mid tB \\ B &\to Bl \quad \mid l \end{aligned}$$

is equivalent to $G_l$. The only difference is in row three, which defines $B$ by a left-recursive rule, instead of the right-recursive rule used in $G_l$. Clearly any derivations of length $n \geqslant 1$

$$B \underset{G_l}{\overset{n}{\Rightarrow}} l^n \qquad \text{and} \qquad B \underset{G_{l3}}{\overset{n}{\Rightarrow}} l^n$$

generate the same language $L_B = l^+$.

### 2.5.5 Erroneous Grammars and Useless Rules

When writing a grammar attention should be paid that all nonterminals are defined and that each one effectively contributes to the production of some sentence. In fact, some rules may turn out to be unproductive.
A grammar $G$ is called *clean* (or *reduced*) under the following conditions:

1. every nonterminal $A$ is *reachable* from the axiom, i.e., there exists derivation $S \overset{*}{\Rightarrow} \alpha A \beta$;
2. every nonterminal $A$ is *well-defined*, i.e., it generates a nonempty language, $L_A(G) \neq \emptyset$.

It is often straightforward to check by inspection whether a grammar is clean. The following algorithm formalizes the checks.

Grammar Cleaning

The algorithm operates in two phases, first pinpointing the nondefined nonterminals, then the unreachable ones. Lastly the rules containing nonterminals of either type can be cancelled.

Phase 1. Compute the set $DEF \subseteq V$ of well-defined nonterminals.
The set $DEF$ is initialized with the nonterminals of terminal rules, those having a terminal string as right part:

$$DEF := \{A \mid (A \to u) \in P, \text{ with } u \in \Sigma^*\}$$

Then the next transformation is applied until convergence is reached:

$$DEF := DEF \cup \{B \mid (B \to D_1 D_2 \ldots D_n) \in P\}$$

where every $D_i$ is a terminal or a nonterminal symbol present in $DEF$. At each iteration two outcomes are possible:

- a new nonterminal is found having as right part a string of symbols that are well-defined nonterminals or terminals, or else
- the termination condition is reached.

The nonterminals belonging to the complement set $V \setminus DEF$ are nondefined and should be eliminated.

Phase 2. A nonterminal is reachable from the axiom, if, and only if, there exists a path in the following graph, which represents a relation between nonterminals, called *produce*:

$$A \xrightarrow{\text{produce}} B$$

saying that $A$ *produces* $B$ if, and only if, there exists a rule $A \to \alpha B \beta$, where $A, B$ are nonterminals and $\alpha, \beta$ are any strings.
Clearly $C$ is reachable from $S$ if, and only if, in this graph there exists an oriented path from $S$ to $C$. The unreachable nonterminals are the complement with respect to $V$. They should be eliminated because they do not contribute to the generation of any sentence.

Quite often the following requirement is added to the above cleanness conditions.

- $G$ should not permit *circular derivations* $A \overset{+}{\Rightarrow} A$ .

The reason is such derivations are inessential, because,if string $x$ is obtained by means of a circular derivation $A \Rightarrow A \Rightarrow x$,it can also be obtained by the shorter derivation $A \Rightarrow x$.
Moreover, circular derivations cause ambiguity (a negative phenomenon later discussed).
In this book we assume grammars are always clean and noncircular.

*Example 2.35.* Unclean examples

- The grammar with rules $\{S \to aASb,\ A \to b\}$ generates nothing.
- The grammar $G$ with rules $\{S \to a,\ A \to b\}$ has an unreachable nonterminal $A$; the same language $L(G)$ is generated by the clean grammar $\{S \to a\}$.
- Circular derivation:
  The grammar with rules $\{S \to aASb \mid A,\ A \to S \mid c\}$ presents the circular derivation $S \Rightarrow A \Rightarrow S$. The grammar $\{S \to aSSb \mid c\}$ is equivalent.

- Notice that circularity may also come from the presence of an empty rule, as for instance in the following grammar fragment:

$$X \to XY \mid \ldots \qquad Y \to \varepsilon \mid \ldots$$

Finally we observe a grammar, although clean, may still contain redundant rules, as the next one:

*Example 2.36.* Double rules

$$\begin{array}{ll} 1.\ S \to aASb & 4.\ A \to c \\ 2.\ S \to aBSb & 5.\ B \to c \\ 3.\ S \to \varepsilon & \end{array}$$

One of the pairs (1,4) and (2,5), which generate exactly the same sentences, should be deleted.

### 2.5.6 Recursion and Language Infinity

An essential property of most technical languages is to be infinite. We study how this property follows from the form of grammar rules. In order to generate an unbounded number of strings, the grammar must be able to derive strings of unbounded length. To this end, recursive rules are necessary, as next argued.

An $n \geqslant 1$ steps derivation $A \overset{n}{\Rightarrow} xAy$ is called *recursive* (*immediately* recursive if $n = 1$); similarly nonterminal $A$ is called recursive. If $x$ (resp. $y$) is empty, the recursion is termed *left* (resp. *right*).

*Property 2.37.* Let $G$ be a grammar clean and devoid of circular derivations. The language $L(G)$ is infinite if, and only if, $G$ has a recursive derivation.

Proof. Clearly without recursive derivations, any derivation has bounded length, therefore any sentence too is bounded in length, and $L(G)$ would be finite.
Conversely, assume $G$ offers a recursive derivation $A \overset{n}{\Rightarrow} xAy$, with not both $x$ and $y$ empty by the noncircularity hypothesis. Then the derivation $A \overset{+}{\Rightarrow} x^m Ay^m$ exists, for every $m \geqslant 1$. Since $G$ is clean, $A$ can be reached from the axiom by a derivation $S \overset{*}{\Rightarrow} uAv$, and also $A$ derives at least one terminal string $A \overset{+}{\Rightarrow} w$. Combining the derivations, we obtain

$$S \overset{*}{\Rightarrow} uAv \overset{+}{\Rightarrow} ux^m Ay^m v \overset{+}{\Rightarrow} ux^m wy^m v \ , \ (m \geqslant 1)$$

that generates an infinite language.

In order to see whether a grammar has recursions, we examine the binary relation *produce* of p. 38: a grammar does not have a recursion if, and only if, the graph of the relation has no circuit.

We illustrate by two grammars generating a finite and infinite language.

*Example 2.38.* Finite language

$$S \to aBc \qquad B \to ab \mid Ca \qquad C \to c$$

The grammar does not have a recursion and allows just two derivations, defining the finite language $\{aabc, acac\}$.

The next example is a most common paradigm of so many artificial languages. It will be replicated and transformed over and over in the book.

*Example 2.39.* Arithmetic expressions
The grammar

$$G = (\{E, T, F\},\ \{i, +, *, ), (\},\ P,\ E)$$

contains the rules

$$E \to E + T \mid T \qquad T \to T * F \mid F \qquad F \to (E) \mid i$$

The language

$$L(G) = \{i, i + i + i, i * i, (i + i) * i, \ldots\}$$

is the set of arithmetic expressions over the letter $i$, with signs of sum and product and parentheses. Nonterminal $F$ (factor) is nonimmediately recursive; $T$ (term) and $E$ (expression) are immediately recursive, both to the left. Such properties are evident from the circuits in the graph of the *produce* relation:

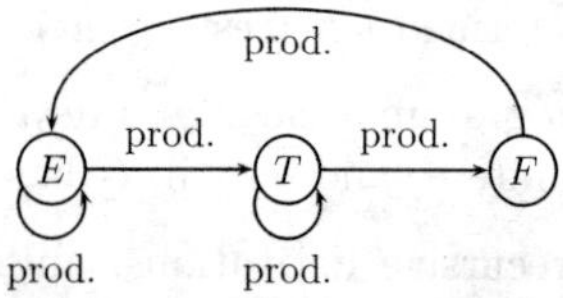


Since the grammar is clean and noncircular, the language is infinite.

### 2.5.7 Syntax Trees and Canonical Derivations

The process of derivation can be visualized as a syntax tree for better legibility. A *tree* is an oriented and ordered graph not containing a circuit, such that every pair of nodes is connected by exactly one oriented path. An arc $\langle N_1 \to N_2 \rangle$ defines the $\langle$father, son$\rangle$ relation, customarily visualized from top to bottom as in genealogical trees. The siblings of a node are ordered from left to right. The *degree* of a node is the number of its siblings. A tree contains one node without father, termed *root.*

Consider an internal node $N$: the *subtree* with root $N$ is the tree having $N$ as root and containing all siblings of $N$, all of their siblings, etc., that is, all *descendants* of $N$. Nodes without sibling are termed *leaves* or *terminal nodes.* The sequence of all leaves, read from left to right, is the *frontier* of the tree.

A *syntax tree* has as root the axiom and as frontier a sentence.

To construct the tree consider a derivation. For each rule $A_0 \to A_1 A_2 \ldots A_r$, $r \geqslant 1$ used in the derivation, draw a small tree having $A_0$ as root and siblings $A_1 A_2 \ldots A_r$, which may be terminals or nonterminals. If the rule is $A_0 \to \varepsilon$, draw one sibling labelled with epsilon. Such trees are then pasted together, by uniting each nonterminal sibling, say $A_i$, with the root node having the same label $A_i$, which is used to expand $A_i$ in the subsequent step of the derivation.

*Example 2.40.* Syntax tree

The grammar is reproduced in Figure 2.1 numbering the rules for reference in the construction of the syntax tree.

1. $E \to E + T$
2. $E \to T$
3. $T \to T * F$
4. $T \to F$
5. $F \to (E)$
6. $F \to i$

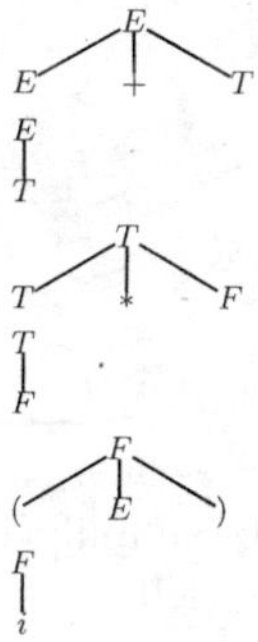


**Fig. 2.1** Grammar rules and corresponding tree fragments.

The derivation

$$E \underset{1}{\Rightarrow} E+T \underset{2}{\Rightarrow} T+T \underset{4}{\Rightarrow} F+T \underset{6}{\Rightarrow} i+T \underset{3}{\Rightarrow} i+T*F \underset{4}{\Rightarrow} i+F*F \underset{6}{\Rightarrow} i+i*F \underset{6}{\Rightarrow} i+i*i \tag{2.2}$$

corresponds to the following syntax tree:

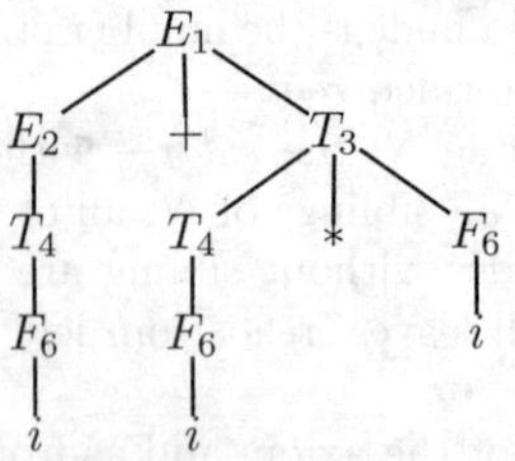


where the labels of the rules applied are displayed. Notice the same tree represents other equivalent derivations, like the next one

$$E \underset{1}{\Rightarrow} E{+}T \underset{3}{\Rightarrow} E{+}T{*}F \underset{6}{\Rightarrow} E{+}T{*}i \underset{4}{\Rightarrow} E{+}F{*}i \underset{6}{\Rightarrow} E{+}i{*}i \underset{2}{\Rightarrow} T{+}i{*}i \underset{4}{\Rightarrow} F{+}i{*}i \underset{6}{\Rightarrow} i{+}i{*}i \quad (2.3)$$

and many others which differ in the order rules are applied. Derivation (2.2) is termed *left* and derivation (2.3) is termed *right.*

A syntax tree of a sentence $x$ can also be encoded in a text, by enclosing each subtree between brackets[18]. Brackets are subscripted with the nonterminal symbol. Thus the preceding tree is encoded by the *parenthesized expression*

$$\Big[\big[[[i]_F]_T\big]_E + \big[[[i]_F]_T * [i]_F\big]_T\Big]_E$$

or by

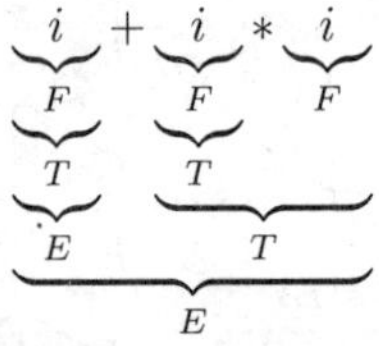


The representation can be simplified by dropping the nonterminal labels, thus obtaining a *skeleton tree* (left):

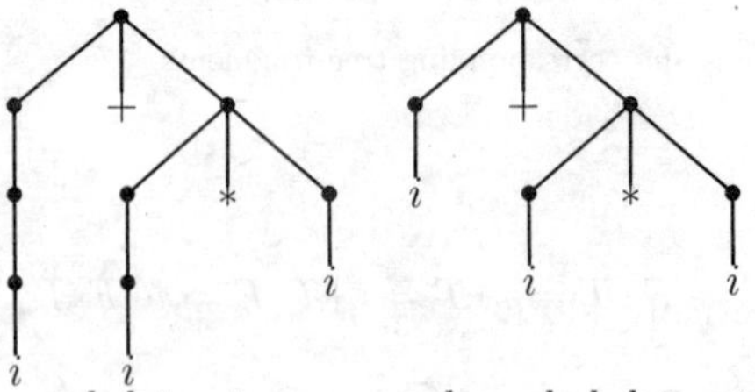


*skeleton tree* *condensed skeleton tree*

or the corresponding parenthesized string:

$$\Big[\big[[[i]]\big] + \big[[[i]] * [i]\big]\Big]$$

[18] Assuming brackets not to be in the terminal alphabet.

A further simplification of the skeleton tree consists in shortening non-bifurcating paths, resulting in the *condensed skeleton tree* (right). The nodes fused together represent copy rules of the grammar. The corresponding parenthesized sentence is

$$[[i]+[[i]*[i]]]$$

Some approaches tend to view a grammar as a device for assigning structure to sentences. From this standpoint a grammar defines a set of syntax trees, that is, a tree language instead of a string language.[19]

### Left and Right Derivations

A derivation

$$\beta_0 \Rightarrow \beta_1 \Rightarrow \ldots \Rightarrow \beta_p$$

where

$$\beta_i = \delta_i A_i \eta_i \text{ and } \beta_{i+1} = \delta_i \alpha_i \eta_i$$

is called *right* or rightmost (resp. *left*) if, for all $0 \leqslant i \leqslant p-1$, it is $\eta_i \in \Sigma^*$ (resp. $\delta_i \in \Sigma^*$).
In words, a right (resp. left) derivation expands at each step the rightmost (resp. leftmost) nonterminal. A letter $r$ or $l$ may be subscripted to the arrow sign, to make explicit the order of the derivation.

Observe that other derivations exist which are neither right nor left, because the nonterminal symbol expanded is not always either rightmost or leftmost, or because it is at some step rightmost and at some other step leftmost.
par Returning to the preceding example, the derivation (2.2) is leftmost and is denoted by $E \overset{+}{\underset{l}{\Rightarrow}} i+i*i$. The derivation 2.3 is rightmost, whereas the derivation

$$\begin{aligned} E \underset{l,r}{\Rightarrow} E+T \underset{r}{\Rightarrow} E+T*F \underset{l}{\Rightarrow} T+T*F \Rightarrow T+F*F \underset{r}{\Rightarrow} \\ T+F*i \underset{l}{\Rightarrow} F+F*i \underset{r}{\Rightarrow} F+i*i \underset{r}{\Rightarrow} i+i*i \end{aligned} \tag{2.4}$$

is neither right nor left. The three derivations are represented by the same tree.

This example actually illustrates an essential property of context-free grammars.

*Property 2.41.* Every sentence of a context-free grammar can be generated by a left (or right) derivation.

Therefore it does no harm to use just right (or left) derivations in the definition (p. 36) of the language generated by a grammar.

---

[19] A reference to the theory of tree languages is [21].

On the other hand, other more complex types of grammars, as the context-sensitive ones, do not share this nice property, which is quite important for obtaining efficient algorithms for string recognition and parsing, as we shall see.

### 2.5.8 Parenthesis Languages

Many artificial languages include parenthesized or nested structures, made by matching pairs of *opening/closing marks*. Any such occurrence may contain other matching pairs.

The marks are abstract elements that have different concrete representations in distinct settings. Thus Pascal block structures are enclosed within 'begin' ... 'end', while in language C curly brackets are used.

A massive use of parenthesis structures characterizes the mark-up language XML, that offers the possibility of inventing new matching pairs. An example is $\langle$*title*$\rangle \ldots \langle$*/title*$\rangle$ used to delimit the document title. Similarly, in the LaTeX notation this book was written in, a mathematical formula is enclosed between the marks `\begin{equation}`...`\end{equation}`.

When a marked construct may contain another construct of the same kind, it is called *self-nested*. Self-nesting is potentially unbounded in artificial languages, whereas in natural languages its use is moderate, because it causes difficulty of comprehension by breaking the flow of discourse. Next comes an example of a complex German sentence [20] with three nested relative clauses:

$$\textit{der Mann } \underbrace{\textit{der die Frau } \underbrace{\textit{die das Kind } \underbrace{\textit{das die Katze füttert}} \textit{ sieht}} \textit{ liebt}} \textit{ schläft}$$

Abstracting from concrete representation and content, this paradigm is known as *Dyck language*. The terminal alphabet contains one or more pairs of opening/closing marks. An example is alphabet $\Sigma = \{')', '(', ']', '['\}$ and sentence $[\,]\,(\,(\,[\,]\,(\,)\,)\,)$.

Dyck sentences are characterized by the following *cancellation rule* that checks parentheses are well nested: given a string, repeatedly substitute the empty string for a pair of adjacent matching parentheses

$$[\,] \Rightarrow \varepsilon \qquad (\,) \Rightarrow \varepsilon$$

thus obtaining another string. Repeat until the transformation no longer applies; the original string is correct if, and only if, the last string is empty.

[20] The man who loves the woman (who sees the child (who feeds the cat)) sleeps.

*Example 2.42.* Dyck language
To aid the eye, we encode left parentheses as $a, b, \ldots$ and right parentheses as $a', b', \ldots$.
With alphabet $\Sigma = \{a, a', b, b'\}$, the Dyck language is generated by grammar:

$$S \rightarrow aSa'S \mid bSb'S \mid \varepsilon$$

Notice we need nonlinear rules (the first two) to generate this language.
To see that, compare with language $L_1$ of example 2.29 on p. 30. The latter, recoding its alphabet $\{b, e\}$ as $\{a, a'\}$, is strictly included in the Dyck language, since $L_1$ disallows any string with two or more nests, e.g.,

$$a\,\underbrace{a\,\underbrace{aa'}\,a'}\,\underbrace{a\,\underbrace{a\,\underbrace{aa'}\,a'}\,a'}\,a'$$

Such sentences have a branching syntax tree that requires nonlinear rules for its derivation.

Another way of constraining the grammar to produce nested constructs, is to force each rule to be parenthesized.

**Definition 2.43.** Parenthesized grammar
Let $G = (V, \Sigma, P, S)$ be a grammar with an alphabet $\Sigma$ not containing parentheses. The parenthesized grammar $G_p$ has alphabet $\Sigma \cup \{'(', ')'\}$ and rules

$$A \rightarrow (\alpha) \text{ where } A \rightarrow \alpha \text{ is a rule of } G$$

The grammar is *distinctly parenthesized* if every rule has form

$$A \rightarrow (_A\ \alpha\ )_A \qquad B \rightarrow (_B\ \alpha\ )_B$$

where $(_A$ and $)_A$ are parentheses subscripted with the nonterminal name.

Clearly each sentence produced by such grammars exhibits parenthesized structure.

*Example 2.44.* Parenthesis grammar
The parenthesized version of the grammar for lists of palindromes (p. 31) is

$$\begin{array}{ll} list \rightarrow (pal, list) & pal \rightarrow () \\ list \rightarrow (pal) & pal \rightarrow (a\ pal\ a) \\ & pal \rightarrow (b\ pal\ b) \end{array}$$

The original sentence $aa$ becomes the parenthesized sentence $((a\,(\,)\,a))$.

A notable effect of the presence of parentheses is to allow a simpler checking of string correctness, to be discussed in Chapter 4.

### 2.5.9 Regular Composition of Context-Free Languages

If the basic operations of regular languages, union, concatenation, and star, are applied to context-free languages, the result remains a member of the $CF$ family, to be shown next.

Let $G_1 = (\Sigma_1, V_1, P_1, S_1)$ and $G_2 = (\Sigma_2, V_2, P_2, S_2)$ be the grammars defining languages $L_1$ and $L_2$. We need the unrestrictive hypothesis that nonterminal sets are disjoint, $V_1 \cap V_2 = \emptyset$. Moreover, we stipulate that symbol $S$, to be used as axiom of the grammar under construction, is not used by either grammar, $S \notin (V_1 \cup V_2)$.

Union: The union $L_1 \cup L_2$ is defined by the grammar containing the rules of both grammars, plus the initial rules $S \to S_1 \mid S_2$. In formulas, the grammar is

$$G = (\Sigma_1 \cup \Sigma_2, \{S\} \cup V_1 \cup V_2, \{S \to S_1 \mid S_2\} \cup P_1 \cup P_2, S)$$

Concatenation: The concatenation $L_1 L_2$ is defined by the grammar containing the rules of both grammars, plus the initial rule $S \to S_1 S_2$. The grammar is

$$G = (\Sigma_1 \cup \Sigma_2, \{S\} \cup V_1 \cup V_2, \{S \to S_1 S_2\} \cup P_1 \cup P_2, S)$$

Star: The grammar $G$ of the starred language $(L_1)^*$ includes the rules of $G_1$ and rules $S \to S S_1 \mid \varepsilon$.

Cross: From the identity $L^+ = L.L^*$, the grammar of the cross language could be written applying the concatenation construction to $L$ and $L^*$, but it is better to produce the grammar directly. The grammar $G$ of language $(L_1)^+$ contains the rules of $G_1$ and rules $S \to S S_1 \mid S_1$.

From all this we have:

*Property 2.45.* The family $CF$ of context-free languages is closed by union, concatenation, star, and cross.

*Example 2.46.* Union of languages
The language

$$L = \{a^i b^i c^* \mid i \geqslant 0\} \cup \{a^* b^i c^i \mid i \geqslant 0\} = L_1 \cup L_2$$

contains sentences of the form $a^i b^j c^k$ with $i = j \vee j = k$, such as

$$a^5 b^5 c^2, a^5 b^5 c^5, b^5 c^5$$

The rules for the component languages are straightforward:

| $G_1$ | $G_2$ |
|---|---|
| $S_1 \to XC$ | $S_2 \to AY$ |
| $X \to aXb \mid \varepsilon$ | $Y \to bYc \mid \varepsilon$ |
| $C \to cC \mid \varepsilon$ | $A \to aA \mid \varepsilon$ |

We just add alternatives $S \to S_1 \mid S_2$, to trigger derivation with either grammar.

A word of caution: if the nonterminal sets overlap, this construction produces a grammar that generates a language typically larger than the union. To see it, replace grammar $G_2$ with the trivially equivalent grammar $G''$:

$$S'' \to AX \qquad X \to bXc \mid \varepsilon \qquad A \to aA \mid \varepsilon$$

Then the putative grammar of the union, $\{S \to S_1 \mid S''\} \cup P_1 \cup P''$, would also allow hybrid derivations using rules from both grammars, thus generating for instance *abcbc*, which is not in the union language.

Notably, property 2.45 holds for both families *REG* and *CF*, but only the former is closed by intersection and complement, to be seen later.

Grammar of Mirror Language

Examining the effect of string reversal on the sentences of a *CF* language, one immediately sees the family is closed with respect to reversal (the same as family *REG*). Given a grammar, the rules generating the mirror language are obtained reversing every right part of a rule.

### 2.5.10 Ambiguity

The common linguistic phenomenon of ambiguity in natural language shows up when a sentence has two or more meanings. Ambiguity is of two kinds, semantic or syntactic. Semantic ambiguity occurs in the clause `a hot spring`, where the noun denotes either a coil or a season. A case of syntactic (or structural) ambiguity is `half baked chicken`, having different meanings depending on the structure assigned:

`[[half baked] chicken]` or `[half [baked chicken]]`.

Although ambiguity may cause misunderstanding in human communication, negative consequences are counteracted by availability of nonlinguistic clues for choosing the intended interpretation.

Artificial languages too can be ambiguous, but the phenomenon is less deep than in human languages. In most situations ambiguity is a defect to be removed or counteracted.

A *sentence* $x$ defined by grammar $G$ is syntactically *ambiguous*, if it is generated with two different syntax trees. Then the *grammar* too is called *ambiguous*.

*Example 2.47.* Consider again the language of arithmetic expressions of example 2.39, p. 40, but define it with a different grammar $G'$ equivalent to the previous one:

$$E \to E + E \mid E * E \mid (E) \mid i$$

The left derivations

$$E \Rightarrow E * E \Rightarrow E + E * E \Rightarrow i + E * E \Rightarrow i + i * E \Rightarrow i + i * i \tag{2.5}$$

$$E \Rightarrow E + E \Rightarrow i + E \Rightarrow i + E * E \Rightarrow i + i * E \Rightarrow i + i * i \tag{2.6}$$

generate the same sentence, with different trees:

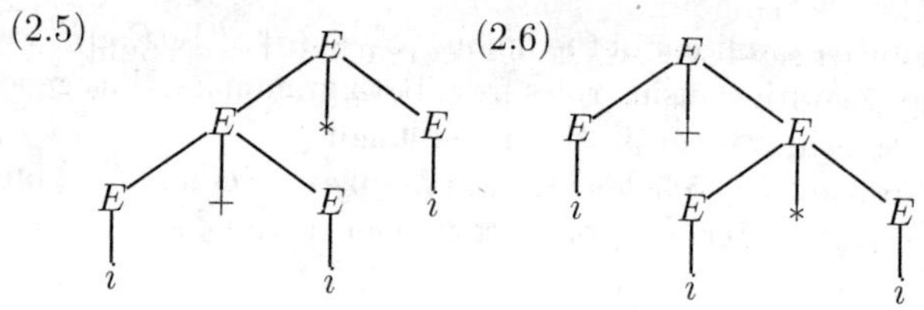


The sentence $i + i * i$ is therefore ambiguous.

Pay attention now to the meaning of the two readings of the same expression. The left tree interprets the sentence as $(i + i) * i$, the right tree assigns the interpretation $i + (i * i)$. The latter is likely to be preferable, because it agrees with the traditional precedence of operators. Another ambiguous sentence is $i + i + i$, having two trees that differ in the order of association of subexpressions: from left to right, or the other way. As a consequence grammar $G'$ is ambiguous.
A major defect of this grammar is that it does not force the expected precedence of product over sum.

On the other hand, for grammar $G$ of example 2.39 on p. 40 each sentence has only one left derivation, therefore all sentences are unambiguous, and the grammar as well.

It may be noticed that the new grammar $G'$ is smaller than the old one $G$: this manifests a frequent property of ambiguous grammars, their conciseness with respect to equivalent unambiguous ones. In special situations, when one wants the simplest possible grammar for a language, ambiguity may be tolerated, but in general conciseness cannot be bought at the cost of equivocation.

The *degree of ambiguity* of a sentence $x$ of language $L(G)$ is the number of distinct syntax trees deriving the sentence. For a grammar the degree of ambiguity is the maximum degree of any ambiguous sentence. The next derivation shows such degree may be unbounded.

*Example 2.48.* (Example 2.47 continued)
The degree of ambiguity is 2 for sentence $i + i + i$ ; it is 5 for $i + i * i + i$, as one sees from the skeleton trees:

$$\underbrace{\underbrace{i+i}*\underbrace{i+i}},\quad \underbrace{\underbrace{i+\underbrace{i*i}}+i},\quad \underbrace{i+\underbrace{\underbrace{i*i}+i}},\quad \underbrace{i+\underbrace{i*\underbrace{i+i}}},\quad \underbrace{\underbrace{\underbrace{i+i}*i}+i}$$

It is easy to see that longer sentences cause the degree of ambiguity to grow unbounded.

An important practical problem is to check a given grammar for ambiguity. This is an example of a seemingly simple problem, for which no general algorithm exists: the problem is undecidable.[21] This means that any general procedure for checking a grammar for ambiguity may be forced to examine longer and longer sentences, without ever reaching the certainty of the answer. On the other hand, for a specific grammar, with some ingenuity, one can often prove nonambiguity by applying some form of inductive reasoning.

In practice this is not necessary, and two approaches usually suffice. First, a small number of rather short sentences are tested, by constructing their syntax trees and checking that they are unique. If the test is passed, one has to check whether the grammar complies with certain conditions characterizing the so-called deterministic context-free languages, to be lengthily studied in Chapters 4 and 5. Such conditions are sufficient to ensure nonambiguity.

Even better is to prevent the problem when a grammar is designed, by avoiding some common pitfalls to be explained next.

### *2.5.11 Catalogue of Ambiguous Forms and Remedies*

Following the definition, an ambiguous sentence displays two or more structures, each one possibly associated with a sensible interpretation. Though the cases of ambiguity are abundant in natural language, clarity of communication is not seriously impaired because sentences are uttered or written in a living context (gestures, intonation, presuppositions, etc.) that helps in selecting the interpretation intended by the author. On the contrary, in artificial languages ambiguity cannot be tolerated because machines are not as good as humans in making use of context, with the negative consequence of unpredictable behavior of the interpreter or compiler.

Now we classify the most common types of ambiguity and we show how to remove them by modifying the grammar, or in some cases the language.

#### Ambiguity from Bilateral Recursion

A nonterminal symbol $A$ is bilaterally recursive if it is both left and right-recursive (i.e., it offers derivations $A \stackrel{+}{\Rightarrow} A\gamma$ and $A \stackrel{+}{\Rightarrow} \beta A$). We distinguish the case the two derivations are produced by the same or by different rules.

[21] A proof can be found in [28].

*Example 2.49.* Bilateral recursion from same rule
The grammar $G_1$:

$$E \to E + E \mid i$$

generates string $i + i + i$ with two different left derivations:

$$E \Rightarrow E + E \Rightarrow E + E + E \Rightarrow i + E + E \Rightarrow i + i + E \Rightarrow i + i + i$$
$$E \Rightarrow E + E \Rightarrow i + E \Rightarrow i + E + E \Rightarrow i + i + E \Rightarrow i + i + i$$

Ambiguity comes from the absence of a fixed order of generation of the string, from the left or from the right. Looking at the intended meaning as arithmetic formulas, this grammar does not specify the order of application of operations.

In order to remove ambiguity, observe this language is a list with separators $L(G_1) = i(+i)^*$, a paradigm we are able to define with a right-recursive rule, $E \to i + E \mid i$; or with a left-recursive rule $E \to E + i \mid i$. Both are unambiguous.

*Example 2.50.* Left and right recursions in different rules
A second case of bilateral recursive ambiguity is grammar $G_2$:

$$A \to aA \mid Ab \mid c$$

This language too is regular: $L(G_2) = a^*cb^*$. It is the concatenation of two lists, $a^*$ and $b^*$, with $c$ interposed. Ambiguity disappears if the two lists are derived by separate rules, thus suggesting the grammar:

$$S \to AcB \qquad A \to aA \mid \varepsilon \qquad B \to bB \mid \varepsilon$$

An alternative remedy is to decide the first list should be generated before the second one (or conversely):

$$S \to aS \mid X \qquad X \to Xb \mid c$$

Remark: a double recursion on the same nonterminal by itself does not cause ambiguity, if the two recursions are not left and right. Observe the grammar

$$S \to +SS \mid \times SS \mid i$$

that defines so-called prefix polish expressions with signs of sum and product (further studied in Chapter 6), such as $+ + ii \times ii$. Although two rules are doubly recursive, since one recursion is right but the other is not left, the grammar is not ambiguous.

## Ambiguity from Union

If languages $L_1 = L(G_1)$ and $L_2 = L(G_2)$ share some sentences, that is, their intersection is not empty, the grammar $G$ of the united languages, constructed as explained on p. 46, is ambiguous. (No need to repeat the two component grammars should have disjoint nonterminal sets.)
Take a sentence $x \in L_1 \cap L_2$. It is obviously produced by two distinct derivations, one using rules of $G_1$, the other using rules of $G_2$. The sentence is ambiguous for grammar $G$ that contains all the rules. Notice a sentence $x$ belonging to the first but not the second language, $x \in L_1 \setminus L_2$, is derived by rules of $G_1$ only, hence is not ambiguous (if the first grammar is so).

*Example 2.51.* Union of overlapping languages
In language and compiler design there are various causes for overlap.

1. When one wants to single out a special pattern requiring special processing, within a general class of phrases. Consider additive arithmetic expressions with constants $C$ and variables $i$. A grammar is

$$E \to E{+}C \mid E{+}i \mid C \mid i \qquad C \to 0 \mid 1D \mid \ldots \mid 9D \quad D \to 0D \mid \ldots \mid 9D \mid \varepsilon$$

Now assume the compiler has to single out such expressions as $i + 1$ or $1 + i$, because they have to be translated to machine code, using increment instead of addition. To this end we add the rules

$$E \to i + 1 \mid 1 + i$$

Unfortunately, the new grammar is ambiguous, since a sentence like $1 + i$ is generated by the original rules too.

2. When the same operator is overloaded, i.e. used with different meanings in different constructs. In language Pascal the sign '+' denotes both addition in

$$E \to E + T \mid T \qquad T \to V \qquad V \to \ldots$$

and set union in

$$E_{set} \to E_{set} + T_{set} \mid T_{set} \qquad T_{set} \to V$$

Such ambiguities need severe grammar surgery to be eliminated: either the two ambiguous constructs are made disjoint or they are fused together. Disjunction of constructs is not feasible in the previous examples, because string '1' cannot be removed from the set of integer constants derived from nonterminal $C$. To enforce a special treatment of value '1', if one accepts a syntactic change to the language, it suffices to add operator *inc* (for increment by 1) and replace rule $E \to i + 1 \mid 1 + i$ with rule $E \to inc\ i$.

In the latter example ambiguity is semantic, caused by the double meaning (polysemy) of operator '+'. A remedy is to collapse together the rules for arithmetic expressions (generated from $E$) and set expressions (generated

from $E_{set}$), thus giving up a syntax-based separation. The semantic analyzer will take care of it. Alternatively, if modifications are permissible, one may replace '+' by character '∪' in set expressions.
In the following examples removal of overlapping constructs actually succeeds.

*Example 2.52.* (McNaughton)

1. Grammar $G$:
$$S \to bS \mid cS \mid D \qquad D \to bD \mid cD \mid \varepsilon$$
is ambiguous since $L(G) = \{b, c\}^* = L_D(G)$. The derivations
$$S \stackrel{+}{\Rightarrow} bbcD \Rightarrow bbc \qquad S \Rightarrow D \stackrel{+}{\Rightarrow} bbcD \Rightarrow bbc$$
produce the same result. Deleting the rules of $D$, which are redundant, we have $S \to bS \mid cS \mid \varepsilon$.
2. Grammar
$$S \to B \mid D \qquad B \to bBc \mid \varepsilon \qquad D \to dDe \mid \varepsilon$$
where $B$ generates $b^n c^n, n \geqslant 0$, and $D$ generates $d^n e^n, n \geqslant 0$, has just one ambiguous sentence: $\varepsilon$. Remedy: generate it directly from axiom:
$$S \to B \mid D \mid \varepsilon \qquad B \to bBc \mid bc \qquad D \to dDe \mid de$$

### Ambiguity from Concatenation

Concatenating languages may cause ambiguity, if a suffix of a sentence of language one is also a prefix of a sentence of language two.
Remember the grammar $G$ of concatenation $L_1 L_2$ (p. 46) contains rule $S \to S_1 S_2$ in addition to the rules of $G_1$ and $G_2$ (by hypothesis not ambiguous). Ambiguity arises in $G$ if the following sentences exist in the languages:

$$u' \in L_1 \qquad u'v \in L_1 \qquad vz'' \in L_2 \qquad z'' \in L_2$$

Then string $u'vz''$ of language $L_1.L_2$ is ambiguous, via the derivations

$$S \Rightarrow S_1 S_2 \stackrel{+}{\Rightarrow} u' S_2 \stackrel{+}{\Rightarrow} u'vz'' \qquad S \Rightarrow S_1 S_2 \stackrel{+}{\Rightarrow} u'vS_2 \stackrel{+}{\Rightarrow} u'vz''$$

*Example 2.53.* Concatenation of Dyck languages
For the concatenation $L = L_1 L_2$ of the Dyck languages (p. 44) $L_1$ and $L_2$ over alphabets (in the order given) $\{a, a', b, b'\}$ and $\{b, b', c, c'\}$, a sentence is $aa'bb'cc'$. The standard grammar of $L$ is

$$S \to S_1 S_2 \qquad S_1 \to aS_1 a' S_1 \mid bS_1 b' S_1 \mid \varepsilon \qquad S_2 \to bS_2 b' S_2 \mid cS_2 c' S_2 \mid \varepsilon$$

The sentence is derived in two ways:

$$\overbrace{aa'bb'}^{S_1}\overbrace{cc'}^{S_2} \qquad \overbrace{aa'}^{S_1}\overbrace{bb'cc'}^{S_2}$$

To remove this ambiguity one should block the movement of a string from the suffix of language one to the prefix of language two (and conversely).

If the designer is free to modify the language, a simple remedy is to interpose a new terminal as separator between the two languages. In our example, with $\sharp$ as separator, the language $L_1\sharp L_2$ is easily defined without ambiguity by a grammar with initial rule $S \to S_1\sharp S_2$.

Otherwise, a more complex unambiguous solution would be to write a grammar, with the property that any string not containing $c$, such as $bb'$, is in language $L_1$ but not in $L_2$. Notice that string $bcc'b'$ is on the other hand, assigned to language two.

### Unique Decoding

A nice illustration of concatenation ambiguity comes from the study of codes in information theory. An information source is a process producing a message, i.e., a sequence of symbols from a finite set $\Gamma = \{A, B, \ldots, Z\}$. Each such symbol is then encoded into a string over a terminal alphabet $\Sigma$ (typically binary); a coding function maps each symbol into a short terminal string, termed its code.

Consider for instance the following source symbols and their mapping into binary codes ($\Sigma = \{0, 1\}$):

$$\Gamma = \{\overbrace{A}^{01}, \overbrace{C}^{10}, \overbrace{E}^{11}, \overbrace{R}^{001}\}$$

Message $ARRECA$ is encoded as 01 001 001 11 10 01; by decoding this string the original text is the only one to be obtained. Message coding is expressed by grammar $G_1$:

$$Mess \to A\,Mess \mid C\,Mess \mid E\,Mess \mid R\,Mess \mid A \mid C \mid E \mid R$$

$$A \to 01 \qquad C \to 10 \qquad E \to 11 \qquad R \to 001$$

The grammar generates a message such as $AC$ by concatenating the corresponding codes, as displayed in the syntax tree:

$$\overbrace{\overbrace{01}^{A}\quad\overbrace{\overbrace{10}^{C}}^{Mess}}^{Mess}$$

As the grammar is clearly unambiguous, every encoded message, i.e., every sentence of language $L(G_1)$, has one and only one syntax tree corresponding to the decoded message.
On the contrary, the next bad choice of codes

$$\Gamma = \{ \overbrace{A}^{00}, \overbrace{C}^{01}, \overbrace{E}^{10}, \overbrace{R}^{010} \}$$

renders ambiguous the grammar

$$Mess \rightarrow A\,Mess \mid C\,Mess \mid E\,Mess \mid R\,Mess \mid A \mid C \mid E \mid R$$

$$A \rightarrow 00 \qquad C \rightarrow 01 \qquad E \rightarrow 10 \qquad R \rightarrow 010$$

Consequently, message 00010010100100 can be deciphered in two ways, as $ARRECA$ or as $ACAEECA$.
The defect has two causes: the identity

$$\underbrace{01}_{\text{first}}.00.10 = \underbrace{010}_{\text{first}}.010$$

holds for two pairs of concatenated codes; and the first codes, 01 and 010, are one prefix of the other.
Code theory studies these and similar conditions that make a set of codes uniquely decipherable.

## Other Ambiguous Situations

The next case is similar to the ambiguity of regular expressions (p. 22).

*Example 2.54.* Consider the grammar

$$S \rightarrow DcD \qquad D \rightarrow bD \mid cD \mid \varepsilon$$

Rule one says a sentence contains at least one $c$; the alternatives of $D$ generate $\{b, c\}^*$. The same language structure would be defined by regular expression $\{b, c\}^*\, c\, \{b, c\}^*$, which is ambiguous: every sentence with two or more $c$ is ambiguous since the distinguished occurrence of $c$ is not fixed. This defect can be repaired imposing the distinguished $c$ is, say, the leftmost one:

$$S \rightarrow BcD \qquad D \rightarrow bD \mid cD \mid \varepsilon \qquad B \rightarrow bB \mid \varepsilon$$

Notice that $B$ may not derive a string containing $c$.

*Example 2.55.* Setting an order on rules
In grammar

$$S \rightarrow bSc \mid bbSc \mid \varepsilon$$

the first two rules may be applied in one or the other order, producing the ambiguous derivations

$$S \Rightarrow bbSc \Rightarrow bbbScc \Rightarrow bbbcc \qquad S \Rightarrow bSc \Rightarrow bbbScc \Rightarrow bbbcc$$

Remedy: oblige rule one to precede rule two:

$$S \to bSc \mid D \qquad D \to bbDc \mid \varepsilon$$

### Ambiguity of Conditional Statements

A notorious case of ambiguity in programming languages with conditional instructions occurred in the first version of language Algol 60,[22] a milestone for applications of $CF$ grammars. Consider grammar

$$S \to if\ b\ then\ S\ else\ S \mid if\ b\ then\ S \mid a$$

where $b$ stands for a boolean condition and $a$ for any nonconditional instruction, both left undefined for brevity. The first alternative produces a *two legs* conditional instruction, the second a *one-leg* construct.
Ambiguity arises when two sentences are nested, with the outermost being a two-way conditional. For instance, examine the two readings:

$$\overbrace{if\ b\ then\ \overbrace{if\ b\ then\ a\ else\ a}} \qquad \overbrace{if\ b\ then\ \overbrace{if\ b\ then\ a}\ else\ a}$$

caused by the "dangling" *else*.

It is possible to eliminate the ambiguity at the cost of complicating the grammar. Assume we decide to choose the left skeleton tree, that binds the *else* to the immediately preceding *if*. The corresponding grammar is:

$$S \to S_E \mid S_T \qquad S_E \to if\ b\ then\ S_E\ else\ S_E \mid a$$

$$S_T \to if\ b\ then\ S_E\ else\ S_T \mid if\ b\ then\ S$$

Observe the syntax class $S$ has been split into two classes: $S_E$ defines a two-legs conditional such that its nested conditionals are in the same class $S_E$. The other syntax class $S_T$ defines a one-leg conditional, or a two-legs conditional such that the first nested conditional is of class $S_E$ and the second is of class $S_T$; this excludes the combinations

$$if\ b\ then\ S_T\ else\ S_T \qquad \text{and} \qquad if\ b\ then\ S_T\ else\ S_E$$

The facts that only $S_E$ may precede *else*, and that only $S_T$ defines a one-leg conditional, disallow derivation of the right skeleton tree.

---

22 The following official version [39] removed the ambiguity.

If the language syntax can be modified, a simpler solution exists: many language designers have introduced a closing mark for delimiting conditional constructs. See the next use of mark *end_if*:

$$S \to if\ b\ then\ S\ else\ S\ end\_if \mid if\ b\ then\ S\ end\_if \mid a$$

Indeed this is a sort of parenthesizing (p. 45) of the original grammar.

## Inherent Ambiguity of Language

In all preceding examples we have found that a language is defined by equivalent grammars, some ambiguous some not. But this is not always the case. A language is called *inherently ambiguous* if every grammar of the language is ambiguous. Surprisingly enough, inherently ambiguous languages exist!

*Example 2.56.* Unavoidable ambiguity from union
Recall example 2.46 on p. 46:

$$L = \{a^i b^j c^k \mid (i, j, k \geqslant 0) \wedge ((i = j) \vee (j = k))\}$$

The language can be equivalently defined by means of the union

$$L = \{a^i b^i c^* \mid i \geqslant 0\} \cup \{a^* b^i c^i \mid i \geqslant 0\} = L_1 \cup L_2$$

of two nondisjoint languages.

We intuitively argue that any grammar of this language is necessarily ambiguous. The grammar on p. 46 unites the rules of the component grammars, and is obviously ambiguous for every sentence $x \in \{\varepsilon, abc, \ldots a^i b^i c^i \ldots\}$, shared by both languages. Any such sentence is produced by $G_1$ using rules checking that $|x|_a = |x|_b$, a check only possible for a syntax structure of the type

$$\underbrace{a \ldots a\ \underbrace{\underbrace{ab}}\ b \ldots b}\, cc \ldots c$$

Now the same string $x$, viewed as a sentence of $L_2$, must be generated with a structure of type

$$a \ldots aa\, \underbrace{b \ldots b\ \underbrace{\underbrace{bc}}\ c \ldots c}$$

in order to perform the equality check $|x|_b = |x|_c$.

No matter which variation of the grammar we make, the two equality checks on the exponents are unavoidable for such sentences and the grammar remains ambiguous.

In reality, inherent language ambiguity is rare and hardly, if ever, affects technical languages.

### 2.5.12 Weak and Structural Equivalence

It is not enough for a grammar to generate the correct sentences; it should also assign to each one a suitable structure, in agreement with the intended meaning. This requirement of *structural adequacy* has already been invoked at times, for instance when discussing operator precedence in hierarchical lists.

We ought to reexamine the notion of grammar in the light of structural adequacy. Recall the definition on p. 36: two grammars are equivalent if they define the same language, $L(G) = L(G')$. Such definition, to be qualified now as *weak equivalence*, poorly fits with the real possibility of substituting one grammar for the other in technical artifacts such as compilers. The reason is the two grammars are not guaranteed to assign the same meaningful structure to every sentence.

We need a more stringent definition of equivalence, which is only relevant for unambiguous grammars. Grammars $G$ and $G'$ are *strongly or structurally equivalent*, if $L(G) = L(G')$ and in addition $G$ and $G'$ assign to each sentence two syntax trees, which may be considered *structurally similar*.

The last condition should be formulated in accordance with the intended application. A plausible formulation is: two syntax trees are structurally similar if the corresponding condensed skeleton trees (p. 43) are equal.

Strong equivalence implies weak equivalence, but the former is a decidable property, unlike the latter. [23]

*Example 2.57.* Structural adequacy of arithmetic expressions

The difference between strong and weak equivalence is manifested by the case of arithmetic expressions, such as $3+5\times 8+2$, first viewed as a list of digits separated by plus and times signs.

- First grammar $G_1$:

$$E \to E + C \qquad E \to E \times C \qquad E \to C$$
$$C \to 0 \mid 1 \mid 2 \mid 3 \mid 4 \mid 5 \mid 6 \mid 7 \mid 8 \mid 9$$

  The syntax tree of the previous sentence is

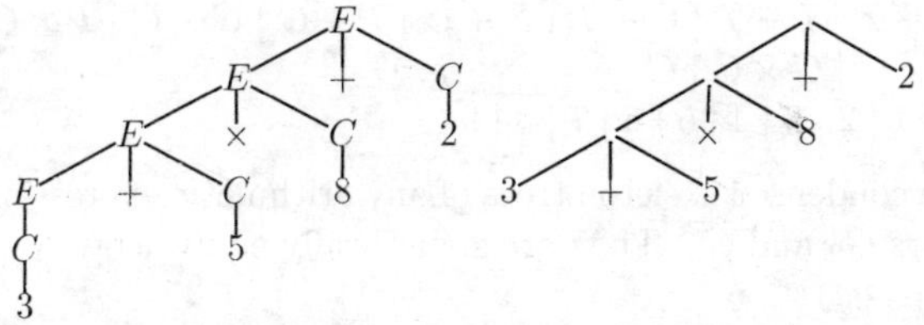


  In the condensed skeleton (right), nonterminals and copy rules have been dropped.

[23] The decision algorithm, e.g., in [47], is similar to the one for checking the equivalence of finite automata, to be presented in next chapter.

- A second grammar $G_2$ for this language is

$$E \to E + T \qquad E \to T \qquad T \to T \times C \qquad T \to C$$
$$C \to 0 \mid 1 \mid 2 \mid 3 \mid 4 \mid 5 \mid 6 \mid 7 \mid 8 \mid 9$$

  The two grammars are weakly equivalent. Observing now the syntax tree of the same sentence:

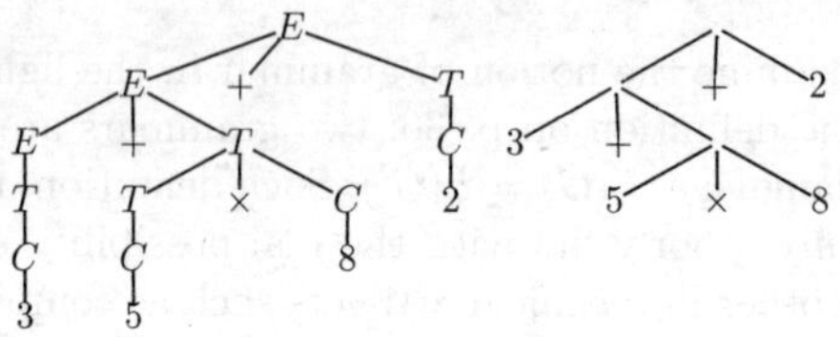


  we see its skeleton differs from the previous one: it contains a subtree with frontier 5 × 8, associated with a multiplication. Therefore the grammars are not structurally equivalent.

Is either one of the grammars preferable? Concerning ambiguity, both grammars are all right. But only grammar $G_2$ is structurally adequate, if one considers also meaning. In fact, sentence $3{+}5{\times}8{+}2$ denotes a computation, to be executed in the traditional order: $3+(5\times 8)+2 = (3+40)+2 = (43+2) = 45$: this is the *semantic interpretation*. The parentheses specifying the order of evaluation $((3 + (5 \times 8)) + 2)$ can be mapped on the subtrees of the skeletal tree produced by $G_2$.
On the contrary, grammar $G_1$ produces the parenthesizing $(((3 + 5) \times 8) + 2)$ which is not adequate, because by giving precedence to the first sum over the product, it returns the wrong semantic interpretation, 66.
Incidentally, the second grammar is more complex because enforcing operator precedence requires more nonterminals and rules.

It is crucial for a grammar intended for driving a compiler to be structurally adequate, as we shall see in the last chapter on syntax-directed translations.

- A case of structural equivalence is illustrated by the next grammar $G_3$[24]:

$$E \to E + T \mid T + T \mid C + T \mid E + C \mid T + C \mid C + C \mid T \times C \mid C \times C \mid C$$
$$T \to T \times C \mid C \times C \mid C$$
$$C \to 0 \mid 1 \mid 2 \mid 3 \mid 4 \mid 5 \mid 6 \mid 7 \mid 8 \mid 9$$

  Now the condensed skeleton trees of any arithmetic expression coincide for grammars $G_2$ and $G_3$. They are structurally equivalent.

---

[24] This grammar has more rules because it does not exploit copy rules to express inclusion of syntax classes. Categorization and ensuing taxonomies reduce the complexity of descriptions in any area of knowledge.

### Generalized Structural Equivalence

Sometimes a looser criterion of similarity than strict identity of condensed skeleton trees is more suitable. This consists in requesting that the two corresponding trees should be easily mapped one on the other by some simple transformation. The idea can be differently materialized: one possibility is to have a bijective correspondence between the subtrees of one tree and the subtrees of the other. For instance, the grammars

$$\{S \rightarrow Sa \mid a\} \qquad \text{and} \qquad \{X \rightarrow aX \mid a\}$$

are just weakly equivalent in generating $L = a^+$, since the condensed skeleton trees differ, as in the example of sentence $aa$:

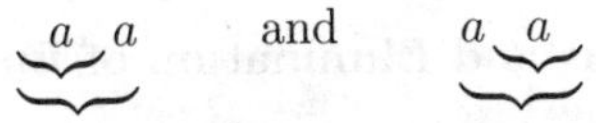


However, the two grammars may be considered structurally equivalent in a generalized sense because each left-linear tree of the first grammar corresponds to a right-linear tree of the second. The intuition that the two grammars are similar is satisfied because their trees are specularly identical, i.e., they become coincident by turning left-recursive rules into right-recursive (or conversely).

## *2.5.13 Grammar Transformations and Normal Forms*

We are going to study a range of transformations that are useful to obtain grammars having certain desired properties, without affecting the language. Normal forms are restricted rule patterns, yet allowing any context-free language to be defined. Such forms are widely used in theoretical papers, to simplify statements and proofs of theorems. Otherwise, in applied work, grammars in normal form are rarely used because they are much larger and less readable.

Several grammar transformations (e.g., the movement of recursion from left to right) are useful for parsing algorithms. We start the survey of transformations from simple ones.

Let grammar $G = (V, \Sigma, P, S)$ be given.

### Nonterminal Expansion

A general-purpose transformation preserving language is *nonterminal expansion*, consisting of replacing a nonterminal with its alternatives.

Replace rule $A \rightarrow \alpha B \gamma$ with rules

$$A \to \alpha\beta_1\gamma \mid \alpha\beta_2\gamma \mid \ldots \mid \alpha\beta_n\gamma$$

where $B \to \beta_1 \mid \beta_2 \mid \ldots \mid \beta_n$ are all the alternatives of $B$. Clearly the language does not change, since the two-step derivation $A \Rightarrow \alpha B\gamma \Rightarrow \alpha\beta_i\gamma$ becomes the immediate derivation $A \Rightarrow \alpha\beta_i\gamma$, to the same effect.

### Axiom Elimination from Right Parts

At no loss of generality, every right part of a rule may exclude the presence of the axiom, i.e., be a string over alphabet $(\Sigma \cup (V \setminus \{S\}))$. To this end, just introduce a new axiom $S_0$ and rule $S_0 \to S$.

### Nullable Nonterminals and Elimination of Empty Rules

A nonterminal $A$ is *nullable* if it can derive the empty string, i.e., $A \overset{+}{\Rightarrow} \varepsilon$. Consider the set named $Null \subseteq V$ of nullable nonterminals. The set is computed by the following logical clauses, to be applied in any order until the set ceases to grow, i.e., a fixed point is reached:

$A \in Null$ if $A \to \varepsilon \in P$
$A \in Null$ if $(A \to A_1 A_2 \ldots A_n \in P$ with $A_i \in V \setminus \{A\}) \wedge \forall A_i (A_i \in Null)$

Row one finds the nonterminals that are immediately nullable; row two finds those which derive a string of nullable nonterminals.

*Example 2.58.* Computing nullable nonterminals

$$S \to SAB \mid AC \qquad A \to aA \mid \varepsilon \qquad B \to bB \mid \varepsilon \qquad C \to cC \mid c$$

Result: $Null = \{A, B\}$.

Notice that, if rule $S \to AB$ were added to the grammar, the result would include $S \in Null$.

The *normal form without nullable nonterminals*, for brevity *nonnullable*, is defined by the condition that no nonterminal other than the axiom is nullable. Moreover, the axiom is nullable if, and only if, the empty string is in the language.

To construct the non-nullable form, first compute the set $Null$, then do as follows:

- for each rule $A \to A_1 A_2 \ldots A_n \in P$, with $A_i \in V \cup \Sigma$, add as alternatives the strings obtained from the right part, deleting in all possible ways any nullable nonterminal $A_i$;
- remove the empty rules $A \to \varepsilon$, for every $A \neq S$.

If the grammar thus obtained is unclean or circular, it should be cleaned with the known algorithms (p. 37).

*Example 2.59.* (Example 2.58 continued)
In Table 2.4, column one lists nullability. The other columns list the original rules, those produced by the transformation, and the final clean rules.

**Table 2.4** Elimination of copy rules.

| *Nullable* | *G original* | *G′ to be cleaned* | *G′ nonnullable normal* |
|---|---|---|---|
| F | $S \to SAB \mid AC$ | $S \to SAB \mid SA \mid SB \mid S \mid AC \mid C$ | $S \to SAB \mid SA \mid SB \mid AC \mid C$ |
| V | $A \to aA \mid \varepsilon$ | $A \to aA \mid a$ | $A \to aA \mid a$ |
| V | $B \to bB \mid \varepsilon$ | $B \to bB \mid b$ | $B \to bB \mid b$ |
| F | $C \to cC \mid c$ | $C \to cC \mid c$ | $C \to cC \mid c$ |

## Copies or Subcategorization Rules and Their Elimination

A *copy* (or *subcategorization*) rule has the form $A \to B$, with $B \in V$, a nonterminal symbol. Any such rule is tantamount as the relation $L_B(G) \subseteq L_A(G)$: the syntax class $B$ is included in the class $A$.
For a concrete example, the rules

$$iterative\_phrase \to while\_phrase \mid for\_phrase \mid repeat\_phrase$$

introduce three subcategories of iterative phrases: `while`, `for`, and `repeat`. Although copy rules can be eliminated, many more alternatives have to be introduced and grammar legibility usually deteriorates. Notice that copy elimination reduces the height of syntax trees by shortening derivations.
For grammar $G$ and nonterminal $A$, we define the set $Copy(A) \subseteq V$ containing the nonterminals that are immediate or transitive copies of $A$:

$$Copy(A) = \{B \in V \mid \text{ there is a derivation } A \overset{*}{\Rightarrow} B\}$$

Note: if nonterminal $C$ is nullable, the derivation may take the form

$$A \overset{+}{\Rightarrow} BC \Rightarrow B$$

For simplicity we assume the grammar is nonnullable and the axiom does not occur in a right part.
To compute the set $Copy$, apply the following logical clauses until a fixed point is reached:

$$A \in Copy(A) \qquad \text{- - initialization}$$
$$C \in Copy(A) \; if \; (B \in Copy(A)) \wedge (B \to C \in P)$$

Then construct the rules $P'$ of a new grammar $G'$, equivalent to $G$ and copy-free, as follows:

$P' := P \setminus \{A \to B \mid A, B \in V\}$ -- copy cancellation
$P' := \{A \to \alpha \mid \alpha \in ((\Sigma \cup V)^* \setminus V)\}$ where $(B \to \alpha) \in P \wedge B \in Copy(A)$

The effect is that the old grammar derivation $A \overset{+}{\Rightarrow} B \Rightarrow \alpha$ shrinks to the immediate derivation $A \Rightarrow \alpha$.
Notice the transformation keeps all original noncopy rules. In Chapter 3 the same transformation will be applied to remove spontaneous moves from an automaton.

*Example 2.60.* Copy-free rules for arithmetic expressions
Applying the algorithm to grammar $G_2$

$$E \to E+T \mid T \qquad T \to T \times C \mid C \ .$$
$$C \to 0 \mid 1 \mid 2 \mid 3 \mid 4 \mid 5 \mid 6 \mid 7 \mid 8 \mid 9$$

we obtain

$$Copy(E) = \{E, T, C\}, \qquad Copy(T) = \{T, C\}, \qquad Copy(C) = \{C\}$$

The equivalent copy-free grammar is

$$E \to E+T \mid T \times C \mid 0 \mid 1 \mid 2 \mid 3 \mid 4 \mid 5 \mid 6 \mid 7 \mid 8 \mid 9$$
$$T \to T \times C \mid 0 \mid 1 \mid 2 \mid 3 \mid 4 \mid 5 \mid 6 \mid 7 \mid 8 \mid 9$$
$$C \to 0 \mid 1 \mid 2 \mid 3 \mid 4 \mid 5 \mid 6 \mid 7 \mid 8 \mid 9$$

It is worth repeating that copy rules are very convenient for reusing certain blocks of rules, corresponding to syntactic subcategories; the grammar is concise and evidences the generalization and specialization of language constructs. For these reasons, reference manuals of technical languages cannot do without copy rules.

### Chomsky or Binary Normal Form

There are two types of rules:

1. *homogeneous binary*: $A \to BC$, where $B, C \in V$
2. *terminal with singleton right part*: $A \to a$, where $a \in \Sigma$

Moreover, if the empty string is in the language, there is rule $S \to \varepsilon$ but the axiom is not allowed in any right part.

With such constraints any internal node of a syntax tree may have either two nonterminal siblings or one terminal son.

Given a grammar, by simplifying hypothesis without nullable nonterminals, we explain how to obtain a Chomsky normal form. Each rule $A_0 \to A_1 A_2 \ldots A_n$ of length $n > 2$ is converted to a length 2 rule, singling out the first symbol $A_1$ and the remaining suffix $A_2 \ldots A_n$. Then a new ancillary nonterminal is created, named $\langle A_2 \ldots A_n \rangle$, and the new rule

$$\langle A_2 \ldots A_n \rangle \to A_2 \ldots A_n$$

Now the original rule is replaced by

$$A_0 \to A_1 \langle A_2 \dots A_n \rangle$$

If symbol $A_1$ is terminal, we write instead the rules:

$$A_0 \to \langle A_1 \rangle \langle A_2 \dots A_n \rangle \qquad \langle A_1 \rangle \to A_1$$

where $\langle A_1 \rangle$ is a new ancillary nonterminal.
Continue applying the same series of transformations to the grammar thus obtained, until all rules are in the form requested.

*Example 2.61.* Conversion to Chomsky normal form
The grammar

$$S \to dA \mid cB \qquad A \to dAA \mid cS \mid c \qquad B \to cBB \mid dS \mid d$$

becomes

$$S \to \langle d \rangle A \mid \langle c \rangle B \qquad A \to \langle d \rangle \langle AA \rangle \mid \langle c \rangle S \mid c \qquad B \to \langle c \rangle \langle BB \rangle \mid \langle d \rangle S \mid d$$

$$\langle d \rangle \to d \qquad \langle c \rangle \to c \qquad \langle AA \rangle \to AA \qquad \langle BB \rangle \to BB$$

This form is used in mathematical essays, but rarely in practical work.

### Conversion of Left to Right Recursions

Another normal form termed *not left-recursive* is characterized by the absence of left-recursive rules or derivations (l-recursions); it is indispensable for the top-down parsers to be studied in Chapter 4. We explain how to transform l-recursions to right recursions.

#### Transformation of Immediate l-Recursions

The more common and easier case is when the l-recursion to be eliminated is immediate. Consider the l-recursive alternatives of a nonterminal $A$:

$$A \to A\beta_1 \mid A\beta_2 \mid \dots \mid A\beta_h \,, h \geqslant 1$$

where no $\beta_i$ is empty, and let

$$A \to \gamma_1 \mid \gamma_2 \mid \dots \mid \gamma_k \,, k \geqslant 1$$

be the remaining alternatives.
Create a new ancillary nonterminal $A'$ and replace the previous rules with the next ones:

$$A \rightarrow \gamma_1 A' \mid \gamma_2 A' \mid \ldots \mid \gamma_k A' \mid \gamma_1 \mid \gamma_2 \mid \ldots \mid \gamma_k$$

$$A' \rightarrow \beta_1 A' \mid \beta_2 A' \mid \ldots \mid \beta_h A' \mid \beta_1 \mid \beta_2 \mid \ldots \mid \beta_h$$

Now every original l-recursive derivation, as for instance

$$A \Rightarrow A\beta_2 \Rightarrow A\beta_3\beta_2 \Rightarrow \gamma_1\beta_3\beta_2$$

is replaced with the equivalent right-recursive derivation

$$A \Rightarrow \gamma_1 A' \Rightarrow \gamma_1\beta_3 A' \Rightarrow \gamma_1\beta_3\beta_2$$

*Example 2.62.* Converting immediate l-recursions to right recursion
In the usual grammar of expressions

$$E \rightarrow E + T \mid T \qquad T \rightarrow T * F \mid F \qquad F \rightarrow (E) \mid i$$

nonterminals $E$ and $T$ are immediately l-recursive. Applying the transformation, the right-recursive grammar is obtained:

$$E \rightarrow TE' \mid T \qquad E' \rightarrow +TE' \mid +T$$

$$T \rightarrow FT' \mid F \qquad T' \rightarrow *FT' \mid *F \qquad F \rightarrow (E) \mid i$$

Actually, in this case but not always, a simpler solution is possible, to specularly reverse the l-recursive rules, obtaining

$$E \rightarrow T + E \mid T \qquad T \rightarrow F * T \mid F \qquad F \rightarrow (E) \mid i$$

### Transformation of Nonimmediate Left Recursions

The next algorithm is used to transform nonimmediate l-recursions. We present it under the simplifying assumptions that grammar $G$ is homogeneous, nonnullable, with singleton terminal rules; in other words, the rules are like in Chomsky normal form, but more than two nonterminals are permitted in a right part.

There are two nested loops; the external loop employs nonterminal expansion to change non-immediate into immediate l-recursions, thus shortening the length of derivations. The internal loop converts immediate l-recursions to right recursions; in so doing it creates ancillary nonterminals.

Let $V = \{A_1, A_2, \ldots, A_m\}$ be the nonterminal alphabet and $A_1$ the axiom. For orderly scanning, we view the nonterminals as an (arbitrarily) ordered set, from 1 to $m$.

Algorithm for Left Recursion Elimination

for $i := 1$ to $m$ do
 for $j := 1$ to $i-1$ do
 replace every rule of type $A_i \to A_j\alpha$, where $i > j$, with the rules:
 $A_i \to \gamma_1\alpha \mid \gamma_2\alpha \mid \ldots \mid \gamma_k\alpha$
 (- - possibly creating immediate l-recursions)
 where $A_j \to \gamma_1 \mid \gamma_2 \mid \ldots \mid \gamma_k$ are the alternatives of nonterminal $A_j$
 end do
 eliminate, by means of the previous algorithm, any immediate l-recursion that may have arisen as alternative of $A_i$, creating the ancillary nonterminal $A'_i$
end do

The idea[25] is to modify the rules in such a way that, if the right part of a rule $A_i \to A_j \ldots$ starts with a nonterminal $A_j$, then it is $j > i$, i.e., the latter nonterminal follows in the ordering.

*Example 2.63.* Applying the algorithm to grammar $G_3$

$$A_1 \to A_2a \mid b \qquad A_2 \to A_2c \mid A_1d \mid e$$

which has the l-recursion $A_1 \Rightarrow A_2a \Rightarrow A_1da$, we list in Table 2.5 the steps producing grammar $G'_3$, which has no l-recursion.

**Table 2.5** Turning recursion from left to right.

| *i j* | | *Grammar* |
|---|---|---|
| 1 | Eliminate immediate l-recursions of $A_1$ (none) | idem |
| 2 1 | Replace $A_2 \to A_1d$ with the rules constructed expanding $A_1$, obtaining: | $A_1 \to A_2a \mid b$<br>$A_2 \to A_2c \mid A_2ad \mid bd \mid e$ |
| | Eliminate the immediate l-recursion, obtaining $G'_3$: | $A_1 \to A_2a \mid b$<br>$A_2 \to bdA'_2 \mid eA'_2 \mid bd \mid e$<br>$A'_2 \to cA'_2 \mid adA'_2 \mid c \mid ad$ |

It would be straightforward to modify the algorithm to transform right recursions to left ones, a conversion sometimes applied to speed up the bottom-up parsing algorithms of Chapter 5.

[25] A proof of correctness may be found in [28] or in [14].

### Greibach and Real-Time Normal Form

In the *real-time* normal form every rule starts with a terminal:

$$A \to a\alpha \quad \text{where } a \in \Sigma, \quad \alpha \in \{\Sigma \cup V\}^*$$

A special case of this is *Greibach* normal form:

$$A \to a\alpha \quad \text{where } a \in \Sigma, \quad \alpha \in V^*$$

Every rule starts with a terminal, followed by zero or more nonterminals. To be exact, both forms exclude the empty string from the language.
The designation 'real time' will be later understood, as a property of the parsing algorithm: at each step it reads and consumes a terminal character, thus the total number of steps equals the length of the string to be parsed.
Assuming for simplicity the given grammar to be nonnullable, we explain how to proceed to obtain the above forms.
For the real-time form: first eliminate all left-recursions; then, by elementary transformations, expand any nonterminal that occurs in first position in a right part, until a terminal prefix is produced. Then continue for the Greibach form: if in any position other than the first, a terminal occurs, replace it by an ancillary nonterminal and add the terminal rule that derives it.

*Example 2.64.* The grammar

$$A_1 \to A_2 a \qquad A_2 \to A_1 c \mid bA_1 \mid d$$

is converted to Greibach form by the following steps.

1. Eliminate l-recursions by the step

$$A_1 \to A_2 a \qquad A_2 \to A_2 ac \mid bA_1 \mid d$$

and then

$$A_1 \to A_2 a \qquad A_2 \to bA_1A_2' \mid dA_2' \mid d \mid bA_1 \qquad A_2' \to acA_2' \mid ac$$

2. Expand the nonterminals in first position until a terminal prefix is produced:

$$A_1 \to bA_1A_2'a \mid dA_2'a \mid da \mid bA_1a \qquad A_2 \to bA_1A_2' \mid dA_2' \mid d \mid bA_1$$
$$A_2' \to acA_2' \mid ac$$

3. Substitute ancillary nonterminals for any terminal in a position other than one:

$$A_1 \to bA_1A_2'\langle a\rangle \mid dA_2'\langle a\rangle \mid d\langle a\rangle \mid bA_1\langle a\rangle \qquad A_2 \to bA_1A_2' \mid dA_2' \mid d \mid bA_1$$

$$A'_2 \rightarrow a\langle c\rangle A'_2 \mid a\langle c\rangle$$

$$\langle a\rangle \rightarrow a \qquad \langle c\rangle \rightarrow c$$

Halting before the last step, the grammar would be in real-time but not in Greibach's form.

Although not all preceding transformations, especially not the Chomsky and Greibach ones, will be used in this book, practicing with them is recommended as an exercise for becoming fluent in grammar design and manipulation, a skill certainly needed in language and compiler engineering.

## 2.6 Grammars of Regular Languages

Since regular languages are a rather limited class of context-free languages, it is not surprising that their grammars admit severe restrictions, to be next considered. Furthering the study of regular languages, we shall also see that longer sentences present unavoidable repetitions, a property that can be exploited to prove that certain context-free languages are not regular. Other contrastive properties of the $REG$ and $CF$ families will emerge in chapters 3 and 4 from consideration of the amount of memory needed to check whether a string is in the language, which is finite for the former and unbounded for the latter family.

### *2.6.1 From Regular Expressions to Context-Free Grammars*

Given an r.e. it is straightforward to write a grammar for the language, by analyzing the expression and mapping its subexpressions into grammar rules. At the heart of the construction, the iterative operators (star and cross) are replaced by unilaterally recursive rules.

*Algorithm.* From r.e. to grammar
First we identify and number the subexpressions contained in the given r.e. $r$. From the very definition of r.e., the possible cases and corresponding grammar rules (with uppercase nonterminals) are in Table 2.6. Notice we allow the empty string as term. For shortening the grammar, if in any row a term $r_i$ is a terminal or $\varepsilon$, we do not introduce a corresponding nonterminal $E_i$, but write it directly in the rule.

Notice that rows 3 and 4 offer the choice of left or right-recursive rules. To apply this conversion scheme, each subexpression label is assigned as a distinguishing subscript to a nonterminal. The axiom is associated with the

**Table 2.6** From subexpressions to grammar rules.

| | *subexpression* | *grammar rule* |
|---|---|---|
| 1 | $r = r_1.r_2.\ldots.r_k$ | $E \to E_1E_2\ldots E_k$ |
| 2 | $r = r_1 \cup r_2 \cup \ldots \cup r_k$ | $E \to E_1 \cup E_2 \cup \ldots \cup E_k$ |
| 3 | $r = (r_1)^*$ | $E \to EE_1 \mid \varepsilon$ or $E \to E_1E \mid \varepsilon$ |
| 4 | $r = (r_1)^+$ | $E \to EE_1 \mid E_1$ or $E \to E_1E \mid E_1$ |
| 5 | $r = b \in \Sigma$ | $E \to b$ |
| 6 | $r = \varepsilon$ | $E \to \varepsilon$ |

first step, i.e., to the whole r.e. An example should suffice to understand the procedure.

*Example 2.65.* From r.e. to grammar
The expression

$$E = (abc)^* \cup (ff)^+$$

is analyzed into the arbitrarily numbered subexpressions shown in the tree, which is a sort of syntax tree of the r.e. with added numbering:

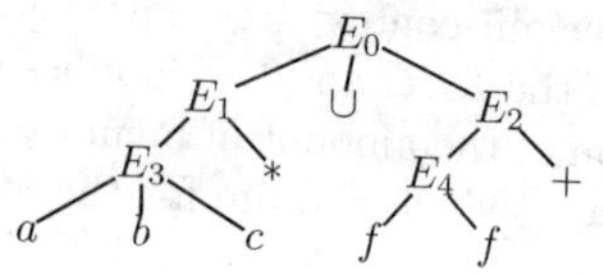


We see that $E_0$ is union of subexpressions $E_1$ and $E_2$, $E_1$ is star of subexpression $E_3$, etc.

The mapping scheme of Table 2.6 yields the rules in Table 2.7. The axiom derives the sentential forms $E_1$ and $E_2$; nonterminal $E_1$ generates the string forms $E_3^*$, and from them $(abc)^*$. Similarly $E_2$ generates strings $E_4^+$ and finally $(ff)^+$.

**Table 2.7** Mapping the r.e. of example 2.65 on grammar rules.

| Mapping | Subexpression | Grammar rule |
|---|---|---|
| 2 | $E_1 \cup E_2$ | $E_0 \to E_1 \mid E_2$ |
| 3 | $E_3^*$ | $E_1 \to E_1\ E_3 \mid \varepsilon$ |
| 4 | $E_4^+$ | $E_2 \to E_2\ E_4 \mid E_4$ |
| 1 | $a\ b\ c$ | $E_3 \to a\ b\ c$ |
| 1 | $f\ f$ | $E_4 \to f\ f$ |

Notice that if the r.e. is ambiguous (p. 22), the grammar is so (see example 2.68 on p. 70).

We have thus seen how to map each operator of an r.e. on equivalent rules, to generate the same language. It follows that every regular language is context-free. Since we know of context-free languages which are not regular (e.g., palindromes and Dyck language), the following property holds.

*Property 2.66.* The family of regular languages $REG$ is strictly included in the family of context-free languages $CF$, that is, $REG \subset CF$.

## 2.6.2 Linear Grammars

Algorithm 2.6.1 converts an r.e. to a grammar substantially preserving the structure of the r.e. But for a regular language it is possible to constrain the grammar to a very simple form of rules, called unilinear or of type 3. Such form gives evidence to some fundamental properties and leads to a straightforward construction of the automaton which recognizes the strings of a regular language.
par We recall a grammar is *linear* if every rule has the form

$$A \to uBv \quad \text{where } u, v \in \Sigma^*, B \in (V \cup \varepsilon)$$

i.e., at most one nonterminal is in the right part.

Visualizing a corresponding syntax tree, we see it never branches into two subtrees but it has a linear structure made by a stem with leaves directly attached to it. Linear grammars are not powerful enough to generate all context-free languages (an example is Dyck language), but already exceed the power needed for regular languages. For instance, the following well-known subset of Dyck language is generated by a linear grammar but is not regular (to be proved on p. 77).

*Example 2.67.* Nonregular linear language

$$L_1 = \{b^n e^n \mid n \geqslant 1\} = \{be, bbee, \ldots\}$$

Linear grammar: $S \to bSe \mid be$

A rule of the following form is called *right-linear*:

$$A \to uB \text{ where } u \in \Sigma^*, B \in (V \cup \epsilon)$$

Symmetrically, a *left-linear* rule has the form

$$A \to Bu, \text{ with the same stipulations.}$$

Clearly both cases are linear and are obtained by deleting on either side a terminal string embracing nonterminal $B$.
A grammar such that all the rules are right-linear or all the rules are left-linear is termed *unilinear* or of *type 3*.[26]

[26] Within Chomsky hierarchy (p. 87).

For a right-linear grammar every syntax tree has an oblique stem oriented towards the right (towards the left for a left-linear grammar). Moreover, if the grammar is recursive, it is necessarily right-recursive.

*Example 2.68.* The strings containing $aa$ and ending with $b$ are defined by the (ambiguous) r.e.

$$(a \mid b)^* aa(a \mid b)^* b$$

The language is generated by the unilinear grammars:

1. Right-linear grammar $G_r$:

$$S \to aS \mid bS \mid aaA \qquad A \to aA \mid bA \mid b$$

2. Left-linear grammar $G_l$:

$$S \to Ab \qquad A \to Aa \mid Ab \mid Baa \qquad B \to Ba \mid Bb \mid \varepsilon$$

An equivalent nonunilinear grammar is constructed by the algorithm on p. 67:

$$E_1 \to E_2 aa E_2 b \qquad E_2 \to E_2 a \mid E_2 b \mid \varepsilon$$

With grammar $G_l$ the leftwards syntax trees of the ambiguous sentence $baaab$ are

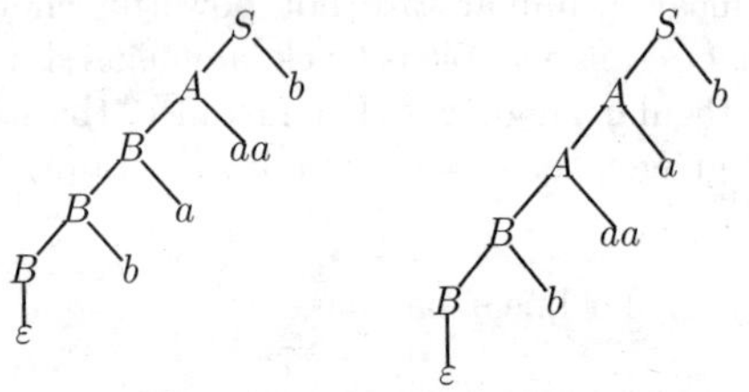


*Example 2.69.* Parenthesis-free arithmetic expressions
The language

$$L = \{a, a + a, a * a, a + a * a, \ldots\}$$

is defined by the right-linear grammar $G_r$:

$$S \to a \mid a + S \mid a * S$$

or by the left-linear grammar $G_l$:

$$S \to a \mid S + a \mid S * a$$

By the way, neither grammar is adequate to impose the precedence of arithmetic operations.

Strictly Unilinear Grammars

The unilinear rule form can be further constrained, with the aim of simplifying the coming discussion of theoretical properties and the construction of language recognizing automata. A grammar is *strictly unilinear* if every rule contains at most one terminal character, i.e., if it has the form

$$A \rightarrow aB \quad (\text{or } A \rightarrow Ba), \text{ where } a \in (\Sigma \cup \varepsilon), B \in (V \cup \varepsilon)$$

A further simplification is possible: to impose that the only terminal rules are empty ones. In this case we may assume the grammar contains just the following rule types:

$$A \rightarrow aB \mid \varepsilon \qquad \text{where } a \in \Sigma, B \in V$$

Summarizing the discussion, we may indifferently use a grammar in unilinear form or strictly unilinear form, and we may additionally choose to have as terminal rules only the empty ones.

*Example 2.70.* Example 2.69 continued
By adding ancillary nonterminals, the right-linear grammar $G_r$ is transformed to the equivalent strictly right-linear grammar $G'_r$:

$$S \rightarrow a \mid aA \qquad A \rightarrow +S \mid *S$$

and also to the equivalent grammar with null terminal rules:

$$S \rightarrow aA \qquad A \rightarrow +S \mid *S \mid \varepsilon$$

### 2.6.3 Linear Language Equations

Continuing the study of unilinear grammars, we show the languages they generate are regular. The proof consists of transforming the rules to a set of linear equations, having regular languages as their solution. In Chapter 3 we shall see that every regular language can be defined by a unilinear grammar, thus proving the identity of the languages defined by r.e. and by unilinear grammars.

For simplicity take a grammar $G = (V, \Sigma, P, S)$ in strictly right-linear form (the case of left-linear grammar is analogous) with null terminal rules. Any such rule can be transcribed into a linear equation having as unknowns the languages generated from each nonterminal, that is, for nonterminal $A$

$$L_A = \{x \in \Sigma^* \mid A \stackrel{+}{\Rightarrow} x\}$$

and in particular, $L(G) \equiv L_S$.

A string $x \in \Sigma^*$ is in language $L_A$ if:

- $x$ is the empty string and $P$ contains rule $A \to \varepsilon$;
- $x$ is the empty string, $P$ contains rule $A \to B$ and $\varepsilon \in L_B$;
- $x = ay$ starts with character $a$, $P$ contains rule $A \to aB$ and string $y \in \Sigma^*$ is in language $L_B$.

Let $n = |V|$ be the number of nonterminals. Each nonterminal $A_i$ is defined by a set of alternatives

$$A_i \to aA_1 \mid bA_1 \mid \ldots \mid \ldots \mid aA_n \mid bA_n \mid \ldots \mid A_1 \mid \ldots \mid A_n \mid \varepsilon$$

some possibly missing.[27] We write the corresponding equation:

$$L_{A_i} = aL_{A_1} \cup bL_{A_1} \cup \ldots \cup aL_{A_n} \cup bL_{A_n} \cup \ldots \cup L_{A_1} \cup \ldots \cup L_{A_n} \cup \varepsilon$$

The last term disappears if the rule does not contain the alternative $A_i \to \varepsilon$. This system of $n$ simultaneous equations in $n$ unknowns (the languages generated by the nonterminals) can be solved by the well-known method of Gaussian elimination, by applying the following formula to break recursion.

*Property 2.71.* Arden identity
The equation

$$X = KX \cup L \tag{2.7}$$

where $K$ is a nonempty language and $L$ any language, has one and only one solution

$$X = K^*L \tag{2.8}$$

It is simple to see language $K^*L$ is a solution of (2.7) because, substituting it for the unknown in both sides, the equation turns into the identity

$$K^*L = (KK^*L) \cup L$$

It would also be possible to prove that equation (2.7) has no solution other than (2.8).

*Example 2.72.* Language equations
The right-linear grammar

$$S \to sS \mid eA \qquad A \to sS \mid \varepsilon$$

defines a list of (possibly missing) elements $e$, divided by separator $s$. It is transcribed to the system

$$\begin{cases} L_S = sL_S \cup eL_A \\ L_A = sL_S \cup \varepsilon \end{cases}$$

Substitute the second equation into the first:

---

[27] In particular, alternative $A_i \to A_i$ is never present since the grammar is noncircular.

$$\begin{cases} L_S &= sL_S \cup e(sL_S \cup \varepsilon) \\ L_A &= sL_S \cup \varepsilon \end{cases}$$

Then apply the distributive property of concatenation over union, to factorize variable $L_S$ as a common suffix:

$$\begin{cases} L_S &= (s \cup es)L_S \cup e \\ L_A &= sL_S \cup \varepsilon \end{cases}$$

Apply Arden identity to the first equation, obtaining

$$\begin{cases} L_S &= (s \cup es)^* e \\ L_A &= sL_S \cup \varepsilon \end{cases}$$

and then $L_A = s(s \cup es)^* e \cup \varepsilon$.

Notice that it is straightforward to write the equations also for unilinear grammars, which are not strictly so. We have thus proved that every unilinearly generated language is regular.

An alternative method for computing the r.e. of a language defined by a finite automaton will be described in Chapter 3.

## 2.7 Comparison of Regular and Context-Free Languages

It is important to understand the scope of regular languages, in order to realize which constructs can be thus defined, and which require the full power of context-free grammars. To this end we present a structural property of regular languages. Recall first that, in order to generate an infinite language, a grammar must be recursive (property 2.37, p. 39), because only recursive derivations, such as $A \stackrel{+}{\Rightarrow} uAv$, can be iterated $n$ (unbounded) times, producing the string $u^n A v^n$. This fact leads to the observation that any sufficiently large sentence necessarily includes a recursive derivation in its generation; therefore it contains certain substrings that can be unboundedly repeated, producing a longer sentence of the language.
This observation will be stated more precisely, first for unilateral, then for context-free grammars.

*Property 2.73.* Pumping of strings
Take a unilinear grammar $G$. For any sufficiently long sentence $x$, meaning of length greater than some grammar dependent constant, it is possible to find a factorization $x = tuv$, where string $u$ is not empty, such that, for every $n \geqslant 0$, the string $tu^n v$ is in the language. (It is customary to say the given sentence can be "pumped" by injecting arbitrarily many times the substring $u$.)

Proof. Take a strictly right-linear grammar and let $k$ be the number of nonterminal symbols. Observe the syntax tree of any sentence $x$ of length $k$ or more; clearly two nodes exist with the same nonterminal label $A$:

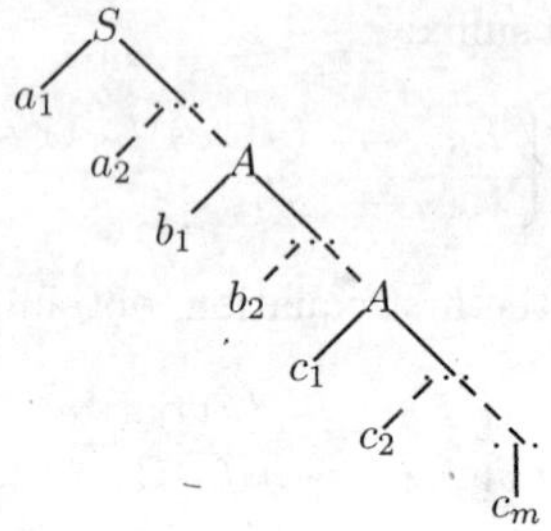


Consider the factorization into $t = a_1 a_2 \dots$, $u = b_1 b_2 \dots$, and $v = c_1 c_2 \dots c_m$. Therefore there is a recursive derivation:

$$S \stackrel{+}{\Rightarrow} tA \stackrel{+}{\Rightarrow} tuA \stackrel{+}{\Rightarrow} tuv$$

that can be repeated to generate the strings $tuuv$, $tu \dots uv$ and $tv$.
This property is next exploited to demonstrate that a language is not regular.

*Example 2.74.* Language with two equal powers
Consider the familiar context-free language

$$L_1 = \{b^n e^n \mid n \geqslant 1\}$$

and assume by contradiction it is regular. Take a sentence $x = b^k e^k$, with $k$ large enough, and decompose it into three substrings, $x = tuv$, with $u$ not empty. Depending on the positions of the two divisions, the strings $t, u$, and $v$ are as in the following scheme:

$$\underbrace{b \dots b}_{t}\underbrace{b \dots b}_{u}\underbrace{b \dots b e \dots e}_{v}$$

$$\underbrace{b \dots b}_{t}\underbrace{b \dots b e \dots e}_{u}\underbrace{e \dots e}_{v}$$

$$\underbrace{b \dots b e \dots e}_{t}\underbrace{e \dots e}_{u}\underbrace{e \dots e}_{v}$$

Pumping the middle string will lead to contradiction in all cases. For row one, if $u$ is repeated twice, the number of $b$ exceeds the number of $e$, causing the pumped string not to be in the language. For row two, repeating twice $u$, the string $tuuv$ contains a pair of substrings $be$ and does not conform to the language structure. Finally for row three, repeating $u$, the number of $e$ exceeds the number of $b$. In all cases the pumped strings are not valid and property 2.73 is contradicted. This completes the proof that the language is not regular.

This example and the known inclusion of the families $REG \subseteq CF$ justify the following statement.

*Property 2.75.* Every regular language is context-free and there exist context-free languages which are not regular.

The reader should be convinced by this example, that the regular family is too narrow for modelling some typical simple constructs of technical languages. Yet it would be foolish to discard regular expressions, because they are perfectly fit for modelling some most common parts of technical languages: on one hand there are the substrings that make the so-called lexicon (for instance, numerical constants and identifiers), on the other hand, many constructs that are variations over the list paradigm (e.g., lists of procedure parameters or of instructions).

## Role of Self-Nested Derivations

Having ascertained that regular languages are a smaller family than context-free ones, it is interesting to focus on what makes some typical languages (as the two powers language, Dyck or palindromes) not regular. Careful observation reveals that their grammars have a common feature: they all use some recursive derivation which is neither left nor right, but is called *self-nested*:

$$A \stackrel{+}{\Rightarrow} uAv \qquad u \neq \varepsilon \text{ and } v \neq \varepsilon$$

On the contrary, such derivations cannot be obtained with unilinear grammars which permit only unilateral recursions.

Now, it is the absence of self-nesting recursion that permitted us to solve linear equations by Arden identity. The higher generative capacity of context-free grammars essentially comes from such derivations, as next stated.

*Property 2.76.* Any context-free grammar not producing self-nesting derivations generates a regular language.

*Example 2.77.* Not self-nesting grammar
The grammar $G$:

$$S \rightarrow AS \mid bA \qquad A \rightarrow aA \mid \varepsilon$$

though not unilinear, does not permit self-nested derivations. Therefore $L(G)$ is regular, as we can see by solving the language equations.

$$\begin{cases} L_S &= L_A L_S \cup bL_A \\ L_A &= aL_A \cup \varepsilon \end{cases}$$

$$\begin{cases} L_S &= L_A L_S \cup bL_A \\ L_A &= a^* \end{cases}$$

$$L_S = a^* L_S \cup ba^*$$

$$L_S = (a^*)^* b a^*$$

Context-Free Languages of Unary Alphabet

The converse of property 2.76 is not true in general: in some cases self-nesting derivations do not cause the language to be nonregular. On the way to illustrate this fact, we take the opportunity to mention a curious property of context-free languages having a one-letter alphabet.

*Property 2.78.* Every language defined by a context-free grammar over a one-letter (or unary) alphabet, $|\Sigma| = 1$, is regular.

Observe that the sentences $x$ with unary alphabet are in bijective correspondence with integer numbers, via the mapping $x \Leftrightarrow n$, if and only if $|x| = n$.

*Example 2.79.* The grammar

$$G = \{S \to aSa \mid \varepsilon\}$$

has the self-nesting derivation $S \Rightarrow aSa$, but $L(G) = (aa)^*$ is regular. A right-linear, equivalent grammar is easily obtained, by shifting to suffix the nonterminal that is, positioned in the middle of the first rule:

$$\{S \to aaS \mid \varepsilon\}$$

## 2.7.1 Limits of Context-Free Languages

In order to understand what cannot be done with context-free grammars, we study the unavoidable repetitions which are found in longer sentences of such languages, much as we did for regular languages. We shall see that longer sentences necessarily contain two substrings, which can be repeated the same unbounded number of times by applying a self-nested derivation. This property will be exploited to prove that context-free grammars cannot generate certain languages where three or more parts are repeated the same number of times.

*Property 2.80.* Language with three equal powers
The language

$$L = \{a^n b^n c^n \mid n \geqslant 1\}$$

is not context-free.

*Proof.* By contradiction, assume grammar $G$ of $L$ exists and imagine the syntax tree of sentence $x = a^n b^n c^n$. Focus now on the paths from the root (axiom $S$) to the leaves. At least one path must have a length that increases with the length of sentence $x$, and since $n$ can be arbitrarily large, such path necessarily traverses two nodes with identical nonterminal label, say $A$. The situation is depicted in the scheme:

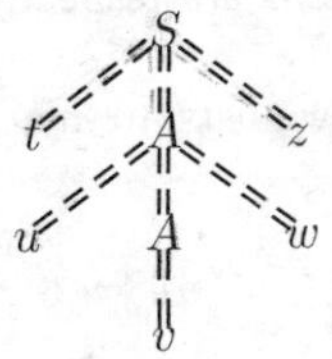


where $t, u, v, w, z$ are terminal strings. This scheme denotes the derivation

$$S \stackrel{+}{\Rightarrow} tAz \stackrel{+}{\Rightarrow} tuAwz \stackrel{+}{\Rightarrow} tuvwz$$

This contains a recursive subderivation from $A$ to $A$, which can be repeated any number $j$ of times, producing strings of type

$$y = t\,\overbrace{u \ldots u}^{j}\,v\,\overbrace{w \ldots w}^{j}\,z$$

Now, examine all possible cases for strings $u, w$:

- Both strings contain just one and the same character, say $a$; therefore, as $j$ increases, string $y$ will have more $a$ than $b$, hence cannot be in the language.
- String $u$ contains two or more different characters, for instance $u = \ldots a \ldots b \ldots$. Then, by repeating the recursive part of the derivation, we obtain $uu = \ldots a \ldots b \ldots a \ldots b \ldots$, where characters $a$ and $b$ are mixed up, hence $y$ is not in the language.
  We do not discuss the analogous case when string $w$ contains two different characters.
- String $u$ contains only one character, say $a$, and string $w$ only one different character, say $b$. When $j$ increases, string $y$ contains a number of $a$ greater than the number of $c$, hence it is not valid.

This reasoning exploits the possibility of pumping the sentences by repeating a recursive derivation. It is a useful conceptual tool for proving that certain languages are not in the $CF$ family.

Although the language with three equal powers has no practical relevance, it illustrates a kind of agreement or concordance that cannot be enforced by context-free rules. The next case considers a construct more relevant for technical languages.

### Language of Copies or Replica

An outstanding abstract paradigm is the *replica*, to be found in many technical contexts, whenever two lists contain elements that must be identical

or more generally must agree with each other. A concrete case is provided by procedure declaration/invocation: the correspondence between the formal parameter list and the actual parameter list. An example inspired by English is: cats, vipers, crickets, and lions are respectively mammals, snakes, insects, and mammals.
In the most abstract form the two lists are made with the same alphabet and the replica is the language

$$L_{\text{replica}} = \{uu \mid u \in \Sigma^+\}$$

Let $\Sigma = \{a, b\}$. A sentence $x = abbb\,abbb = uu$ is in some respect analogous to a palindrome $y = abbb\,bbba = uu^R$, but string $u$ is copied in the former language, specularly reversed in the latter. We may say the symmetry of sentences $L_{\text{replica}}$ is translational, not specular. Strange enough, whereas palindromes are a most simple context-free language, the language of replicas is not context-free. This comes from the fact that the two forms of symmetry require quite different control mechanisms: a LIFO (last in first out) push-down stack for specular, and a FIFO (first in first out) queue for translational symmetry. We shall see in chapter 4 that the algorithms (or automata) recognizing context-free languages use a LIFO memory.

In order to show that replica is not in $CF$, one should apply again the pumping reasoning; but before doing so, we have to filter the language to render it similar to the three equal powers language.
We focus on the following subset of $L_{\text{replica}}$, obtained by means of intersection with a regular language:

$$L_{abab} = \{a^m b^n a^m b^n \mid m, n \geqslant 1\} = L_{\text{replica}} \cap a^+b^+a^+b^+$$

We state (anticipating the proof on p. 160) that the intersection of a context-free language with a regular one is always a context-free language. Therefore, if we prove that $L_{abab}$ is not context-free, we may conclude the same for $L_{\text{replica}}$.
For brevity, we omit the analysis of the possible cases of the strings to be pumped, since it closely resembles the discussion in the previous proof (p. 76).

### 2.7.2 Closure Properties of REG and CF

We know language operations are used to combine languages into new ones with the aim of extending, filtering, or modifying a given language. But not all operations preserve the class or family the given languages belong to. When the result of the operation exits from the starting family, it can no longer be generated with the same type of grammar.

Continuing the comparison between regular and context-free languages, we resume in Table 2.8 the closure properties with respect to language operations: some are already known, others are immediate, and a few need to await the results of automata theory for their proofs. We denote as $L$ and $R$ a generic context-free language and regular language, respectively.

**Table 2.8** Closure properties of $REG$ and $CF$.

| *reflection* | *star* | *union* or *concatenation* | *complement* | *intersection* |
|---|---|---|---|---|
| $R^R \in REG$ | $R^* \in REG$ | $R_1 \oplus R_2 \in REG$ | $\neg R \in REG$ | $R_1 \cap R_2 \in REG$ |
| $L^R \in CF$ | $L^* \in CF$ | $L_1 \oplus L_2 \in CF$ | $\neg L \notin CF$ | $L_1 \cap L_2 \notin CF$<br>$L \cap R \in CF$ |

Comments and examples follow.

- A nonmembership (such as $\neg L \notin CF$) means that the left term does not always belong to the family; but this does not exclude, for instance, that the complement of some context-free language is context-free.
- The mirror language of $L(G)$ is generated by the *mirror grammar*, the one obtained reversing the right parts of the rules. Clearly, if grammar $G$ is right-linear the mirror grammar is left-linear and defines a regular language.
- We know the star, union, and concatenation of context-free languages are context-free. Let $G_1$ and $G_2$ be the grammars of $L_1$ and $L_2$, let $S_1$ and $S_2$ be their axioms, and suppose that the nonterminal sets are disjoint, $V_1 \cap V_2 = \emptyset$. To obtain the new grammar in the three cases, add to the rules of $G_1$ and $G_2$ the following initial rules:

$$\begin{array}{ll} \text{Star:} & S \to SS_1 \mid \varepsilon \\ \text{Union:} & S \to S_1 \mid S_2 \\ \text{Concatenation:} & S \to S_1 S_2 \end{array}$$

  In the case of union, if the grammars are right-linear, so is the new grammar. On the contrary, the new rules introduced for concatenation and star are not right-linear but we know that an equivalent right-linear grammar for the resulting languages exists, because they are regular (property 2.23, p. 24) and family $REG$ is closed by such operations.
- The proof that the complement of a regular language is regular is in Chapter 3 (p.137).
- The intersection of two context-free languages is not context-free (in general), as witnessed by the known language with three equal powers (example 2.80 on p. 76)

$$\{a^n b^n c^n \mid n \geqslant 1\} = \{a^n b^n c^+ \mid n \geqslant 1\} \cap \{a^+ b^n c^n \mid n \geqslant 1\}$$

  where the two components are easily defined by context-free grammars.

- As a consequence of De Morgan identity, the complement of a context-free language is not context-free (in general): since $L_1 \cap L_2 = \neg(\neg L_1 \cup \neg L_2)$, if the complement were context-free, a contradiction would ensue since the union of two context-free languages is context-free.
- On the other hand, the intersection of a context-free and a regular language is context-free. The proof will be given on p. 160.

The last property can be applied, in order to make a grammar more discriminatory, by filtering the language with a regular language which forces some constraints on the original sentences.

*Example 2.81.* Regular filters on Dyck language (p. 45)
It is instructive to see how the freely parenthesized sentences of a Dyck language $L_D$ of alphabet $\Sigma = \{a, a'\}$ can be filtered, by intersecting with the regular languages:

$$L_1 = L_D \cap \neg(\Sigma^* a' a' \Sigma^*) = (aa')^*$$
$$L_2 = L_D \cap \neg(\Sigma^* a' a \Sigma^*) = \{a^n (a')^n \mid n \geqslant 0\}$$

The first intersection preserves the sentences that do not contain substring $a'a'$, i.e., it eliminates all the sentences with nested parentheses. The second filter preserves the sentences having exactly one nest of parentheses. Both results are context-free languages, but the former is also regular.

### *2.7.3 Alphabetic Transformations*

It is a common experience to find conceptually similar languages that differ by the concrete syntax, i.e., by the choice of terminals. For instance, multiplication may be represented by sign $\times$, by an asterisk, or by a dot in different languages.
The term *transliteration* or *alphabetic homomorphism* refers to the linguistic operation that replaces individual characters by other ones.

**Definition 2.82.** Transliteration (or alphabetic homomorphism[28])
Consider two alphabets: *source* $\Sigma$ and *target* $\Delta$. An alphabetic transliteration is a function:

$$h : \Sigma \to \Delta \cup \{\varepsilon\}$$

The transliteration or image of character $c \in \Sigma$ is $h(c)$, an element of the target alphabet. If $h(c) = \varepsilon$, character $c$ is erased. A transliteration is *nonerasing* if, for no source character $c$, it is $h(c) = \varepsilon$.

The image of a source string $a_1 a_2 \ldots a_n$, $a_i \in \Sigma$ is the string $h(a_1)h(a_2)\ldots h(a_n)$ obtained concatenating the images of individual characters. Notice the image of the empty string is itself.

[28] This is a simple case of the translation functions to be studied in Chapter 6.

Such transformation is compositional: the image of the concatenation of two strings $v$ and $w$ is the concatenation of the images of the strings:

$$h(v.w) = h(v).h(w)$$

*Example 2.83.* Printer
An obsolete printer cannot print Greek characters and instead prints the special character $\square$. Moreover, the test sent to the printer may contain control characters (such as `start-text`, `end-text`) that are not printed. The text transformation (disregarding uppercase letters) is described by the transliteration:

$$\begin{array}{ll} h(c) = c & \text{if } c \in \{a, b, \ldots, z, 0, 1, \ldots, 9\}; \\ h(c) = c & \text{if } c \text{ is a punctuation mark or a blank space;} \\ h(c) = \square & \text{if } c \in \{\alpha, \beta \ldots, \omega\}; \\ h(\textsf{start-text}) = h(\textsf{end-text}) = \varepsilon. & \end{array}$$

An example of transliteration is

$$h(\underbrace{\textsf{start-text} \text{ the const. } \pi \text{ has value } 3.14 \textsf{ end-text}}_{\text{source string}}) = \underbrace{\text{the const. } \square \text{ has value } 3.14}_{\text{target string}}$$

An interesting special case of erasing homomorphism is the *projection*: it is a function that erases some source characters and leaves the others unchanged.

### Transliteration to Words

The preceding qualification of transliteration as alphabetic means the image of a character is a character (or the empty string), not a longer string. Otherwise the transliteration or homomorphism may no longer be qualified as alphabetic. An example is the conversion of an assignment statement $a \leftarrow b+c$ to the form $a := b + c$ by means of a (nonalphabetical) transliteration:

$$h(\leftarrow) = \text{':='} \qquad h(c) = c \qquad \text{for any other } c \in \Sigma$$

This case is also called transliteration *to words*.

Another example: vowels with umlaut of German alphabet have as image a string of two characters:

$$h(\text{ä}) = ae, \qquad h(\text{ö}) = oe, \qquad h(\text{ü}) = ue$$

### Language Substitution

A further generalization leads us to a language transformation termed *substitution* (already introduced in the discussion of linguistic abstraction on

p. 27). Now a source character can be replaced by any string of a specified language. Substitution is very useful in early language design phases, in order to leave a construct unspecified in the working grammar. The construct is denoted by a symbol (for instance ⟨identifier⟩). As the project progresses, the symbol will be substituted with the definition of the corresponding language (for instance with $(a \dots z)\,(a \dots z \mid 0 \dots 9)^*$).
par Formally, given a source alphabet $\Sigma = \{a, b, \dots\}$, a substitution $h$ associates each character with a language $h(a) = L_a, h(b) = L_b, \dots$ of target alphabet $\Delta$. Applying substitution $h$ to a source string $a_1 a_2 \dots a_n, a_i \in \Sigma$ we obtain a set of strings:

$$h(a_1 a_2 \dots a_n) = \{y_1 y_2 \dots y_n \mid y_i \in L_{a_i}\}$$

We may say a transliteration to words is a substitution such that each image language contains one string only; if the string has length one or zero, the transliteration is alphabetic.

### Closure under Alphabetic Transformation

Let $L$ be a source language, context-free or regular, and $h$ a substitution such that for every source character, its image is a language in the same family as the source language. Then the substitution maps the set of source sentences (i.e., $L$) on a set of image strings, called the *image* or *target* language, $L' = h(L)$. Is the target language a member of the same family as the source language? The answer is yes, and will be given by means of a construction that is, valuable for modifying without effort the regular expression or the grammar of the source language.

*Property 2.84.* The family $CF$ is closed by the operation of substitution with languages of the same family (therefore also by the operation of transliteration).

*Proof.* Let $G$ be the grammar of $L$ and $h$ a substitution such that, for every $c \in \Sigma$, $L_c$ is context-free. Let this language be defined by grammar $G_c$ with axiom $S_c$. Moreover, we assume the nonterminal sets of grammars $G, G_a, G_b, \dots$ are pairwise disjoint (otherwise it suffices to rename the overlapping nonterminals).

Next we construct the grammar $G'$ of language $h(L)$ by transliterating the rules of $G$ with the following mapping $f$:

$f(c) = S_c$, for every terminal $c \in \Sigma$;
$f(A) = A$, for every nonterminal symbol $A$ of $G$.

The rules of grammar $G'$ are constructed next:

- to every rule $A \to \alpha$ of $G$ apply transliteration $f$, to the effect of replacing each terminal character with the axiom of the corresponding target grammar;

- add the rules of grammars $G_a, G_b, \ldots$

It should be clear that the new grammar generates language $h(L(G))$.

In the simple case where the substitution $h$ is a transliteration, the construction of grammar $G'$ is more direct: replace in $G$ any terminal character $c \in \Sigma$ with its image $h(c)$.

For regular languages an analogous result holds.

*Property 2.85.* The family *REG* is closed by substitution (therefore also by transliteration) with regular languages.

Essentially the same construction of the proof of property 2.84 can be applied to the r.e. of the source language, to compute the r.e. of the target language.

*Example 2.86.* Grammar transliterated
The source language $i(;i)^*$, defined by rules

$$S \rightarrow i; S \mid i$$

schematizes a program including a list of instructions $i$ separated by semicolon. Imagine that instructions have to be now defined as assignments. Then the following transliteration to words is appropriate:

$$g(i) = v \leftarrow e$$

where $v$ is a variable and $e$ an arithmetic expression. This produces the grammar

$$S \rightarrow A; S \mid A \qquad A \rightarrow v \leftarrow e$$

As next refinement, the definition of expressions can be plugged in by means of a substitution $h(e) = L_E$, where the image language is the well-known one. Suppose it is defined by a grammar with axiom $E$. The grammar of the language after expression expansion is

$S \rightarrow A; S \mid A \qquad A \rightarrow v \leftarrow E \qquad E \rightarrow \ldots$ -- usual rules for arith. expr.

As a last refinement, symbol $v$, which stands for a variable, should be replaced with the regular language of identifier names.

### *2.7.4 Grammars with Regular Expressions*

The legibility of r.e. is especially good for lists and similar structures, and it would be a pity to do without them when defining technical languages by means of grammars. Since we know recursive rules are indispensable for parenthesis structures, the idea arises to combine r.e. and grammar rules in a notation, called *extended context-free grammar*, or *EBNF*[29] that takes the best of each formalism: simply enough we allow the right part of a rule to be an r.e. Such grammars have a nice graphical representation, the syntax charts to be shown in Chapter 4 on p. 174, which represents the blueprint of the flowchart of the syntax analyzer.

First observe that, since family $CF$ is closed by all the operations of r.e., the family of languages defined by $EBNF$ grammars coincide with family $CF$.

In order to appreciate the clarity of extended rules with respect to basic ones, we examine a few typical constructs of programming languages.

*Example 2.87.* $EBNF$ grammar of a block language: declarations
Consider a list of variable declarations:

*char* text1, text2; *real* temp, result; *int* alpha, beta2, gamma;

to be found with syntactic variations in most programming languages.

The alphabet is $\Sigma = \{c, i, r, v, ',' , ';'\}$, where $c, i, r$ stand for *char, int, real* and $v$ for a variable name. The language of lists of declarations is defined by r.e. $D$:

$$((c \mid i \mid r)v(, v)^*;)^+$$

The iteration operators used to generate lists are dispensable: remember any regular language can be defined by a grammar, even a unilinear one.

The lists can be defined by the basic grammar

$$D \to DE \mid E \qquad E \to AN; \qquad A \to c \mid i \mid r \qquad N \to v, N \mid v$$

with two recursive rules (for $D$ and $N$). The grammar is a bit longer than the r.e. and subjectively less perspicuous in giving evidence to the two-level hierarchical structure of declarations, which is evident in the r.e. Moreover, the choice of metasymbols $A, E, N$ is to some extent mnemonic but arbitrary and may cause confusion, when several individuals jointly design a grammar.

**Definition 2.88.** An *extended context-free* or *EBNF grammar* $G = (V, \Sigma, P, S)$ contains exactly $|V|$ rules, each one in the form $A \to \alpha$ , where $A$ is a nonterminal and $\alpha$ is an r.e. of alphabet $V \cup \Sigma$.
For better legibility and concision, other derived operators (cross, power, option) too may be permitted in the r.e. .

We continue the preceding example, adding typical block structures to the language.

*Example 2.89.* Algol-like language
A block $B$ embraces an optional declarative part $D$ followed by the imperative part $I$, between the marks $b$ (begin) and $e$ (end):

---

[29] Extended BNF.

$$B \to b\,[D]I\ e$$

The declarative part $D$ is taken from the preceding example:

$$D \to ((c \mid i \mid r)v(,v)^*;)^+$$

The imperative part $I$ is a list of phrases $F$ separated by semicolon:

$$I \to F(;F)^*$$

Last, a phrase $F$ can be an assignment $a$ or a block $B$:

$$F \to a \mid B$$

As an exercise, yet worsening legibility, we eliminate as many nonterminals as possible by applying nonterminal expansion to $D$:

$$B \to b\Big[\big((c \mid i \mid r)v(,v)^*;\big)^+\Big]Ie$$

A further expansion of $I$ leads to

$$B \to b\big((c \mid i \mid r)v(,v)^*;\big)^* F(;F)^* e$$

Last $F$ can be eliminated obtaining a one-rule grammar $G'$

$$B \to b\big((c \mid i \mid r)v(,v)^*;\big)^*(a \mid B)(;(a \mid B))^* e$$

This cannot be reduced to an r.e. because nonterminal $B$ cannot be eliminated, as it is needed to generate nested blocks ($bb \ldots ee$) by a self-nesting derivation (in agreement with property 2.76, p. 75).

Usually language reference manuals specify grammars by $EBNF$ rules, but beware that excessive grammar conciseness is often contrary to clarity. Moreover, if a grammar is split into smaller rules, it may be easier for the compiler writer to associate simple specific semantic actions to each rule, as we shall see in Chapter 5.

### Derivations and Trees in Extended Context-Free Grammars

The right part $\alpha$ of an extended rule $A \to \alpha$ of grammar $G$ is an r.e., which in general derives an infinite set of strings: each one can be viewed as the right part of a nonextended rule having unboundedly many alternatives.

For instance, $A \to (aB)^+$ stands for a set of rules

$$A \to aB \mid aBaB \mid \ldots$$

The notion of derivation can be defined for extended grammars too, via the notion of derivation for r.e. introduced on p. 20.

Shortly, for an $EBNF$ grammar $G$ consider a rule $A \to \alpha$, where $\alpha$ is an r.e. possibly containing choice operators (star, cross, union, and option); let $\alpha'$ be a string deriving from $\alpha$ (using the definition of derivation of r.e.), not containing any choice operator. For any (possibly empty) strings $\delta$ and $\eta$ there is a one-step derivation:

$$\delta A \eta \underset{G}{\Rightarrow} \delta \alpha' \eta$$

Then one can define multi-step derivations starting from the axiom and producing terminal strings, and finally the language generated by an $EBNF$ grammar, in the same manner as for basic grammars. Exemplification should be enough.

*Example 2.90.* Derivation for extended grammar of expressions
The grammar $G$:

$$E \to [+ \mid -]T((+ \mid -)T)^* \qquad T \to F((\times \mid /)F)^* \qquad F \to (a \mid \text{'('}E\text{')'})$$

generates arithmetic expressions with the four infix operators, and the prefix operators $\pm$, parentheses, and terminal $a$ standing for a numeric argument. Square brackets denote option. The left derivation

$$E \Rightarrow T+T-T \Rightarrow F+T-T \Rightarrow a+T-T \Rightarrow a+F-T \Rightarrow a+a-T \Rightarrow$$
$$\Rightarrow a+a-F \times F \Rightarrow a+a-a \times F \Rightarrow a+a-a \times a$$

produces the syntax tree:

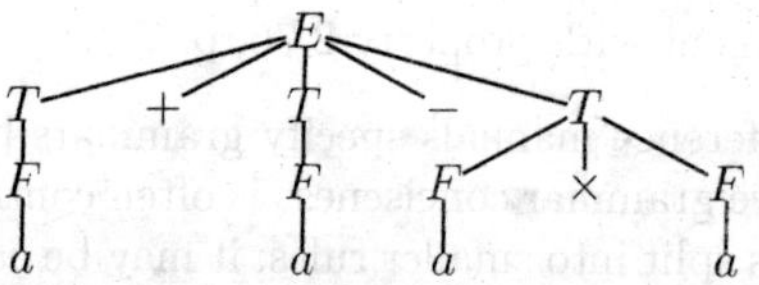


Observe that the degree of a node can be unbounded, with the consequence that the breadth of the tree increases and the height decreases, in comparison with the tree of an equivalent basic grammar.

### Ambiguity in Extended Grammars

It is obvious that an ambiguous basic grammar remain such also when viewed as an $EBNF$ grammar. On the other hand, a different form of ambiguity may arise in an $EBNF$ grammar, caused by the ambiguity of the r.e. present in the rules. Recall an r.e. is ambiguous (p. 22) if it derives a string with two different left derivations.

For instance, the r.e. $a^*b \mid ab^*$, numbered $a_1^*b_2 \mid a_3b_4^*$, is ambiguous because the string $ab$ can be derived as $a_1b_2$ or as $a_3b_4$. As a consequence the extended grammar

$$S \rightarrow a^*bS \mid ab^*S \mid c$$

is ambiguous.

## 2.8 More General Grammars and Language Families

We have seen context-free grammars cover the main constructs occurring in technical languages, namely, parentheses structures and hierarchical lists, but fail with other syntactic structures even simple, such as the replica or the three equal powers language on p. 76.
Such shortcomings have motivated, from the early days of language theory, much research on more powerful formal grammars. It is fair to say that none of the formal models have been successful; the more powerful are too obscure and difficult to use, and the models marginally superior to the context-free do not offer significant advantages. In practice, application of such grammars to compilation has been episodic and quickly abandoned. Since the basis of all subsequent developments is the classification of grammars due to the linguist Noam Chomsky, it is appropriate to briefly present it for reference, before moving on to more applied aspects in the coming chapters.

### *2.8.1 Chomsky Classification*

The historical classification of phrase structure grammars based on the form of the rewriting rules is in Table 2.9. Surprisingly enough, very small difference in the rule form, determine substantial changes in the properties of the corresponding family of languages, both in terms of decidability and algorithmic complexity.
A rewriting rule has a left part and a right part, both strings on the terminal alphabet $\Sigma$ and nonterminal set $V$. The left part is replaced by the right part. The four types are characterized as follows:

- a rule of *type 0* can replace an arbitrary not empty string over terminals and nonterminals, with another arbitrary string;
- a rule of *type 1* adds a constraint to the form of type 0: the right part of a rule must be at least as long as the left part;
- a rule of *type 2* is context-free: the left part is one nonterminal;
- a rule of *type 3* coincides with the unilinear form we have studied.

For completeness Table 2.9 lists the names of the automata (abstract string recognition algorithms) corresponding to each type, although the notion of automata will not be introduced until next chapter. The language families

**Table 2.9** Chomsky classification of grammars and corresponding languages and machines.

| *grammar* | *form of rules* | *language family* | *type of recognizer* |
|---|---|---|---|
| *Type 0* | $\beta \to \alpha$ where $\alpha, \beta \in (\Sigma \cup V)^+$ and $\beta \neq \varepsilon$ | Recursively enumerable | Turing machine |
| *Type 1* context dependent (or context sensitive) | $\beta \to \alpha$ where $\alpha, \beta \in (\Sigma \cup V)^+$ and $\|\beta\| \leqslant \|\alpha\|$ | Contextual or context-dependent | Turing machine with space complexity limited by the length of the source string |
| *Type 2* context-free or BNF | $A \to \alpha$ where $A$ is a nonterminal and $\alpha \in (\Sigma \cup V)^*$ | Context-free $CF$ or algebraic | Push-down automaton |
| *Type 3* unilinear (right-linear or left-linear) | Right-linear: $A \to uB$ Left linear: $A \to Bu$, where $A$ is a nonterminal, $u \in \Sigma^*$ and $B \in (V \cup \varepsilon)$ | Regular $REG$ or rational or finite-state | Finite automaton |

are strictly included one into the next from bottom to top, which justifies the name of hierarchy.

Partly anticipating later matters, the difference between rule types is mirrored by differences in the computational resources needed to recognize the strings. Concerning space, i.e., memory complexity for string recognition, type 3 uses a finite memory, the others need unbounded memory.

Other properties are worth mentioning, without any claim to completeness. All four language families are closed by union, concatenation, star, reflection, and intersection with a regular language. But for other operators, properties differ: for instance families 1 and 3, but not 0 and 2, are closed by complement.

Concerning decidability of various properties, the difference between the apparently similar types 0 and 1 is striking. For type 0 it is undecidable (more precisely semi-decidable) whether a string is in the language generated by a grammar. For type 1 grammars the problem is decidable, though its time complexity is not polynomial. Last, only for type 3 the equivalence problem for two grammars is decidable.

We finish with two examples of type 1 grammars and languages.

*Example 2.91.* Type 1 grammar of the three equal powers language
The language, proved on p. 76 to be not $CF$, is

$$L = \{a^n b^n c^n \mid n \geqslant l\}$$

It is generated by the context-sensitive grammar

| | | |
|---|---|---|
| 1. $S \to aSBC$ | 3. $CB \to BC$ | 5. $bC \to bc$ |
| 2. $S \to abC$ | 4. $bB \to bb$ | 6. $cC \to cc$ |

For type 0 and 1 grammars a derivation cannot be represented as a tree, because the left part of a rule typically contains more than one symbol.

However, the derivation can be visualized as a graph, where the application of a rule such as $BA \rightarrow AB$ is displayed by a bundle of arcs (hyper-edge) connecting the left part nodes to the right part ones.

Coming from our experience with context-free grammars, we would expect to be able to generate all sentences by left derivations. But if we try to generate sentence *aabbcc* proceeding from left to right

$$S \Rightarrow aSBC \Rightarrow aabCBC \Rightarrow aabcBC \Rightarrow \text{ block!}$$

surprisingly, the derivation is stuck, before all nonterminal symbols are eliminated. In order to generate this string we need a not leftmost derivation, shown in Figure 2.2.

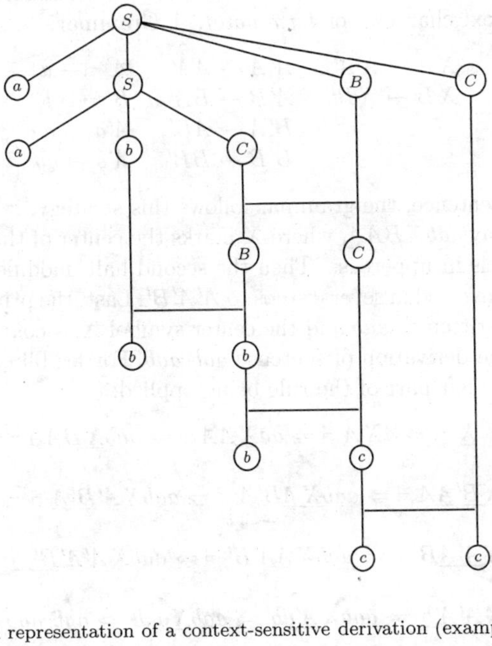

**Fig. 2.2** Graph representation of a context-sensitive derivation (example 2.91).

Intuitively the derivation produces the requested number of $a$ with rule 1 (a type 2 self-nesting rule) and then with rule 2. In the sentential form, letters $b$, $B$, and $C$ appear with the correct number of occurrences, but mixed up. In order to produce the valid string, all $C$'s must be shifted to the right, using rule 3. $CB \rightarrow BC$, until they reach the suffix position.

The first application of 3. reorders the sentential form, to the aim that $B$ becomes adjacent to $b$. This enables derivation 4. $bB \Rightarrow bb$. Then the derivation continues in the same manner, alternating steps 3. and 4., until the sentential form is left with just $C$ as nonterminal. The occurrences of

$C$ are transformed to terminals $c$, by means of rule $bC \to bc$, followed by repeated applications of rule $cC \to cc$.

We stress the finding that the language generated by type 1 grammars may not coincide with the sentences generated by left derivations, unlike for type 2 grammars. This is a cause of difficulty in string recognition algorithms.

Type 1 grammars have the power to generate the language of replicas, or lists with agreements between elements, a construct that we have singled out as practically relevant and exceeding the power of context-free grammars.

*Example 2.92.* Type 1 grammar of replica with center
Language $L = \{ycy \mid y \in \{a,b\}^+\}$ contains sentences such as $aabcaab$, where a prefix and a suffix, divided by the central separator $c$, must be equal.
To simplify the grammar, we assume sentences are terminated to the right by the end-of-text character or *terminator*, $\dashv$. Grammar:

$$\begin{array}{lllll} S \to X \dashv & XA \to XA' & A'A \to AA' & A' \dashv \to a & B'a \to ba \\ X \to aXA & XB \to XB' & A'B \to BA' & B' \dashv \to b & B'b \to bb \\ X \to bXB & & B'A \to AB' & A'a \to aa & Xa \to ca \\ & & B'B \to BB' & A'b \to ab & Xb \to cb \end{array}$$

To generate a sentence, the grammar follows this strategy: it first generates a palindrome, say $aabXBAA$, where $X$ marks the center of the sentence and the second half is in uppercase. Then the second half, modified as $B'AA$, is reflected and converted in several steps to $A'A'B'$. Last, the primed uppercase symbols are rewritten as $aab$ and the center symbol $X$ is converted to $c$.
We illustrate the derivation of sentence $aabcaab$. For legibility, at each step we underline the left part of the rule being applied:

$$\underline{S} \Rightarrow \underline{X} \dashv \Rightarrow a\underline{X}A \dashv \Rightarrow aa\underline{X}AA \dashv \Rightarrow aab\underline{XB}AA \dashv \Rightarrow$$

$$aabX\underline{B'A}A \dashv \Rightarrow aab\underline{XA}B'A \dashv \Rightarrow aabXA'\underline{B'A} \dashv \Rightarrow$$

$$aabX\underline{A'A}B' \dashv \Rightarrow aab\underline{XA}A'B' \dashv \Rightarrow aabXA'A'\underline{B' \dashv} \Rightarrow$$

$$aabXA'\underline{A'b} \Rightarrow aabX\underline{A'a}b \Rightarrow aab\underline{Xa}ab \Rightarrow aabcaab$$

We observe that the same strategy used in generation, if applied in reverse order, would allow to check whether a string is a valid sentence. Starting from the given string, the algorithm should store on a memory tape the strings obtained after each reduction (i.e., the reverse of derivation). Such procedure is essentially the computation of a Turing machine that never goes out of the portion of tape containing the original string, but may overprint its symbols.

Such examples should have persuaded the reader of the difficulty to design and apply context-sensitive rules even for very simple languages. The fact is that interaction of grammar rules is hard to understand and control.

In other words, type 1 and 0 grammars can be viewed as a particular notation for writing algorithms. All sorts of problems could be programmed in this way, even mathematical ones, by using the very simple mechanism of string rewriting[30]. It is not surprising that using such elementary mechanism as the only data and control structure, makes the algorithm description very entangled.

Undoubtedly the development of language theory towards models of higher computational capacity has mathematical and speculative interests but is almost irrelevant for language engineering and compilation[31].

In conclusion, we have to admit that the state of the art of formal language theory does not entirely satisfy the need of a powerful and practical formal grammar model, capable of accurately defining the entire range of constructs found in technical languages. Context-free grammars are the best available compromise between expressivity and simplicity. The compiler designer will supplement their weaknesses by other methods and tools, termed semantic, coming from general-purpose programming methods. They will be introduced in Chapter 6.

---

30 An extreme case is a type 1 grammar presented in [47] to generate prime numbers encoded in unary base, i.e., the language $\{a^n \mid n \text{ prime number}\}$.

31 For historical honesty, we mention that context-sensitive grammars have been occasionally considered by language and compiler designers. The language Algol 68 has been defined with a special class of type 1 grammars termed 2-level grammars, also known as VW-grammars from Van Wijngarten [55]; see also Cleaveland and Uzgalis [13] .

# Chapter 3
# Finite Automata as Regular Language Recognizers

## 3.1 Introduction

Regular expressions and grammars are widely used in technical specifications of languages but the actual design and implementation of a compiler needs a way to describe the algorithms, termed *recognizers* or *acceptors*, which examine a string and decide if it is a valid sentence of the language. In this chapter we study the recognizers for regular languages and in the next two chapters those of context-free languages.

The need to recognize if a text is valid for a given language is quite common, especially as a first step for text processing or translation. A compiler analyzes a source program to check its correctness; a document processor makes a spell check on words, then verifies syntax; and a graphic user interface must check that the data are correctly entered. Such control is done by a *recognition* procedure, which can be conveniently specified using minimalist models, termed *abstract machines* or *automata*. The advantages are that automata do not depend on programming languages and techniques, i.e., on implementation, and that their properties (such as time and memory complexity) are in this way more clearly related with the family of the source language.

In this chapter we briefly introduce more general automata, then focus on those having a finite memory that match the regular language family and have countless applications in computer science and beyond. First we consider the deterministic machines and describe useful methods for cleaning and minimizing. Then we motivate and introduce nondeterministic models, and we show they correspond to the unilinear grammars of the previous chapter. Conversion back to deterministic models follows.

A central section deals with transformations back and forth from regular expressions to automata. On the way to proving their convertibility, we introduce the subfamily of local regular languages, which have a simpler recognition procedure making use of a sliding window.

S.C. Reghizzi, *Formal Languages and Compilation*,
Texts in Computer Science, DOI 10.1007/978-1-84882-050-0_3,

Then we return to the operations of complement and intersection on regular languages from the standpoint of their recognizers, and present the composition of automata by cartesian product. The chapter ends with a summary of the interrelation between finite automata, regular expressions, and grammars.

In compilation finite automata have several uses to be described especially in Chapter 6: in lexical analysis to extract the shortest meaningful strings from a text, for making simple translations, and for modelling and analyzing program properties in static flow analysis and optimization.

## 3.2 Recognition Algorithms and Automata

To check if a string is valid for a specified language, we need a *recognition algorithm*, a type of algorithm producing a *yes/no* answer, commonly referred to in computational complexity studies as a *decision* algorithm. For instance, a famous problem is to decide if two given graphs are isomorphic: the problem domain (a pair of graphs) differs from the case of language recognition, but the answer is again yes/no.

For the string membership problem, the input domain is a set of strings of alphabet $\Sigma$. The application of a recognition algorithm $\alpha$ to a given string $x$ is denoted as $\alpha(x)$. We say string $x$ is *recognized* or *accepted* if $\alpha(x) = yes$, otherwise it is *rejected*. The language recognized, $L(\alpha)$, is the set of accepted strings:

$$L(\alpha) = \{x \in \Sigma^* \mid \alpha(x) = yes\}$$

The algorithm is usually assumed to terminate for every input, so that the membership problem is decidable. However, it may happen that, for some string $x$, the algorithm does not terminate, i.e., the value of $\alpha(x)$ is not defined, hence $x$ is not a valid sentence of language $L(\alpha)$. In such case we say that the membership problem for $L$ is *semidecidable*, or also that $L$ is recursively enumerable.

In principle, if for an artificial language the membership problem is semidecidable, we cannot exclude that the compiler falls into an endless loop, for some input strings. In practice we do not have to worry about such decidability issues, central as they are for the theory of computation,[1] because in language processing the only language families of concern are decidable, and efficiently so.

Incidentally, even within the family of context-free languages, some decision problems, different from string membership, are not decidable: we have mentioned in Chapter 2 the problem of deciding if two grammars are weakly equivalent, and of checking if a grammar is ambiguous.

[1] Many books cover the subject e.g.,Bovet and Crescenzi [11], Floyd and Beigel [20], Hopcroft and Ullman [29], Kozen [32], Mandrioli and Ghezzi [34], and McNaughton [35]).

In fact, recognizing a string is just the first step of the compilation process. In Chapter 6 we shall see the translation from a language to another: clearly the codomain of a translation algorithm is much more complex than a pure yes/no, since it is itself a set of strings, the target language.

Algorithms, including those for string recognition, may be ranked in complexity classes, measured by the amount of computational resources (time or memory i.e., space) required to solve the problem. In the field of compilation it is common to consider time rather than space complexity. With rare exceptions, all the problems of interest for compilation have low time complexity: linear or at worst polynomial with respect to the size of the problem input. Time complexity is closely related with electric power consumption, which is an important attribute for portable programmed devices.

A tenet of the theory of computation is that the complexity of an algorithm should be measured by the number of steps, rather than by the actual execution time spent by a program implementing the algorithm. The reason is that the complexity should be a property of the algorithm and should not depend on the actual implementation and processing speed of a particular computer. Even so, several choices are open for computational steps: they may range from a Turing machine move to a machine instruction or to a high-level language statement. Here we consider a step to be an elementary operation of an abstract machine or automaton, as customary in all the theoretical and applied studies on formal languages. This approach has several advantages: it gives evidence to the relation between the algorithmic complexity and the family of languages under consideration; it allows to reuse optimized abstract algorithms with a low cost of adaptation to the language, and it avoids premature commitment and tedious details of implementation. Moreover, sufficient hints will be given for a programmer to easily transform the automaton into a program, by hand or by using widespread compiler generation tools.

### 3.2.1 A General Automaton

An automaton or abstract machine is an ideal computer featuring a very small set of simple instructions. Starting from the Turing machine of the 1930s, research on abstract machines has spawned many models, but only a few are important for language processing.[2] In its more general form a recognizer is schematized in Figure 3.1. It comprises three parts: input tape, control unit, and (auxiliary) memory. The control unit has a limited store, to be represented as a finite set of states; the auxiliary memory on the other hand, has unbounded capacity. The upper tape contains the given input or

---

[2] Other books have a broader and deeper coverage of automata theory, such as Salomaa [47], Hopcroft and Ullman [28, 29], Harrison [25], and the handbook [45]; for finite automata a specific reference is Sakarovitch [46].

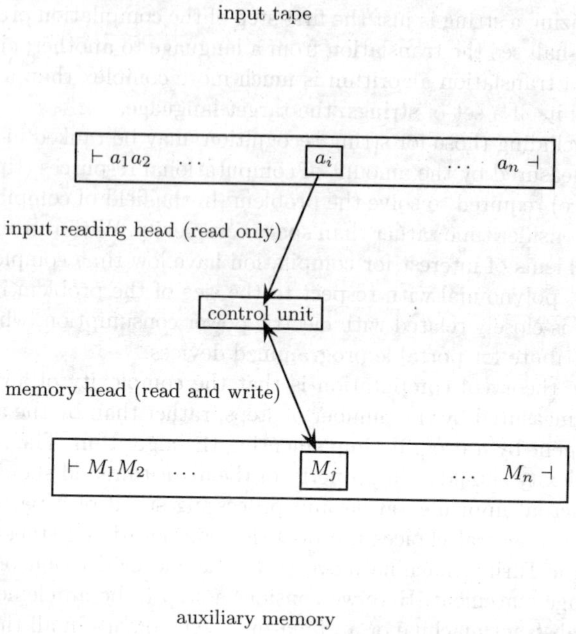


**Fig. 3.1** General automaton.

*source* string, which can be read but not changed. Each case of the tape contains a terminal character; the cases to the left and right of the input contain two delimiters, the start of text mark ⊢ and the end of text mark or terminator ⊣. A peculiarity of automata is that the auxiliary memory is also a tape (instead of the random access memory used in other computational models), containing symbols of another alphabet.

The automaton performs at discrete time instants the following actions: read the *current character* $a_i$ from input, shift the reading head, read from memory the *current symbol* $M_j$ and replace it with another symbol, move the memory head, and change the *current state* of the control unit to the *next* one.

The automaton examines the source by performing a series of moves; the choice of a move depends on the current two symbols (input and memory) and on the current state. A move may have some of the following effects:

- shift the input head left or right by one position;
- overwrite the current memory symbol with another one, and shift the memory head left or right by one position;
- change the state of the control unit.

A machine is *unidirectional* if the input head only moves from left to right: this is the model to be considered in the book, because it well represents text processing by a single scan. For unidirectional machines the start of text mark is superfluous.

At any time the future behavior of the machine depends on a 3-tuple, called an (instantaneous) *configuration*, made by: the suffix of the input string still to be read, that is laying to the right of the head; the contents of the memory tape and the position of the head; the state of the control unit. The *initial configuration* has: the input head positioned on character $a_1$ (i.e., right of the start of text mark), the control unit in an initial state, and the memory containing a specific symbol (or sometimes a fixed string).

Then the machine performs a computation, i.e., a sequence of moves, that leads to new configurations. If for a configuration at most one move can be applied, the change of configuration is *deterministic*. A *nondeterministic* (or indeterministic) automaton is essentially a manner of representing an algorithm that in some situation may explore alternative paths.

A *configuration* is *final* if the control is in a state specified as final, and the input head is on the terminator. Sometimes, instead of, or in addition to being in a final state, a final configuration is qualified by the fact that the memory tape contains a specified symbol or string: a frequent choice is for memory to be empty.

The *source string* $x$ is *accepted* if the automaton, starting in the initial configuration with $x \dashv$ as input, performs a computation leading to a final configuration (a nondeterministic automaton can possibly reach a final configuration by different computations). The *language accepted or recognized* by the machine is the set of accepted strings.

Notice a computation terminates either when the machine has entered a final configuration or when in the current configuration no move can be applied. In the latter case the source string is not accepted by that computation (but perhaps accepted by another computation if the machine is indeterministic).

Two automata accepting the same language are called *equivalent*. Of course two machines, though equivalent, may belong to different models or have different computational complexities.

### Turing Machine

The preceding description substantially reproduces the automaton introduced by A. Turing in 1936 and widely taken as the best available formalization of any sequential algorithm. The family of languages accepted is termed *recursively enumerable*. In addition, a language is termed *decidable* (or recursive) if there exists a Turing machine accepting it and halting for every input string. The family of decidable languages is smaller than the one of recursively enumerable languages.

Such machine is the recognizer of two of the language families of Chomsky classification (p. 87). The languages generated by type 0 grammars are exactly the recursively enumerable. The languages of context-sensitive or type 1 grammars, on the other hand, correspond to the languages accepted by a Turing machine that is constrained in its use of memory: the length of the memory tape is bounded by the length of the input string.

Turing machines are not relevant for practical applications but are a significant term of comparison for the efficient machine models used to recognize and transform technical languages. Such models can be viewed as Turing machines with severe limitation on memory. When no auxiliary memory is available, we have the finite-state or simply finite automaton, the most fundamental type of computing machine which corresponds to the regular languages. If the memory is organized as LIFO (last in first out) store, the machine is termed a pushdown automaton and is the recognizer of context-free languages.

The memory limitations have a profound effect on the properties and in particular the performance of the automata. Considering the worst-case time complexity, which is a primary parameter for program efficiency, a finite automaton is able to recognize a string in linear time, or more exactly in real time, that is, with a number of steps equal to the input length. In contrast the space bounded Turing machine may take a nonpolynomial time to recognize a context-sensitive language, another reason making it unpractical to use. Context-free language recognizers are somehow in between: the number of steps is bounded by a polynomial of small degree of the input string length.

## 3.3 Introduction to Finite Automata

Finite automata are surely the simplest and most fundamental abstract computational device. Their mathematical theory is very stable and deep and is able to support innumerable applications in diverse areas, from digital circuit design to system modelling and communication protocols, to mention just a few. Our presentation will be focused on the aspects that are important for language and compiler design, but in order to make the presentation self-contained we briefly introduce some essential definitions and theoretical results.

Conforming to the general scheme, a finite automaton comprises: the input tape with the source string $x \in \Sigma^*$; the control unit; the reading head, initially placed on the first character of $x$, scanning the string until its end, unless an error occurs before. Upon reading a character, the automaton updates the state of the control unit and advances the reading head. Upon reading the last character, the automaton accepts $x$ if and only if the state is an accepting one.

A well-known representation of an automaton is by a *state-transition diagram* or *graph*. This is a directed graph whose nodes are the states of the control unit. Each arc is labelled with a terminal and represents the change of state or *transition* caused by reading the terminal.

*Example 3.1.* Decimal constants
The set $L$ of decimal constants has the alphabet $\Sigma = \Delta \cup \{0, \bullet\}$ where $\Delta = \{1, 2, 3, 4, 5, 6, 7, 8, 9\}$ is a digit other than zero. The r.e. is

$$L = (0 \cup \Delta(0 \cup \Delta)^*) \bullet (0 \cup \Delta)^+$$

The recognizer is specified by the *state-transition diagram* or by the equivalent *state-transition table* in Figure 3.2.

*State-transition diagram*

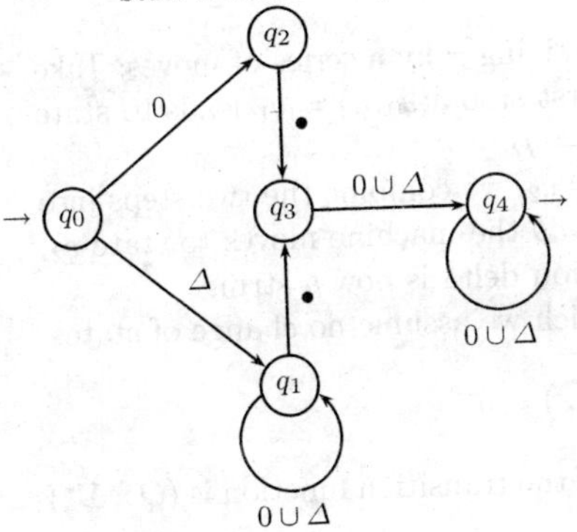


*State-transition table*

| Current state | Current character 0 | 1 | ... | 9 | • |
|---|---|---|---|---|---|
| $\to q_0$ | $q_2$ | $q_1$ | ... | $q_1$ | — |
| $q_1$ | $q_1$ | $q_1$ | ... | $q_1$ | $q_3$ |
| $q_2$ | — | — | ... | — | $q_3$ |
| $q_3$ | $q_4$ | $q_4$ | ... | $q_4$ | — |
| $q_4 \to$ | $q_4$ | $q_4$ | ... | $q_4$ | — |

**Fig. 3.2** State-transition diagram or graph (left) and table (right) for decimal constants (example 3.1).

Notice that if several arcs span the same two nodes, only one is drawn: e.g.,arc $(q_0 \to q_1)$ represents a bundle of 9 arcs with labels $1, 2, \ldots, 9$. The initial state $q_0$ is marked by an ingoing arrow; the final state $q_4$ by an outgoing arrow. The transition table is the incidence matrix of the graph: for each pair (*current state, current character*) the entry contains the next state. Notice the arrows giving evidence to initial/final states.

Given the source string $0 \bullet 2\bullet$, the automaton transits through the states $q_0, q_2, q_3, q_4$. In the last state, since no transition allows reading a $\bullet$ character, the computation stops before the entire input has been consumed. As a consequence, the source string is not accepted. On the other hand, input $0 \bullet 21$ would be accepted.

If we prefer to modify the language so that constants such as $305\bullet$ ending with a decimal point are legal, the state $q_3$ too must be marked as final.

We have seen an automaton may have several final states, but only one initial state (otherwise it would not be deterministic).

## 3.4 Deterministic Finite Automata

The previous ideas are formalized in the next definition.
A *finite deterministic automaton* $M$ comprises five items:

1. $Q$, the *state set* (finite and not empty)
2. $\Sigma$, the *input or terminal alphabet*
3. the *transition function* $\delta : (Q \times \Sigma) \to Q$
4. $q_0 \in Q$, the *initial state*
5. $F \subseteq Q$, the *set of final states.*

Function $\delta$ specifies the moves: the meaning of $\delta(q, a) = r$ is that machine $M$ in the current state $q$ reads $a$ and moves to next state $r$. If $\delta(q, a)$ is undefined, the automaton stops and we can assume it enters the error state; more on that later.

The automaton processes a not empty string $x$ by a series of moves. Take $x = ab$; reading the first character, the first step $\delta(q_0, a) = q_1$ leads to state $q_1$, then to $q_2$ by the second step $\delta(q_1, b) = q_2$.
In short, instead of writing $\delta(\delta(q_0, a), b) = q_2$, we combine the two steps into $\delta(q_0, ab) = q_2$ , to say that reading string $ab$ the machine moves to state $q_2$. Notice that the second argument of function delta is now a string.
A special case is the empty string, for which we assume no change of state:

$$\forall q \in Q \ : \ \delta(q, \varepsilon) = q$$

Following these stipulations, the domain of the transition function is $(Q \times \Sigma^*)$ and the definition is

$$\delta(q, ya) = \delta(\delta(q, y), a), \qquad \text{where } a \in \Sigma \text{ and } y \in \Sigma^*$$

Looking at the graph, if $\delta(q, y) = q'$, then, and only then, there exists a path from node $q$ to node $q'$, such that the concatenated labels of the arrows make string $y$. We say $y$ is the *label* of the path and the path represents a *computation.*
A string $x$ is *recognized* or accepted by the automaton if it is the label of a path from the initial state to a final state, $\delta(q_0, x) \in F$.
Notice the empty string is recognized if, and only if, the initial state is also final, $q_0 \in F$.
The *language recognized* or accepted by automaton $M$ is

$$L(M) = \{x \in \Sigma^* \mid x \text{ is recognized by } M\}$$

The languages accepted by such automata are termed *finite-state recognizable.* Two automata are *equivalent* if they accept the same language.

*Example 3.2.* (Example 3.1 continued)
The automaton $M$ of p. 99 is defined by:

$Q = \{q_0, q_1, q_2, q_3, q_4\}$
$\Sigma = \{1, 2, 3, 4, 5, 6, 7, 8, 9, 0, \bullet\}$
$q_0 = q_0$
$F = \{q_4\}$
Examples of transitions:

$$\delta(q_0, 3\bullet 1) = \delta(\delta(q_0, 3\bullet), 1) = \delta(\delta(\delta(q_0, 3), \bullet), 1) = \delta(\delta(q_1, \bullet), 1) = \delta(q_3, 1) = q_4$$

Since $q_4 \in F$, string $3 \bullet 1$ is accepted. On the contrary, since $\delta(q_0, 3\bullet) = q_3$ is not final, string $3\bullet$ is rejected, as well as string 02 because function $\delta(q_0, 02) = \delta(\delta(q_0, 0), 2) = \delta(q_2, 2)$ is undefined.

Observing that for each input character the automaton executes one step, the total number of steps is exactly equal to the length of the input string. Therefore such machines are very efficient as they can recognize strings in real time by a single left-to-right scan.

### *3.4.1 Error State and Total Automata*

If the move is not defined in state $q$ when reading character $a$, we say that the automaton falls into the *error state* $q_{err}$. The error state is such that for any character the automaton remains in it, thus justifying its other name of *sink* or trap state. Obviously the error state is not final.

The state transition function can be made *total* by adding the error state and the transitions from/to it:

$$\forall \text{ state } q \in Q \text{ and } \forall a \in \Sigma, \text{ if } \delta(q, a) \text{ is undefined set } \delta(q, a) = q_{err}$$
$$\forall a \in \Sigma \quad \text{set } \delta(q_{err}, a) = q_{err}$$

The recognizer of decimal constants, completed with error state, is shown in Figure 3.3.

Clearly any computation reaching the error state gets trapped in it and cannot reach a final state. As a consequence, the total automaton accepts the same language as the original one. It is customary to leave the error state implicit, neither drawing a node nor specifying the transitions for it.

### *3.4.2 Clean Automata*

An automaton may contain useless parts not contributing to any accepting computation, which are best eliminated. Notice the following concepts hold as well for nondeterministic finite automata, and in general for any kind of abstract machine.

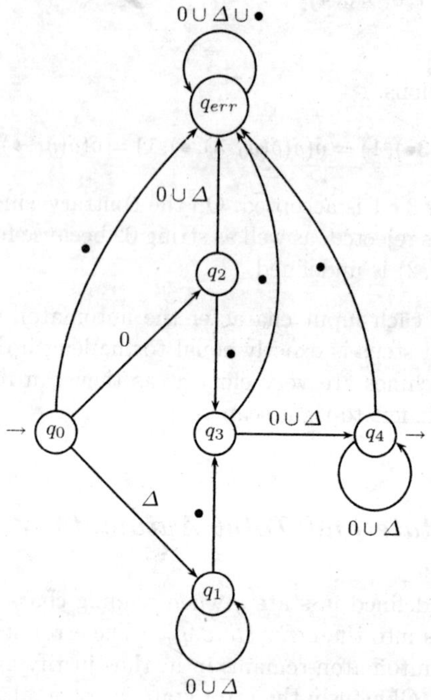


**Fig. 3.3** Recognizer of decimal constants completed with sink (error or trap) state.

A state $q$ is *reachable* from state $p$ if a computation exists going from $p$ to $q$. A state is *accessible* if it can be reached from the initial state; it is *postaccessible* if a final state can be reached from it. A state is called *useful* if it is accessible and postaccessible; otherwise it is *useless*. In other words a useful state lays on some path from the initial state to a final one.

An automaton is *clean* (or reduced) if every state is useful.

*Property 3.3.* For every finite automaton there exists an equivalent clean automaton.

The construction of the clean machine consists of identifying and deleting useless states, together with adjoining transitions.

*Example 3.4.* Elimination of useless states
Figure 3.4 shows a machine with useless states and the corresponding clean machine.

Notice the error state is never postaccessible, hence always useless.

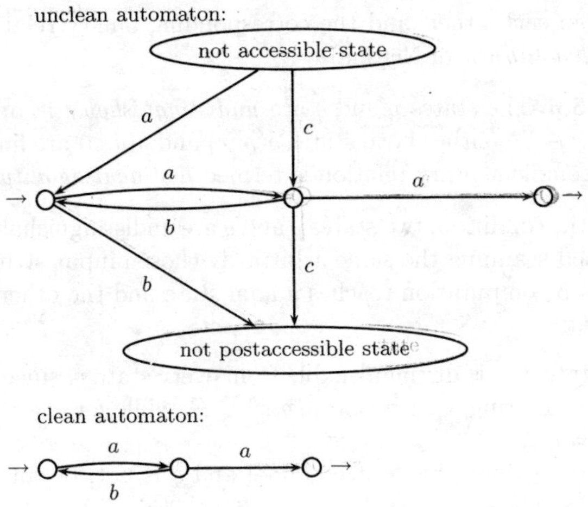


**Fig. 3.4** Useless states (top) and their elimination obtaining a clean automaton (bottom).

### *3.4.3 Minimal Automata*

We focus on properties of the automata recognizing the same language. Their state sets and transition functions are in general different but their computations are equivalent. A central property is that, among such equivalent machines, there exists only one which is the smallest in the following sense.

*Property 3.5.* For every finite-state language, the (deterministic) finite recognizer minimal with respect to the number of states is unique (apart from renaming of states).

Conceptually the statement is fundamental as it permits to represent a collection of equivalent machines by a standard one which moreover is minimal. In practice this is not so important for compiler applications, nevertheless we describe for self-consistency the standard minimization algorithm.

First we need to introduce an algebraic relation between equivalent states, to be computed by the algorithm.[3]

Although we assume the given automaton is clean, some of its states may be redundant, in the sense that they can be fused together at no consequence for strings accepted or rejected. Any two such states are termed *undistin-*

[3] Other more efficient and subtle algorithms have been invented. We refer the reader to the survey in [56].

*guishable* from each other, and the corresponding binary relation is termed *undistinguishability* (or of Nerode).

**Definition 3.6.** The states $p$ and $q$ are *undistinguishable* if, and only if, for every string $x \in \Sigma^*$, either both states $\delta(p, x)$ and $\delta(q, x)$ are final, or neither one is. The complementary relation is termed *distinguishability.*

Spelling out the condition, two states $p$ and $q$ are undistinguishable if, starting from them and scanning the same arbitrarily chosen input string $x$, it never happens that a computation reaches a final state and the other does not.

Notice that:

1. the sink state $q_{err}$ is distinguishable from every state $p$, since for any state there exists a string $x$ such that $\delta(p, x) \in F$, while for every string $x$ it is $\delta(q_{err}, x) = q_{err}$;
2. $p$ and $q$ are distinguishable if $p$ is final and $q$ is not, because $\delta(p, \varepsilon) \in F$ and $\delta(q, \varepsilon) \notin F$;
3. $p$ and $q$ are distinguishable if, for some character $a$, the next states $\delta(p, a)$ and $\delta(q, a)$ are distinguishable.

In particular, $p$ is distinguishable from $q$ if the set of labels attached to the outgoing arrows from $p$ and the similar set from $q$ are different: in that case there exists a character $a$ such that the move from state $p$ reaches state $p'$, while the move from $q$ is not defined (i.e., it reaches the sink); from condition 3. the two states are distinguishable.

Undistinguishability as a relation is symmetric, reflexive, and transitive, i.e., it is an equivalence relation, whose classes are computed by a straightforward procedure to be described next by means of an example.

*Example 3.7.* Equivalence classes of undistinguishable states

For automaton $M$ of Figure 3.5, we construct a table of size $|Q| \times |Q|$, representing the undistinguishability relation; but, since the relation is symmetric, we do not have to fill the cases over the principal diagonal.

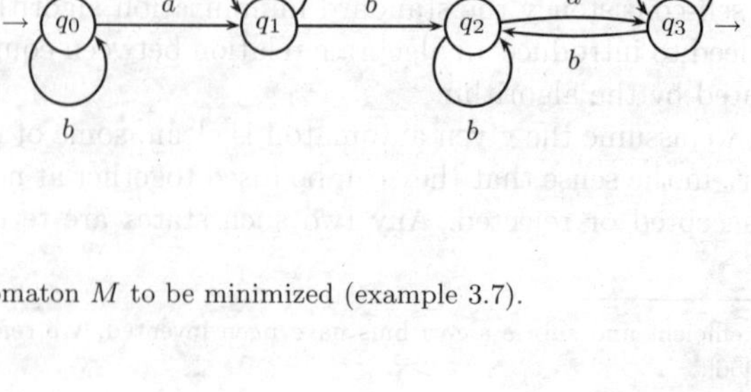


**Fig. 3.5** Automaton $M$ to be minimized (example 3.7).

The procedure will mark with $X$ the case at position $(p, q)$ , when it discovers that the states $p$ and $q$ are distinguishable. We initialize with $X$ the cases such that one state only is final:

| | | | |
|---|---|---|---|
| $q_1$ | | – | – |
| $q_2$ | X | X | – |
| $q_3$ | X | X | |
| | $q_0$ | $q_1$ | $q_2$ |

Then we examine every case $(p, q)$ still unmarked and, for every character $a$, we consider the next states $r = \delta(p, a)$ and $s = \delta(q, a)$. If case $(r, s)$ already contains $X$, meaning that $r$ is distinguishable from $s$, then also $p$ and $q$ are so, therefore case $(p, q)$ is marked $X$. Otherwise, if $(r, s)$ is not marked $X$, the pair $(r, s)$ is written into case $(p, q)$, as a future obligation, if case $(r, s)$ will get marked, to mark case $(p, q)$ as well.

The pairs of next states are listed in the table to the left. The result of this step is the table to the right. Notice case (1,0) is marked because the pair $(0, 2) \equiv (2, 0)$ was already marked:

| | | | |
|---|---|---|---|
| $q_1$ | (1,1),(0,2) | – | – |
| $q_2$ | $X$ | $X$ | – |
| $q_3$ | $X$ | $X$ | (3,3),(2,2) |
| | $q_0$ | $q_1$ | $q_2$ |

| | | | |
|---|---|---|---|
| $q_1$ | $X$ | – | – |
| $q_2$ | $X$ | $X$ | – |
| $q_3$ | $X$ | $X$ | (3,3),(2,2) |
| | $q_0$ | $q_1$ | $q_2$ |

Now all cases (under the principal diagonal) are filled and the algorithm terminates. The cases not marked with $X$ identify the undistinguishable pairs, in our example only the pair $(q_2, q_3)$.

An equivalence class contains all the pairwise undistinguishable states. In the example the equivalence classes are $[q_0], [q_1], [q_2, q_3]$.

It is worthwhile analyzing another example where the transition function is not total. To this end, we modify automaton $M$ of Figure 3.5, erasing the self-loop $\delta(q_3, a) = q_3$, i.e., redefining the function as $\delta(q_3, a) = q_{err}$. As a consequence, states $q_2$ and $q_3$ become distinguishable, because $\delta(q_2, a) = q_3$ and $\delta(q_3, a) = q_{err}$. Now every equivalence class is a singleton, meaning the automaton is already minimal.

### Construction of Minimal Automaton

The minimal automaton $M'$, equivalent to the given $M$, has for states the equivalence classes of the undistinguishability relation. It is simple to construct its transition function: $M'$ contains the arc

$$\overbrace{[\dots, p_r, \dots]}^{C_1} \xrightarrow{b} \overbrace{[\dots, q_s, \dots]}^{C_2}$$

between equivalence classes $C_1$ and $C_2$, if, and only if, $M$ contains an arc

$$p_r \xrightarrow{b} q_s$$

between two states respectively belonging to the two classes. Notice that the same arc of $M'$ may derive from several arcs of $M$.

*Example 3.8.* (Example 3.7 continued)
The minimal automaton $M'$ is in Figure 3.6. This has the least number of states of all equivalent machines. In fact, we could easily check that merging any two states, the resulting machine would not be equivalent, but it would accept a larger language than the original.

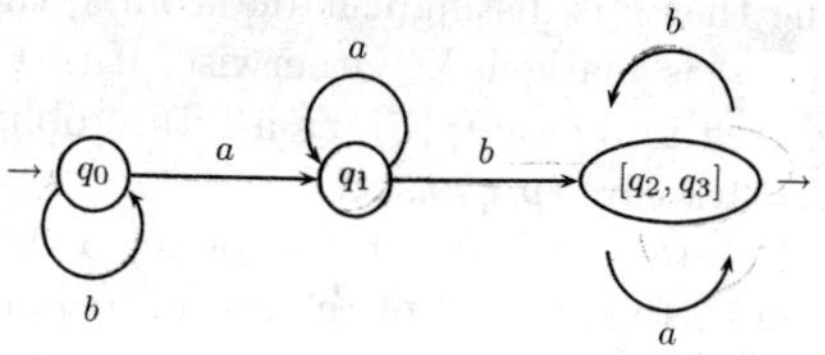


**Fig. 3.6** Result $M'$ of minimization of automaton $M$ of Figure 3.5.

The example has constructively illustrated property 3.5, that the minimal automaton is unique. From this it is a straightforward test to check whether two given machines are equivalent. First minimize both machines; then compare their state-transition graphs to see if they are identical (i.e., isomorphic and with corresponding initial and final states), apart from a change of name of the states.[4]

In practical use, obvious economy reasons make the minimal machine a preferable choice. But the saving is often negligible for the cases of concern in compiler design. What is more, in certain situations state minimization of the recognizer should be avoided: when the automaton is enriched with actions computing an output function, to be seen in Chapter 6, two states that are undistinguishable for the recognizer, can be associated with different output actions. Then merging the states would spoil the intended translation. Finally we anticipate that the uniqueness property of the minimal automaton does not hold for the nondeterministic machines to be introduced next.

### *3.4.4 From Automata to Grammars*

Without much effort we are going to realize that finite automata and unilinear (or type 3) grammars of p. 69 are alternative but equivalent notations defining the same language family.

[4] Other more efficient equivalence tests do without first minimizing the automata.

First we show how to construct a right-linear grammar equivalent to an automaton. Grammar $G$ has as nonterminal set the states $Q$ of the automaton, and the axiom is the initial state. For each move $q \xrightarrow{a} r$ the grammar has the rule $q \to ar$. If state $q$ is final, it has also the terminal rule $q \to \varepsilon$.

It is evident that there exists a bijective correspondence between the computations of the automaton and the derivations of the grammar: a string $x$ is accepted by the automaton if, and only if, it is generated by a derivation $q_0 \stackrel{+}{\Rightarrow} x$.

*Example 3.9.* From the automaton to the right-linear grammar
The automaton and corresponding grammar are

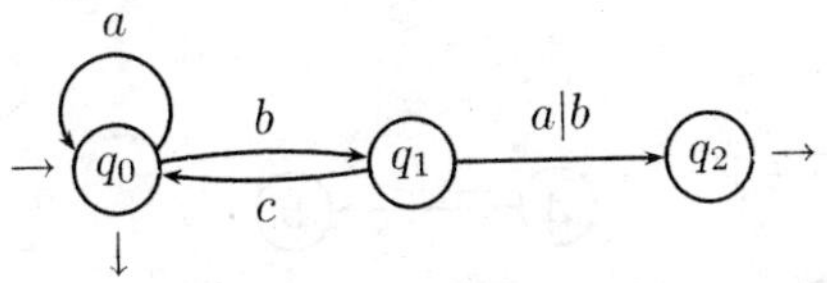


$$q_0 \to aq_0 \mid bq_1 \mid \varepsilon$$
$$q_1 \to cq_0 \mid aq_2 \mid bq_2$$
$$q_2 \to \varepsilon$$

Sentence $bca$ is recognized in 3 steps by the automaton and it derives from the axiom in $3+1$ steps:

$$q_0 \Rightarrow bq_1 \Rightarrow bcq_0 \Rightarrow bcaq_0 \Rightarrow bca\varepsilon$$

Observe the grammar contains empty rules but of course it can be turned into the nonnullable normal form by means of the transformation on p. 60.

For the example, first we find the set of nullable nonterminals $Null = \{q_0, q_2\}$; then we construct the equivalent rules:

$$q_0 \to aq_0 \mid bq_1 \mid a \mid \varepsilon \qquad q_1 \to cq_0 \mid aq_2 \mid bq_2 \mid a \mid b \mid c$$

Now $q_2$ is eliminated because its only rule is empty. At last grammar cleaning produces the rules:

$$q_0 \to aq_0 \mid bq_1 \mid a \mid \varepsilon \qquad q_1 \to cq_0 \mid a \mid b \mid c$$

Of course the empty rule $q_0 \to \varepsilon$ must stay there because $q_0$ is the axiom, which causes the empty string to be a sentence.
In this normal form of the grammar it is evident that a move entering a final state $r$

$$q \xrightarrow{a} r \to$$

may correspond to two rules $q \to ar \mid a$, one producing the nonterminal $r$, the other of the terminal type.

The conversion from automaton to grammar has been straightforward, but to make the reverse transformation from grammar to automaton, we need to modify the machine definition by permitting nondeterministic behavior.

## 3.5 Nondeterministic Automata

A right-linear grammar may contain two alternative rules

$A \to aB \mid aC$ where $a \in \Sigma, A, B, C \in V$

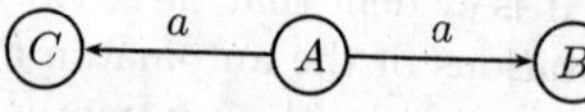


starting with the same character $a$. In this case, converting the rules to machine transitions, two arrows with identical label would exit from the same state $A$ and enter two distinct states $B$ and $C$. This means that in state $A$, reading character $a$, the machine can choose which one of the next states to enter: its behavior is not deterministic. Formally the transition function takes two values, $\delta(A, a) = \{B, C\}$.

Similarly a copy rule

$A \to B$ where $B \in V$

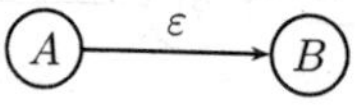


would be converted into an unusual machine transition from state $A$ to state $B$, which does not read any terminal character (it would be odd to say it reads the empty string).

A machine move that does not read an input character is termed *spontaneous* or an *epsilon move*. Spontaneous moves too cause the machine to be nondeterministic, as in the following situation:

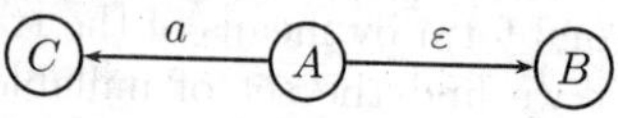


where in state $A$ the automaton can choose to move spontaneously (i.e., without reading) to $B$, or to read a character, and if it is an $a$, to move to $C$.

### *3.5.1 Motivation of Nondeterminism*

The mapping from grammar rules to transitions pushed us to introduce some transitions with multiple destinations and spontaneous moves, which are the main forms of indeterminism. Since this might appear as a useless theoretical concept, we hasten to list several advantages.

#### Concision

Defining a language with a nondeterministic machine often results in a more readable and compact definition, as in the next example.

*Example 3.10.* Penultimate character
A sentence, like *abaabb*, is characterized by the presence of letter $b$ in the penultimate position. The r.e. and indeterministic recognizer are in

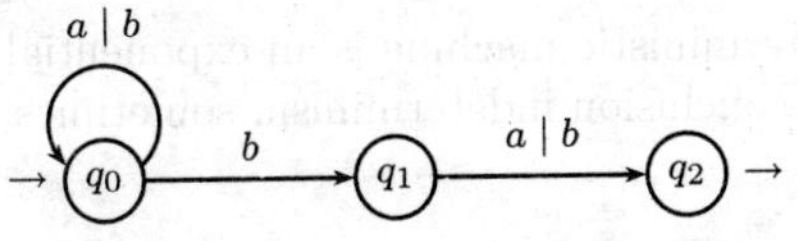


$L_2 = (a \mid b)^* b(a \mid b)$ $N_2$ :

**Fig. 3.7** R.e. and corresponding nondeterministic machine $N_2$ checking the penultimate character is $b$.

Figure 3.7. We have to explain how machine $N_2$ works: given an input string, the machine seeks a computation, i.e., a path from the initial state to the final, labelled with the input characters; if it succeeds, the string is accepted. Thus string *baba* is recognized with the computation

$$q_0 \xrightarrow{b} q_0 \xrightarrow{a} q_0 \xrightarrow{b} q_1 \xrightarrow{a} q_2$$

Notice other computations are possible, for instance the path

$$q_0 \xrightarrow{b} q_0 \xrightarrow{a} q_0 \xrightarrow{b} q_0 \xrightarrow{a} q_0$$

fails to recognize, because it does not reach the final state.

The same language is accepted by the deterministic automaton $M_2$ in Figure 3.8. Clearly this machine is not just more complicated than the indeterministic type in Figure 3.7, but the latter makes it more perspicuous that the penultimate character must be $b$.

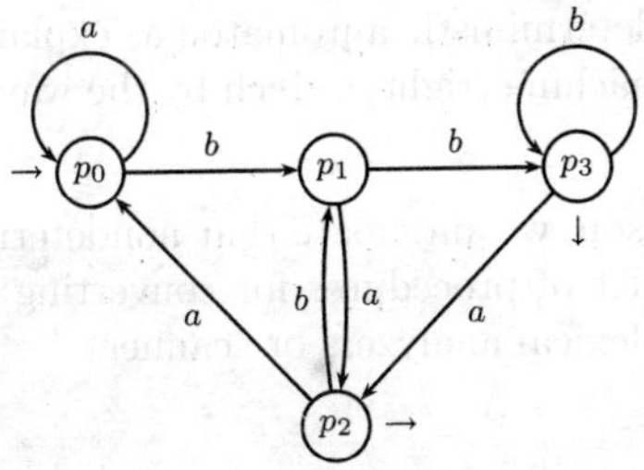


$M_2$:

**Fig. 3.8** Deterministic recognizer $M_2$ of strings having $b$ next to last.

To strengthen the argument consider a generalization of language $L_2$ to language $L_k$, such that, for some $k \geqslant 2$, the $k$-th character before the last is $b$. With little thought we see the nondeterministic automaton would have $k+1$ states, while one could prove that the number of states of the minimal

deterministic machine is an exponential function of $k$.
In conclusion indeterminism sometimes allows much shorter definitions.

### Left Right Interchange and Language Reflection

Nondeterminism also arises in string reversal when a given deterministic machine is transformed to recognize the reflection $L^R$ of language $L$. This is sometimes required when for some reason strings must be scanned from right to left.
The new machine is straightforward to derive: interchange initial and final states[5] and reverse all the arrows. Clearly this may give birth to nondeterministic transitions.

*Example 3.11.* The language having $b$ as penultimate character ($L_2$ of Figure 3.7) is the reflection of the language having the second character equal to $b$:

$$L' = \{x \in \{a, b\}^* \mid b \text{ is the second character of } x\} \qquad L_2 = (L')^R$$

$L'$ is recognized by the deterministic automaton (left):

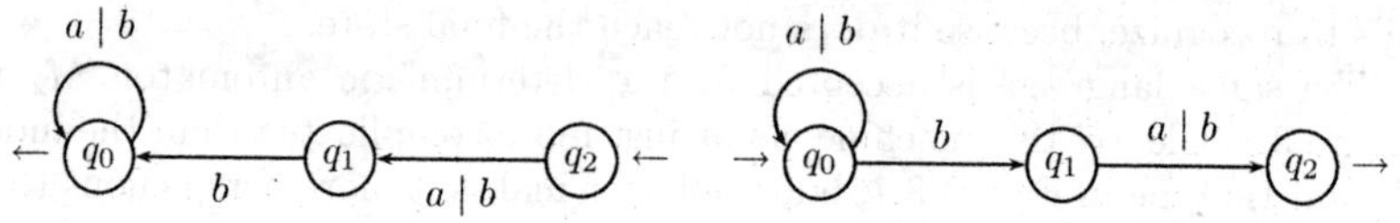


Transforming the deterministic automaton as explained above, we obtain the nondeterministic machine (right), which by the way is identical to the one in Figure 3.7.

As a further reason, we anticipate that nondeterministic machines are the intermediate product of procedures for converting r.e. to automata, widely used for designing lexical analyzers or scanners.

## 3.5.2 Nondeterministic Recognizers

We precisely define the concept of nondeterministic finite-state computation, first without spontaneous moves.

[5] If the machine has several final states, multiple initial states result thus causing another form of indeterminism to be dealt with later.

A *nondeterministic finite automaton* $N$, without spontaneous moves, is defined by:

- the state set $Q$
- the terminal alphabet $\Sigma$
- two subsets of $Q$: the set $I$ of the *initial* states and the set $F$ of *final* states
- the transition relation $\delta$, a subset of the cartesian product $Q \times \Sigma \times Q$.

Remarks. This machine may have several initial states. In the graphic representation a transition $(q_1, a, q_2)$ is an arc labelled $a$, from the first to the second state.

As before, a *computation* is a series of transitions such that the origin of each one coincides with the destination of the preceding one:

$$q_0 \xrightarrow{a_1} q_1 \xrightarrow{a_2} q_2 \dots \xrightarrow{a_n} q_n$$

The computation *origin* is $q_0$, the *termination* is $q_n$, and the *length* is the number $n$ of transitions or moves. A computation of length one is just a transition. The computation *label* is the concatenation $a_1 a_2 \dots a_n$ of the characters read by each transition. In brief, the computation is also written $q_0 \xrightarrow{a_1 a_2 \dots a_n} q_n$.

A string $x$ is *recognized or accepted* by the automaton, if it is the label of a computation originating in some initial state, terminating in some final state, and having label $x$.

Let us focus on the empty string. We stipulate that every state is the origin and termination of a computation of length 0, having the empty string $\varepsilon$ as label. It follows that the empty string is accepted by an automaton if, and only if, there exists an initial state which is also final.

The *language* $L(N)$ *recognized* by automaton $N$ is the set of accepted strings:

$$L(N) = \{x \in \Sigma^* \mid q \xrightarrow{x} r \text{ with } q \in I, r \in F\}$$

*Example 3.12.* Searching a text for a word

Given a string or word $y$ and a text $x$, does $x$ contain $y$ as substring? The following machine recognizes the texts which contain one or more occurrences of $y$, that is, the language $(a \mid b)^* y (a \mid b)^*$. We illustrate with the word $y = bb$:

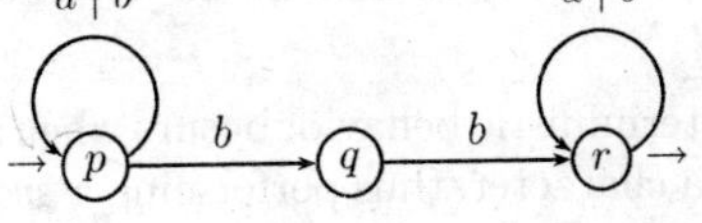


String *abbb* is the label of several computations originating in the initial state:

$$p \xrightarrow{a} p \xrightarrow{b} p \xrightarrow{b} p \xrightarrow{b} p \qquad p \xrightarrow{a} p \xrightarrow{b} p \xrightarrow{b} p \xrightarrow{b} q$$
$$p \xrightarrow{a} p \xrightarrow{b} p \xrightarrow{b} q \xrightarrow{b} r \qquad p \xrightarrow{a} p \xrightarrow{b} q \xrightarrow{b} r \xrightarrow{b} r$$

The first two computations do not find the word looked for. The last two find the word respectively at position $ab\underbrace{bb}$ and $a\underbrace{bb}b$.

#### Transition Function

The moves of a nondeterministic automaton can still be considered as a finite function, but one computing sets of values. For a machine $N = (Q, \Sigma, \delta, I, F)$, devoid of spontaneous moves, the functionality of the state-transition function $\delta$ is:

$$\delta : (Q \times (\Sigma \cup \varepsilon)) \rightarrow \text{powerset of } Q$$

Now the meaning of $\delta(q, a) = [p_1, p_2, \ldots, p_k]$ is that the machine reading $a$ in the current state $q$, can arbitrarily move to any of the states $p_1, \ldots, p_k$. As we did for deterministic machines, we extend the function to any string $y$ including the empty one:

$$\forall q \in Q : \ \delta(q, \varepsilon) = [q]$$

$$\forall q \in Q, y \in \Sigma^* \ : \ \delta(q, y) = [p \mid q \xrightarrow{y} p]$$

In other words, it is $p \in \delta(q, y)$ if there exists a computation labelled $y$ from $q$ to $p$.

The previous definitions allow a reformulation of the language accepted by automaton $N$:

$$L(N) = \{x \in \Sigma^* \mid \exists q \in I : \ \delta(q, x) \cap F \neq \emptyset\}$$

i.e., the set computed by function delta must contain a final state, for a string to be recognized.

*Example 3.13.* (Example 3.12 continued)

$$\delta(p, a) = [p], \quad \delta(p, ab) = [p, q], \quad \delta(p, abb) = [p, q, r]$$

### *3.5.3 Automata with Spontaneous Moves*

Another kind of nondeterministic behavior occurs when an automaton changes state without reading a character, thus performing a *spontaneous move*, to be depicted in the state-transition diagram as an arc labelled $\varepsilon$ (named $\varepsilon$-arc). Such arcs will prove to be expedient for assembling the automata recognizing a regular composition of finite-state languages. The next example illustrates the case for union and concatenation.

*Example 3.14.* Compositional definition of decimal constants
This language includes constants such as $90 \bullet 01$. The part preceding the

decimal point may be missing (as in •02); but it may not contain leading zeroes. Trailing zeroes are permitted at the end of the fractional part. The language is defined by the r.e.

$$L = (0 \mid \varepsilon \mid N) \bullet (0 \ldots 9)^{+} \text{ where } N = (1 \ldots 9)(0 \ldots 9)^{*}$$

The automaton in Figure 3.9 mirrors the structure of the expression. Notice that the presence of spontaneous moves does not affect the way a machine performs recognition: a string $x$ is *recognized* by a machine with spontaneous moves if it is the label of a computation originating in an initial state and terminating in a final state. Observe that taking the spontaneous move from

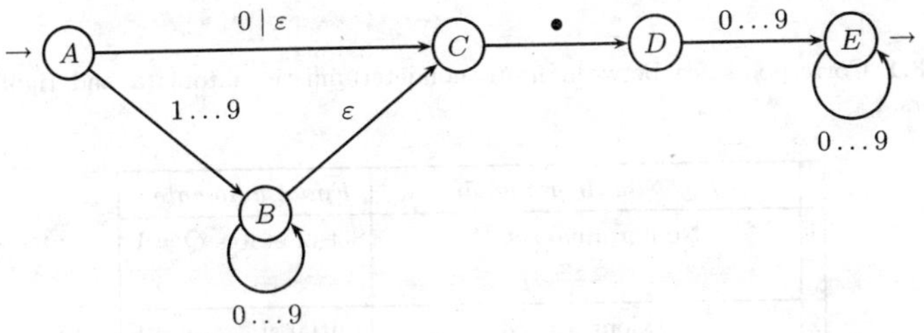


**Fig. 3.9** Decimal constant definition with spontaneous moves (example 3.14).

$A$ to $C$, the integer part $N$ vanishes. The string 34 • 5 is accepted with the computation

$$A \xrightarrow{3} B \xrightarrow{4} B \xrightarrow{\varepsilon} C \xrightarrow{\bullet} D \xrightarrow{5} E$$

But the number of steps of the computation (i.e., the length of the path in the graph) can exceed the length of the input string, because of the presence of $\epsilon$-arcs. As a consequence, the recognition algorithm no longer works in real time. Yet time complexity remains linear, because it is possible to assume that there are no cycles of spontaneous moves in any computation.

The family of languages recognized by such nondeterministic automata is also called *finite-state*.

### Uniqueness of Initial State

The official definition of nondeterministic machine allows two or more initial states, but it is easy to construct an equivalent machine with only one: add to the machine a new state $q_0$, which will be the only initial state, and the $\epsilon$-arcs going from it to the former initial states of the automaton. Clearly any computation on the new automaton accepts a string if, and only if, the old automaton does so.

The transformation has changed one form of indeterminism, linked with multiple initial states, to another form related to spontaneous moves. We shall see on p. 120 that such moves can be eliminated.

### 3.5.4 *Correspondence between Automata and Grammars*

We collect in Table 3.1 the mapping between nondeterministic automata, also with spontaneous moves, and unilinear grammars. The correspondence is so direct that it witnesses the two models are essentially notational variants.

**Table 3.1** Correspondence between finite nondeterministic automata and right-linear grammars.

| | *Right-linear grammar* | *Finite automaton* |
|---|---|---|
| 1 | Nonterminal set $V$ | Set of states $Q = V$ |
| 2 | Axiom $S = q_0$ | Initial state $q_0 = S$ |
| 3 | $p \to aq$, where $a \in \Sigma$ and $p, q \in V$ | $a$ 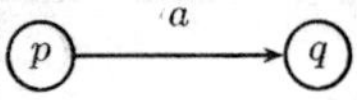 |
| 4 | $p \to q$, where $p, q \in V$ | $\varepsilon$ 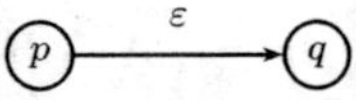 |
| 5 | $p \to \varepsilon$ | Final state 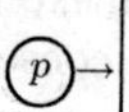 |

Consider a right-linear grammar $G = (V, \Sigma, P, S)$ and a nondeterministic automaton $N = (Q, \Sigma, \delta, q_0, F)$ , which we may assume from the preceding discussion to have a single initial state. First assume the grammar rules are strictly unilinear (p. 71). The states $Q$ of the automaton match the nonterminals $V$ of the grammar. The initial state corresponds to the axiom. Notice (row 3) that the pair of alternatives $p \to aq \mid ar$ correspond to two nondeterministic moves. A copy rule (row 4) matches a spontaneous move. A final state (row 5) matches a nonterminal having an empty rule.

It is easy to see that every grammar derivation matches a machine computation, and conversely, so that the following statement ensues.

*Property 3.15.* A language is recognized by a finite automaton if, and only if, it is generated by a unilinear grammar.

Notice that the statement concerns also left-linear grammars, since we know from Chapter 2 they have the same capacity as right-linear grammars.

If the grammar contains nonempty terminal rules of type $p \to a$ where $a \in \Sigma$, the automaton is modified, to include a new final state $f$, different from those produced by row 5 of Table 3.1, and the move 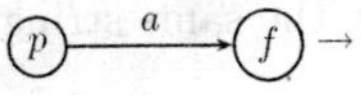


*Example 3.16.* Right-linear grammar and nondeterministic automaton
The grammar matching the automaton of decimal constants (Figure 3.9 on p. 113) is

$$A \to 0C \mid C \mid 1B \mid \ldots \mid 9B \qquad B \to 0B \mid \ldots \mid 9B \mid C$$
$$C \to \bullet D \qquad D \to 0E \mid \ldots \mid 9E$$
$$E \to 0E \mid \ldots \mid 9E \mid \varepsilon$$

where $A$ is the axiom.

Next we drop the assumption of unilinearity in the strict sense. Observe the right-linear grammar (left) and matching automaton (right) below:

$$S \to aaX \mid \varepsilon$$
$$X \to bX \mid b$$

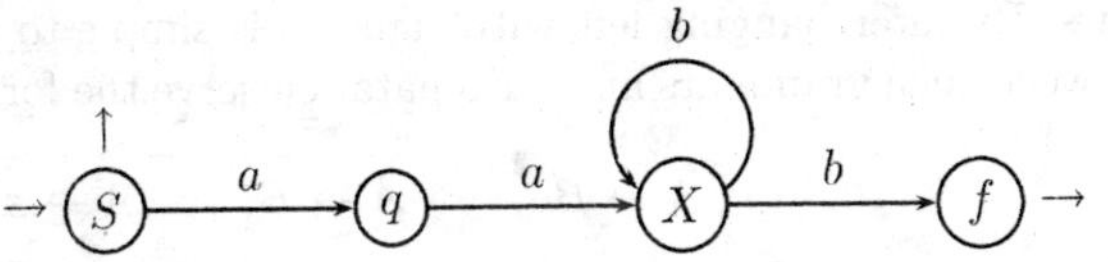


The not strictly right-linear rule $S \to aaX$ is simply converted to a cascade of two arcs, with an intermediate state $q$ after the first $a$. Moreover, the new final state $f$ has been added to mirror the last step of a derivation using rule $X \to b$.

### 3.5.5 Ambiguity of Automata

An *automaton* is *ambiguous* if it accepts a string with two different computations. Clearly it follows from the definition that a deterministic automaton is never ambiguous. It is interesting to link the notion of ambiguity for automata and for unilinear grammars. Knowing that there is a bijective correspondence between computations and grammar derivations, it follows that an automaton is ambiguous if, and only if, the right-linear equivalent grammar is ambiguous, i.e., if it generates a sentence with two distinct syntax trees.

*Example 3.17.* Ambiguity of automaton and grammar
The automaton of example 3.12 on p. 111, reproduced below

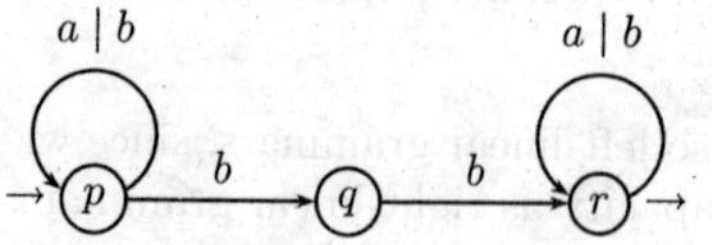


$$p \rightarrow ap \mid bp \mid bq$$
$$r \rightarrow ar \mid br \mid \varepsilon$$
$$q \rightarrow br$$

recognizes string *abbb* in two ways. The equivalent grammar (right) generates the same string with the trees:

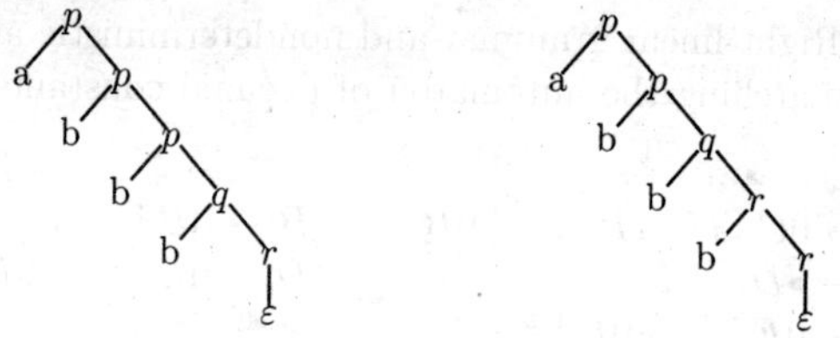

## 3.5.6 Left-Linear Grammars and Automata

Remember that the *REG* family can also be defined using left-linear grammars. By interchanging left with right, it is simple to discover the mapping between such grammars and automata. Observe the forms of left-linear rules:

$$A \rightarrow Ba, \qquad A \rightarrow B, \qquad A \rightarrow \varepsilon$$

Consider such a grammar $G$ and the specular language $L^R = (L(G))^R$: this language is generated by the reflected grammar, denoted $G_R$, obtained (p. 79) transforming the rules of the first form to $A \rightarrow aB$, while the remaining two forms do not change. Since the reflected grammar $G_R$ is right-linear, we know how to construct a finite automaton $N_R$ for $L^R$. In order to obtain the automaton of the original language $L$, we modify $N_R$, reversing the arrows of transitions and interchanging initial and final states.

*Example 3.18.* From left-linear grammar to automaton
Given grammar $G$:

$$S \rightarrow Aa \mid Ab \qquad A \rightarrow Bb \qquad B \rightarrow Ba \mid Bb \mid \varepsilon$$

the reflected grammar $G_R$ is

$$S \rightarrow aA \mid bA \qquad A \rightarrow bB \qquad B \rightarrow aB \mid bB \mid \varepsilon$$

The corresponding automaton $N^R$ recognizing the mirror language and the recognizer $N$ for language $L(G)$ are:

*Recognizer* $N_R$ *of* $(L(G))^R$

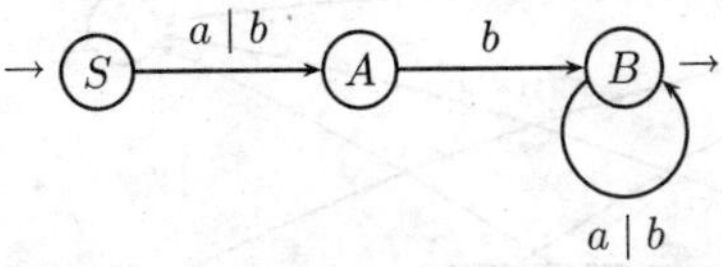


*Recognizer* $N$ *of* $L(G)$

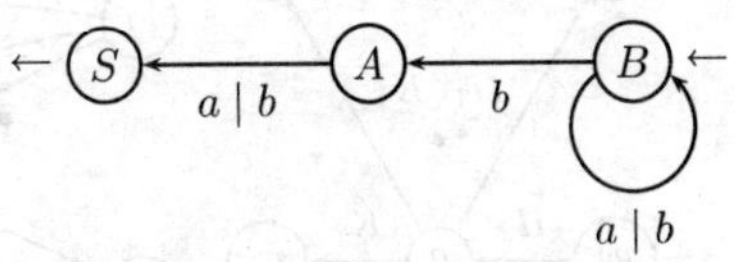


Incidentally, the language has a $b$ in the position before the last.

## 3.6 Directly from Automata to Regular Expressions: BMC Method

In applied work one has sometimes to compute an r.e. for the language defined by a machine. We already know a rather indirect method: since an automaton is easily converted to an equivalent right-linear grammar, the r.e. of the language can be computed solving the linear simultaneous equations, seen on p. 71. The next direct *elimination method* BMC is named after Brzozowski and McCluskey .

Suppose for simplicity the initial state $i$ is unique and no arc enters in it; similarly the final state $t$ is unique and without outgoing arcs. Otherwise, just add a new initial state $i$ connected by spontaneous moves to the ex-initial states; similarly introduce a new unique final state $t$. Every state other than $i$ and $t$ is called *internal*.

We construct an equivalent automaton, termed *generalized*, which is more flexible as it allows arc labels to be not just terminal characters, but also regular languages (i.e., a label can be an r.e.). The idea is to eliminate one by one the internal states, while compensating by introducing new arcs labelled with r.e., until only the initial and final states are left. Then the label of arc $i \rightarrow t$ is the r.e. of the language.

Observe in Figure 3.10 to the left an internal state $q$ with all adjoining arcs; to the right, the same fragment of machine, after eliminating state $q$ and with compensatory arcs labelled with the same strings produced when traversing state $q$.

To avoid too many superpositions some labels are not printed, but of course, for every pair of states $p_i$ and $r_j$ there should be an arc $p_i \xrightarrow{H_i J^* K_j} r_j$. Notice that in the scheme some states $p_i, r_j$ may coincide. It is evident that the set of strings which may be read when the original automaton moves from state $p_i$ to state $r_j$, coincide with the language labelling the arc $p_i \rightarrow r_j$ of the new automaton.

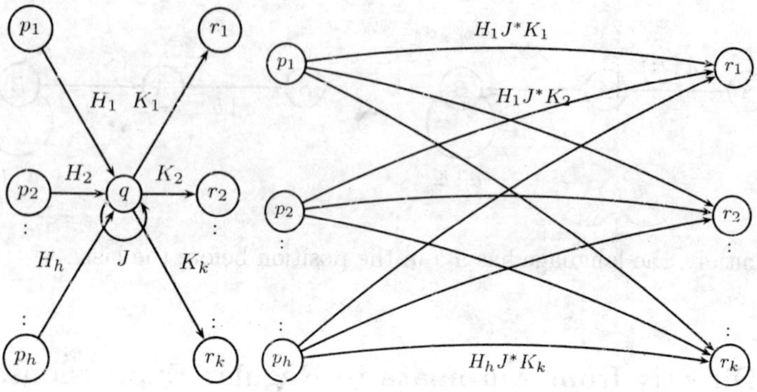


**Fig. 3.10** Deleting a node and compensating with new generalized arcs.

In order to compute the r.e. of the language of a given automaton, the above transformation is applied over and over eliminating each time an internal state.

*Example 3.19.* (from Sakarovitch)
The automaton is shown in Figure 3.11 before and after normalization.

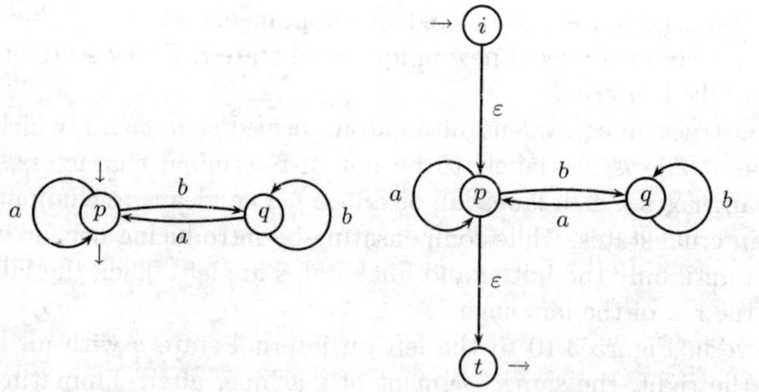


**Fig. 3.11** Automaton before (left) and after (right) normalization (example 3.19).

We trace in Figure 3.12 the execution of the BMC algorithm, eliminating the states in the order $q, p$.

The elimination order does not affect the result, but, as in the solution of simultaneous equations by elimination, it may yield more or less complex

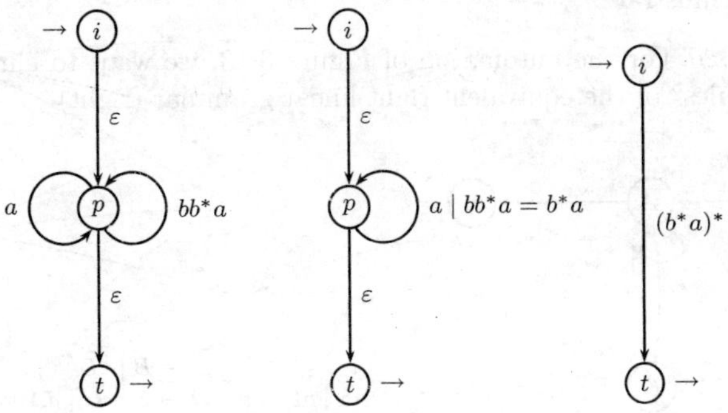


**Fig. 3.12** Left to right: the automaton of Figure 3.11 after elimination of node $q$, simplification of r.e., and elimination of node $p$.

yet equivalent solutions. For instance, the order $p, q$ would produce the r.e. $(a^*b)^+a^+ \mid a^*$.

## 3.7 Elimination of Nondeterminism

We have argued for the use of nondeterministic machines in language specifications and transformations, but the final stage of a project usually requires an efficient implementation, which can only be provided by a deterministic machine. There are exceptions, like when the cost to be minimized is the time needed to construct the automaton, instead of the time spent to recognize strings: this happens for instance in a text editor, when implementing a searching algorithm by means of an automaton to be used only one time to find a string in a text.

Next we describe a procedure for turning a nondeterministic automaton into an equivalent deterministic one; as a corollary every unilinear grammar can be made nonambiguous. The transformation operates in two phases:

1. Elimination of spontaneous moves, obtaining a machine that in general is nondeterministic. Because spontaneous moves match the copy rules of the equivalent grammar, this phase applies the grammar transformation that removes such rules (p. 61).
2. Replacing several not deterministic transitions with one transition entering a new state: this phase is called *powerset construction*, because the new states correspond to the subsets of the set of states.

Elimination of Spontaneous Moves

For phase one we avoid repeating the algorithm for copy rule elimination and proceed to illustrate.

*Example 3.20.* For the automaton of Figure 3.13, we want to eliminate all the copy rules[6] of the equivalent right-linear grammar (right).

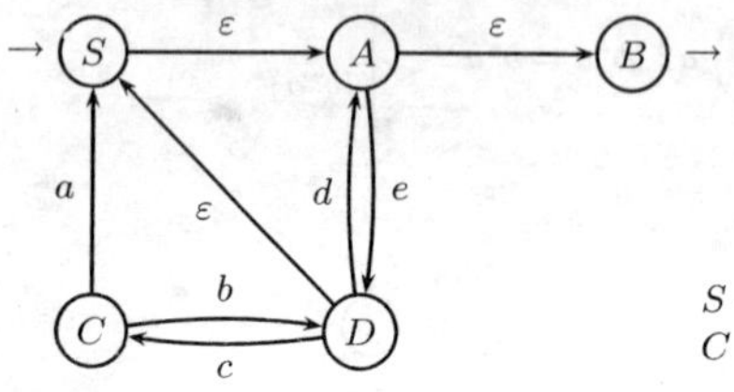


$S \to A$ $\quad A \to B \mid eD$ $\quad B \to \varepsilon$

$C \to aS \mid bD$ $\quad D \to S \mid cC \mid dA$

**Fig. 3.13** Automaton with spontaneous moves and equivalent grammar.

First we compute the sets of copies:

| | *copy* |
|---|---|
| $S$ | $S, A, B$ |
| $A$ | $A, B$ |
| $B$ | $B$ |
| $C$ | $C$ |
| $D$ | $D, S, A, B$ |

Then we construct the copy-less grammar and the equivalent machine without spontaneous moves shown in Figure 3.14, where state $B$, not accessible from the initial state, should be deleted. Observe that a whole path of the graph of Figure 3.13 (e.g., $D \xrightarrow{\varepsilon} S \xrightarrow{\varepsilon} A \xrightarrow{e} D$), made with a chain of spontaneous moves ended by a reading move, is replaced with a direct move ($D \xrightarrow{e} D$) in Figure 3.14.

The last remark suggests that elimination can be directly performed on the graph, without going through the grammar. It suffices to identify every path made by spontaneous moves and ending with a reading move and to replace it with a reading move to the same effect. After all such paths have been similarly analyzed, the *varepsilon*-arcs are erased.
After this machine transformation, if the result is not deterministic, the next transformation must be applied.

[6] Notice that the algorithm of p. 61 can be applied, although the grammar contains $\varepsilon$-rules, because in a unilinear grammar every right part contains at most one nonterminal.

$$S \to \varepsilon \mid eD \qquad A \to \varepsilon \mid eD \qquad B \to \varepsilon$$
$$C \to aS \mid bD \qquad D \to \varepsilon \mid eD \mid cC \mid dA$$

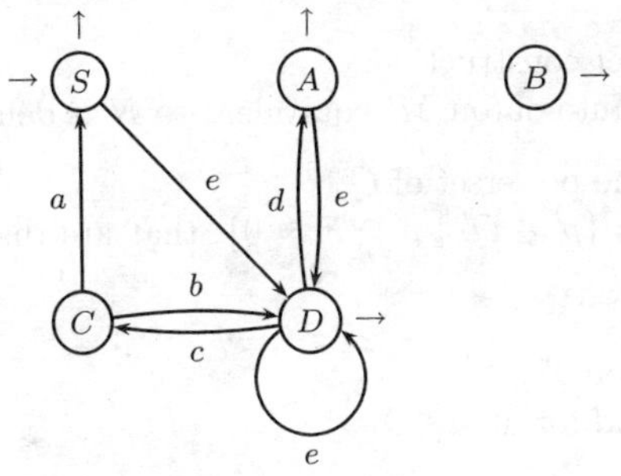


**Fig. 3.14** Copy-less grammar and automaton without spontaneous moves, equivalent to the machine of Figure 3.13.

## *3.7.1 Construction of Accessible Subsets*

Given $N$, a nondeterministic automaton without spontaneous moves, we explain how to construct an equivalent deterministic machine $M'$. The main idea is that, if $N$ contains the moves

$$p \xrightarrow{a} p_1, \qquad p \xrightarrow{a} p_2, \qquad \ldots, \qquad p \xrightarrow{a} p_k$$

after reading $a$, machine $N$ can be in any one of the next states $p_1, p_2, \ldots, p_k$, i.e., it is in a state of uncertainty. Then we create in $M'$ a new collective state named

$$[p_1, p_2, \ldots, p_k]$$

that will simulate the uncertainty.

To connect the new state to the others, we construct the outgoing arcs according to the following rule. If a collective state contains the states $p_1, p_2, \ldots, p_k$ , for each one we consider in $N$ the outgoing arcs labelled with the same letter $a$

$$p_1 \xrightarrow{a} [q_1, q_2, \ldots], \qquad p_2 \xrightarrow{a} [r_1, r_2, \ldots], \qquad \text{etc.}$$

and we merge together the next states

$$[q_1, q_2, \ldots] \cup [r_1, r_2, \ldots] \cup \ldots$$

thus obtaining the collective state reached by transition

$$[p_1, p_2, \ldots, p_k] \xrightarrow{a} [q_1, q_2, \ldots, r_1, r_2, \ldots, \ldots]$$

If such state does not exist in $M'$, it is added to the current state set.

*Algorithm.* Powerset construction.
The deterministic automaton $M'$ equivalent to $N$ is defined by:

1. state set $Q'$ is the powerset of $Q$
2. final states $F' = \{p' \in Q' \mid p' \cap F \neq \emptyset\}$, that are the states containing a final state of $N$
3. initial state[7] $[q_0]$
4. transition function $\delta'$ :
   for all $p' \in Q'$ and for all $a \in \Sigma$

$$p' \xrightarrow{a} [s \mid q \in p' \wedge (\text{arc } q \xrightarrow{a} s \text{ is in } N)]$$

In step 4., if an arc $q \xrightarrow{a} q_{err}$ leads to the error state, it is not added to the collective state: in fact, any computation entering the sink never recognizes any string and can be ignored.

Because the states of $M'$ are the subsets of $Q$, the cardinality of $Q'$ is in the worst case exponentially larger than the cardinality of $Q$. This confirms previous findings that deterministic machines may be larger: remember the exponential explosion of the number of states in the language having a specific character $k$ positions before the last (p. 108).

The algorithm can be improved: $M'$ often contains states inaccessible from the initial state, hence useless. Instead of erasing them with the clean-up procedure, it is better to altogether avoid their creation: we draw only the collective states which can be reached from the initial state.

*Example 3.21.* The nondeterministic automaton in Figure 3.15 (top) is transformed to the deterministic one below.

Explanations: from $\delta(A, b) = \{A, B\}$ we draw the collective state $[A, B]$; from this the transitions

$$[A, B] \xrightarrow{a} (\delta(A, a) \cup \delta(B, a)) = [A]$$

$$[A, B] \xrightarrow{b} (\delta(A, b) \cup \delta(B, b)) = [A, B, C]$$

Then we create the transitions originating from the new collective state $[A, B, C]$:

$$[A, B, C] \xrightarrow{a} (\delta(A, a) \cup \delta(B, a) \cup \delta(C, a)) = [A, C, D], \text{final collective state}$$

---

7 If the given automaton $N$ has several initial states, the initial state of $M'$ is the set of all initial states.

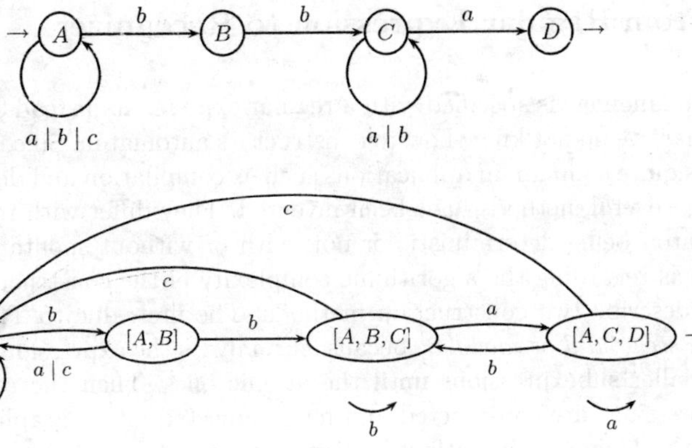


**Fig. 3.15** From nondeterministic $N$ (top) to deterministic $M'$ (bottom).

$$[A, B, C] \xrightarrow{b} (\delta(A, b) \cup \delta(B, b) \cup \delta(C, b)) = [A, B, C], \text{self-loop}$$

etc. The algorithm ends when step 4, applied to the current set $Q'$ of states, does not generate any new state. Notice that not all subsets of $Q$ correspond to an accessible state: e.g., the subset and state $[A, C]$ would be useless.

To justify the correctness of the algorithm, we show that a string $x$ is recognized by $M'$ if, and only if, it is accepted by $N$.

If a computation of $N$ accepts $x$, there exists a labelled path $x$ from the initial state $q_0$ to a final state $q_f$. The algorithm ensures then that in $M'$ there exists a labelled path $x$ from $[q_0]$ to a state $[\ldots, q_f, \ldots]$ containing $q_f$.

Conversely, if $x$ is the label of a valid computation of $M'$, from $[q_0]$ to a final state $p \in F'$, then by definition $p$ contains at least one final state $q_f$ of $N$. By construction there exists in $N$ a labelled path $x$ from $q_0$ to $q_f$.

We summarize with a fundamental statement.

*Property 3.22.* Every finite-state language can be recognized by a deterministic automaton.

This property ensures that the recognition algorithm of finite-state languages works in real time, i.e., completes the job within a number of transitions equal to the length of the input string (fewer if an error occurs before the string has been entirely scanned).

As a corollary, for every language recognized by a finite automaton, there exists an unambiguous unilinear grammar, the one naturally (p. 106) corresponding to the deterministic automaton. This also says that for any regular language we have a procedure to eliminate ambiguity from the grammar, in other words a regular language cannot be inherently ambiguous (p. 56).

## 3.8 From Regular Expression to Recognizer

When a language is specified with a regular expression, instead of a unilinear grammar, we do not know how to construct its automaton. Since this requirement is quite common in applications such as compilation and document processing, several methods have been invented. They differ with respect to the automaton being deterministic or not, with or without spontaneous moves, as well as regarding the algorithmic complexity of the construction.

We describe two construction methods. The first, due to Thompson, is termed *structural* or *modular*, because it analyzes the expression into smaller and smaller subexpressions until the atomic ones. Then the recognizers of subexpressions are constructed and interconnected into a graph that implements the language operations (union, concatenation, and star) present in the expression. The result is in general nondeterministic with spontaneous moves.

The second method, named after Glushkov, or McNaughton and Yamada, builds a nondeterministic machine without spontaneous moves, of a size related to the length of the r.e.

Both methods can be combined with previous determinization algorithms, to the effect of directly producing a deterministic automaton.

Eventually we will be able to transform language specifications back and forth from automata, grammars and regular expressions, thus proving the three models are equivalent.

### *3.8.1 Thompson Structural Method*

Given an r.e. we analyze it into simple parts, we produce corresponding component automata, and we interconnect them to obtain the complete recognizer.

In this construction each component machine is assumed to have exactly one initial state without incoming arcs and one final state without outgoing arcs: if not so, simply introduce two new states, as for the BMC algorithm of p. 117.

Thompson algorithm[8] incorporates the mapping rule between simple r.e. and automata schematized in Table 3.2. Observing the machines in Table 3.2 one sees many nondeterministic bifurcations, with outgoing $\epsilon$-arcs.

The validity of Thompson's method comes from it being an operational reformulation of the closure properties of regular languages by concatenation, union, and star (stated in the preceding chapter, p. 24).

[8] Originally presented in [53]. It forms the base of the popular tool *lex* (or GNU *flex*) used for building scanners.

**Table 3.2** From component subexpression to component subautomata. A rectangle depicts a component subautomaton with its initial state (left) and final state (right).

*Atomic expressions:*

*Concatenation of expressions:*

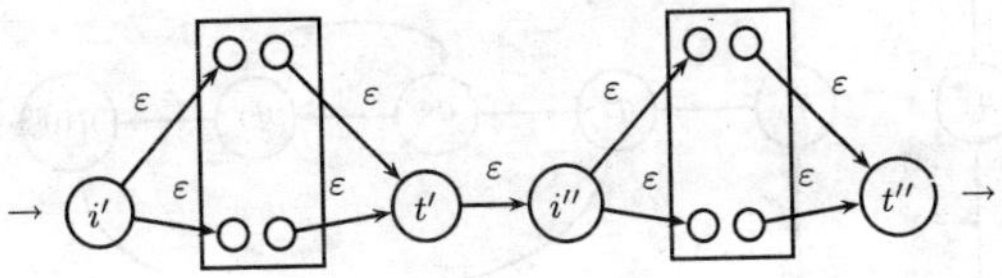


*Union of expressions:*

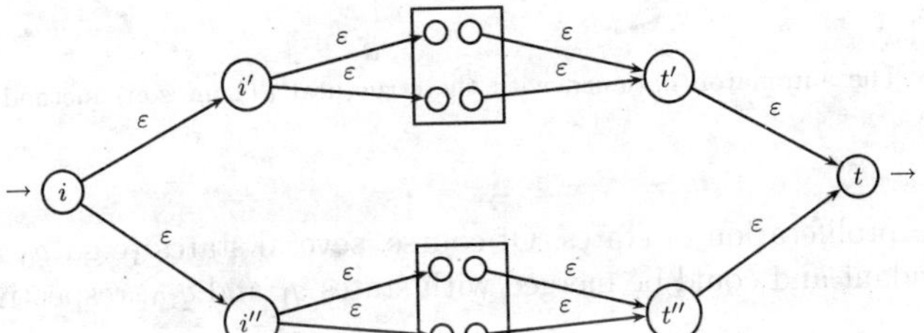


*Star of expression:*

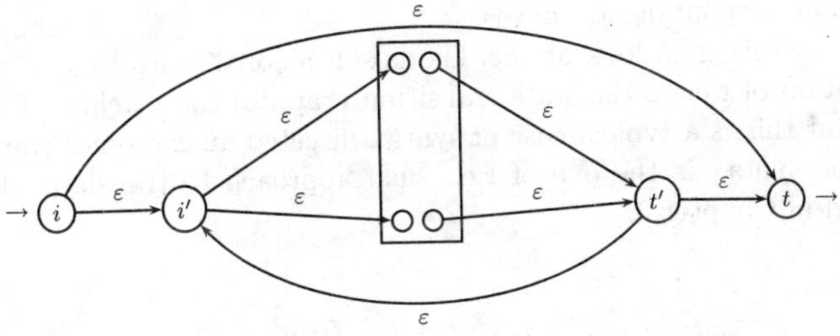


*Example 3.23.* Take the r.e. $(a \cup \varepsilon).b^*$ and decompose it into the subexpressions

$$\overbrace{\overbrace{(\overbrace{a}^{E_{2,3}} \cup \overbrace{\varepsilon}^{E_{4,5}})}^{E_{1,6}} \; . \; \overbrace{\overbrace{b}^{E_{8,9}} \; *}^{E_{7,10}}}^{E_{0,11}}$$

Then apply the mapping to each subexpression, producing the automaton of Figure 3.16. Notice that we have moderately simplified the constructions to

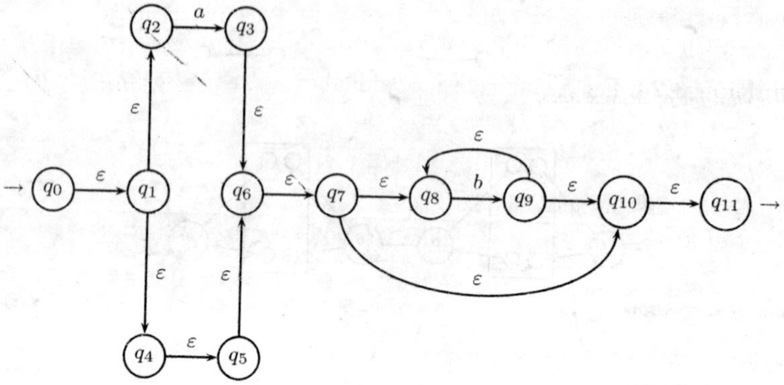


**Fig. 3.16** The automaton obtained with the structural (Thompson) method from r.e. $(a \cup \varepsilon).b^*$.

avoid the proliferation of states. Of course, several states (e.g., $q_0$ and $q_{11}$) are redundant and could be merged with states $q_1$ and $q_{10}$, respectively.

Existing tools use improved versions of the algorithm to avoid constructing redundant states. Other versions combine the algorithm with the one for elimination of spontaneous moves.

It is interesting to look at the Thompson algorithm as a converter from the notation of r.e. to the state transition graph of the machine. From this standpoint this is a typical case of syntax-directed analysis and translation, where the syntax is the one of r.e.; such approach to translator design is presented in Chapter 6.

### 3.8.2 *Algorithm of Glushkov, McNaughton and Yamada*

Another classical method, GMY, builds a machine whose states are in direct correspondence with the terminals of the expression. Preliminarily it is necessary to define[9] a simple subfamily of regular languages.

[9] Following the conceptual path of Berstel and Pin [10].

## Locally Testable Languages and Local Automata

Some regular languages are extremely simple to recognize, because it suffices to test if certain short substrings are present. An example is the set of strings starting with $b$, ending with $a$ or $b$, and containing $ba$ or $ab$ as substrings.

**Definition 3.24.** For a language $L$ of alphabet $\Sigma$, the *set of initials* is

$$Ini(L) = \{a \in \Sigma \mid a\Sigma^* \cap L \neq \emptyset\}$$

i.e., the starting characters of the sentences of $L$.
The *set of finals* is

$$Fin(L) = \{a \in \Sigma \mid \Sigma^* a \cap L \neq \emptyset\}$$

i.e., the last characters of the sentences of $L$.
The *set of digrams* (or factors) is

$$Dig(L) = \{x \in \Sigma^2 \mid \Sigma^* x \Sigma^* \cap L \neq \emptyset\}$$

i.e., the substrings of length 2 present in the sentences of $L$. The complementary digrams are

$$\overline{Dig}(L) = \Sigma^2 \setminus Dig(L)$$

The three sets will be called *local*.

*Example 3.25.* Locally testable language
The local sets for language $L_1 = (abc)^+$ are

$$Ini(L_1) = a \quad Fin(L_1) = c \quad Dig(L_1) = \{ab, bc, ca\}$$

and the complement of the digram set is

$$\overline{Dig(L_1)} = \{aa, ac, ba, bb, cb, cc\}$$

We observe that the sentences of this language are precisely defined by the three sets, in the sense of the following identity.

$$L_1 \equiv \{x \mid Ini(x) \in Ini(L_1) \wedge Fin(x) \in Fin(L_1) \wedge Dig(x) \subseteq Dig(L_1)\} \quad (3.1)$$

or equivalently

$$L_1 \equiv \{x \mid Ini(x) \in Ini(L_1) \wedge Fin(x) \in Fin(L_1)\} \setminus \Sigma^* \overline{Dig}(L_1) \Sigma^* \quad (3.2)$$

Notice the last term contains the forbidden digrams.

**Definition 3.26.** A language $L$ is called *local* (or locally testable) if it satisfies identity (3.1) (or (3.2)).

Although not all languages are local, it should be clear that any language $L$ (not containing the empty string) satisfies a modified condition 3.1 (or 3.2), where the equal sign is substituted by the inclusion. In fact, by definition every sentence starts (resp. ends) with a character of $Ini(L)$ (resp. of $Fin(L)$) and its digrams are included in the set $Dig(L)$. But such conditions may not suffice to exclude some illegal strings.

*Example 3.27.* Nonlocal regular language
For $L_2 = b(aa)^+b$ we have

$$Ini(L_2) = Fin(L_2) = \{b\} \qquad Dig(L_2) = \{aa, ab, ba\} \qquad \overline{Dig}(L_2) = \{bb\}$$

The sentences of $L_2$ have even length, but among the strings starting and terminating with $b$, which do not contain $bb$ as digram, there are those of odd length such as $baaab$. Therefore the language defined by condition (3.1) (or (3.2)) strictly includes $L_2$.

Our present interest[10] for local languages comes from the notable simplicity of their recognizers. To recognize a string, the machine scans it from left to right, it checks the initial character is in $Ini$, it verifies that any pairs of adjacent characters are not in $\overline{Dig}$, and finally it checks the last character is in $Fin$. We are going to see these checks are easily performed by a finite automaton.

### Algorithm for Constructing the Recognizer of a Local Language

The automaton for a local language, specified by the local sets $Ini, Fin, Dig$, is defined as follows:

- the states are $q_0 \cup \Sigma$;
- the final states are $Fin$;
- the arcs are: $q_0 \xrightarrow{a} a$ if $a \in Ini$; $a \xrightarrow{b} b$ if $ab \in Dig$;
- if the empty string is in the language, the initial state $q_0$ is also final.

The finite automata of local languages, in short *local automata*, are characterized by the following properties:

1. apart from the initial state, the other states one-to-one correspond to the characters of the alphabet
2. no arc enters the initial state
3. all the arcs labelled with the same letter, say $a$, enter the same state, the one named $a$.

Intuitively, the automaton is in the state $b$ if, and only if, the last scanned character is $b$: we may think the machine has a sliding window two characters wide, that allows the transition from the previous state to the current one, if the digram is listed as permitted.

---

[10] In Chapter 6 local languages and automata are used to model the control-flow graph of a program.

*Example 3.28.* The local automaton accepting the local language $(abc)^+$ of example 3.25 is

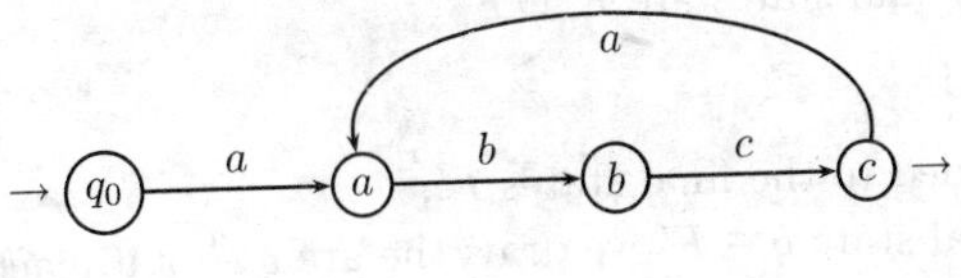


Notice the arc labels are redundant and may be dropped, since they coincide with the name of the destination node.

### Composition of Local Languages with Disjoint Alphabets

Before we apply the sliding window idea to a generic r.e., another conceptual step is needed based on the following observation: the basic language operations preserve the property of being a local language, provided the terminal alphabets of the languages to be combined are disjoint.

*Property 3.29.* Given local languages $L'$ and $L''$ with disjoint alphabets, i.e., $\Sigma' \cap \Sigma'' = \emptyset$, the union $L' \cup L''$, concatenation $L'.L''$ and star $L'^*$ (and cross too) are local languages.

Proof: it is immediate to construct a local automaton for the resulting language by combining the component machines (to be also called $L'$ and $L''$ with a slight abuse) as next explained. Let $q_0', q_0''$ be the respective initial states and $F', F''$ the sets of final states of the component machines. In general the local automaton contains the states of the component machines, with some adjustments on the initial and final states and their arcs, as next described.

For the union $L' \cup L''$:

- the initial state $q_0$ is obtained merging the initial states $q_0'$ and $q_0''$;
- the final states are those of the component machines, $F' \cup F''$; if the empty string belongs to either one or both languages, the new state $q_0$ is marked as final.

For the concatenation $L'.L''$:

- the initial state is $q_0'$;
- the arcs of the recognizer are:
  - the arcs of $L'$ plus
  - the arcs of $L''$, except those exiting from the initial state $q_0''$;

  - the latter are substituted by the arcs $q' \xrightarrow{a} q''$, from every final state $q' \in F'$ to a state $q''$ such that there is in $L''$ an arc $q''_0 \xrightarrow{a} q''$.
- the final states are $F''$, if $\varepsilon \notin L''$; otherwise the final states are $F' \cup F''$.

For the star $L'^*$:

- state $q'_0$ is added to the final states $F'$;
- from each final state $q \in F'$ we draw the arc $q \xrightarrow{a} r$ if machine $L'$ has arc $q_0 \xrightarrow{a} r$ (exiting from the initial state).

It is straightforward to see the above steps correctly produce the recognizer of the union, concatenation, or star of a local language. Clearly such machines have by construction the characteristic properties of local automata. Examples come later.

## Algorithm GMY

Next we show how to transform a generic r.e. into a local language by means of a simple change of alphabet. First we introduce a simple class of regular expressions.

In a generic r.e. a terminal character may of course be repeated. An r.e. is called *linear* if no terminal character is repeated. For instance, $(abc)^*$ is linear whereas $(ab)^*a$ is not, because character $a$ is repeated (but the language is local).

*Property 3.30.* The language defined by a linear r.e. is local.

Proof. From the hypothesis of linearity it follows that the subexpressions have disjoint alphabets. Since the r.e. is obtained by composition of the local languages of the subexpressions, property 3.29 ensures that the language it defines is local.

*Example 3.31.* For the linear r.e. $(ab \cup c)^*$ we trace in Figure 3.17 the construction of the local recognizer, starting with the atomic subexpressions.

Having ascertained that the language of a linear r.e. is local, the problem of constructing its recognizer melts down to the computation of the sets $Ini$, $Fin$, and $Dig$ of the language. We explain how to orderly perform the job.

### Computing Local Sets of Regular Languages

Given regular expressions $e$ and $e'$, the next rules compute the three local sets. First we must check if an r.e. is *nullable*, i.e., it includes the empty string in its language.

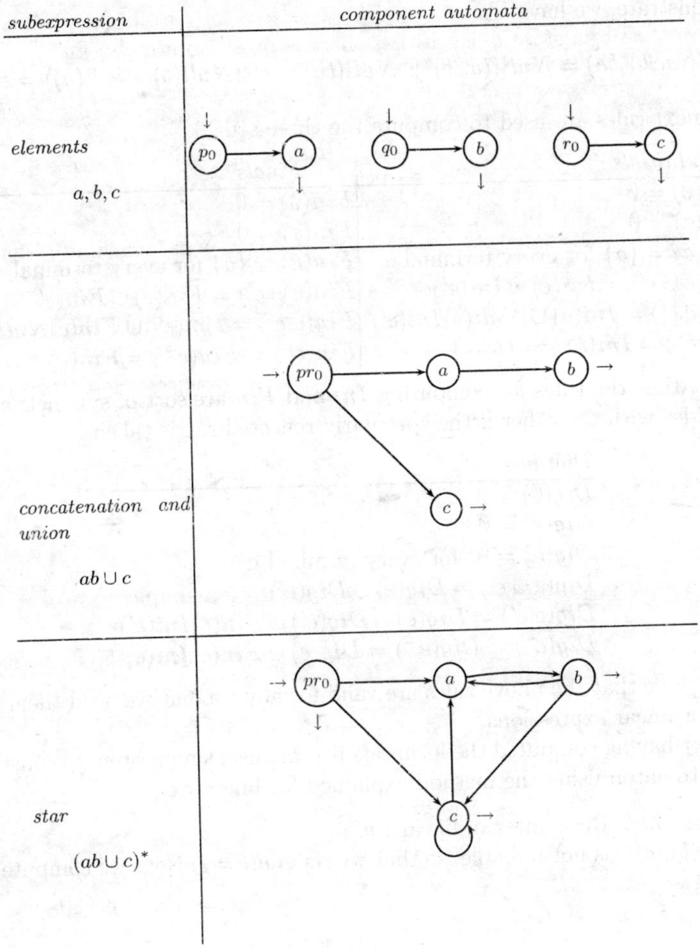


**Fig. 3.17** Step-by-step composition of local automata for the linear r.e. $(ab \cup c)^*$ of example 3.31.

The function $Null(e)$ returns the value $\varepsilon$, if $\varepsilon \in L(e)$; otherwise it returns as value the empty set $\emptyset$. Notice that the function range is not a boolean value. It is computed with the rules:

$Null(\varepsilon) = \varepsilon$
$Null(a) = \emptyset$ for every terminal $a$
$Null(e.e') = Null(e) \cap Null(e')$
$Null(e^+) = Null(e)$

$Null(\emptyset) = \emptyset$
$Null(e \cup e') = Null(e) \cup Null(e')$
$Null(e^*) = \varepsilon$

To illustrate, we have

$$Null((a \cup b)^* ba) = Null((a \cup b)^*) \cap Null(ba) = \varepsilon \cap (Null(b) \cap Null(a)) = \varepsilon \cap \emptyset = \emptyset$$

The next rules are used to compute the three sets:

| *Initials* | *Finals* |
|---|---|
| $Ini(\emptyset) = \emptyset$ | $Fin(\emptyset) = \emptyset$ |
| $Ini(\varepsilon) = \emptyset$ | $Fin(\varepsilon) = \emptyset$ |
| $Ini(a) = \{a\}$ for every terminal $a$ | $Fin(a) = \{a\}$ for every terminal $a$ |
| $Ini(e \cup e') = Ini(e) \cup Ini(e')$ | $Fin(e \cup e') = Fin(e) \cup Fin(e')$ |
| $Ini(e.e') = Ini(e) \cup Null(e) Ini(e')$ | $Fin(e.e') = Fin(e') \cup Fin(e) Null(e')$ |
| $Ini(e^*) = Ini(e^+) = Ini(e)$ | $Fin(e^*) = Fin(e^+) = Fin(e)$ |

Notice that the rules for computing $Ini$ and $Fin$ are sort of symmetric: one coincides with the other if the specularly reflected r.e. is taken.

| *Digrams* |
|---|
| $Dig(\emptyset) = \emptyset$ |
| $Dig(\varepsilon) = \emptyset$ |
| $Dig(a) = \emptyset$, for every terminal $a$ |
| $Dig(e \cup e') = Dig(e) \cup Dig(e')$ |
| $Dig(e.e') = Dig(e) \cup Dig(e') \cup Fin(e) Ini(e')$ |
| $Dig(e^*) = Dig(e^+) = Dig(e) \cup Fin(e) Ini(e)$ |

We observe that the above rules are valid for any r.e. but we need them here only for linear expressions.

After having computed the local sets it remains a simple step: to construct the automaton using the method explained for linear r.e.

*Example 3.32.* Recognizer of linear r.e.
R.e. $a(b \cup c)^*$ is not nullable, so that we set $Null = \emptyset$. Next we compute the local sets:

$Ini = a \qquad Fin = \{b, c\} \cup a = \{a, b, c\} \qquad Dig = \{ab, ac\} \cup \{bb, bc, cb, cc\}$

Applying the algorithm on p. 128, we produce the next local automaton

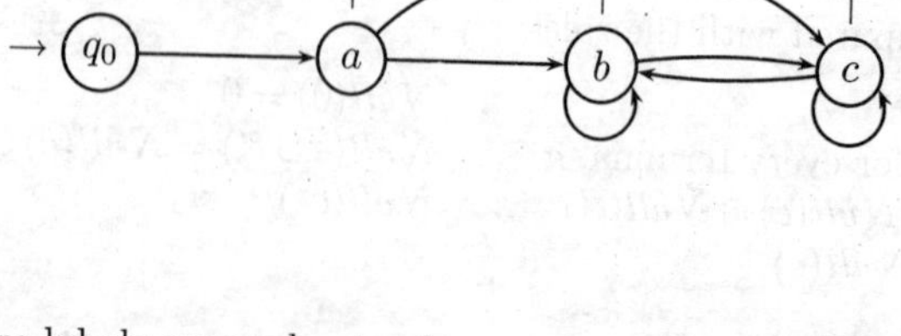


where the arc labels are understood.

Numbered Regular Expressions

At last we show how to apply the construction to a generic r.e. by first making it linear. To this end we make all terminals distinct by progressively numbering, say from left to right, with a subscript. Thus the expression $(ab)^*a$ becomes $(a_1b_2)^*a_3$.

The numbered r.e. is linear for the alphabet of numbered terminals, therefore it defines a local language on this new alphabet. We know how to construct the local recognizer of the numbered r.e. From this we obtain the recognizer of the original language by simply erasing the numbers occurring as subscripts on arc labels.[11]

It should help to recapitulate the various steps of the complete algorithm for constructing the recognizer of a generic r.e.

*Algorithm.* GMY (Glushkov McNaughton Yamada)
The algorithm is divided into four steps:

1. Number the original r.e. $e$ obtaining a linear r.e. $e'$;
2. Compute for $e'$ the nullability function and the local sets $Ini, Fin$, and $Dig$;
3. Construct the recognizer of the local language characterized by the local sets (as explained on p. 128);
4. Erase the numbers from arc labels.

*Example 3.33.* We number the r.e. $(ab)^*a$ obtaining $(a_1b_2)^*a_3$. The expression is not nullable and the local sets are easily computed. From them we construct the recognizer:

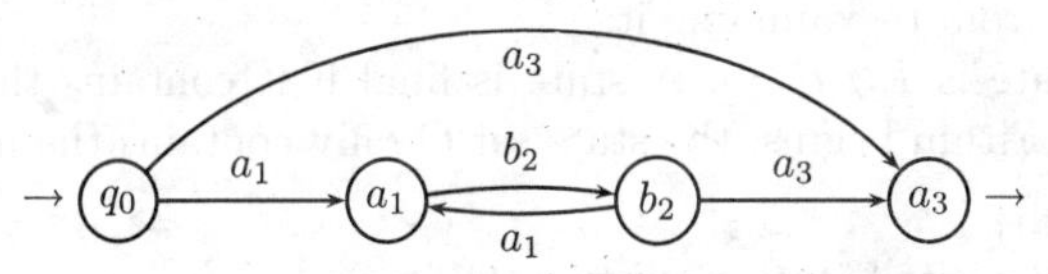


Removing the numbers we obtain the recognizer of the original language:

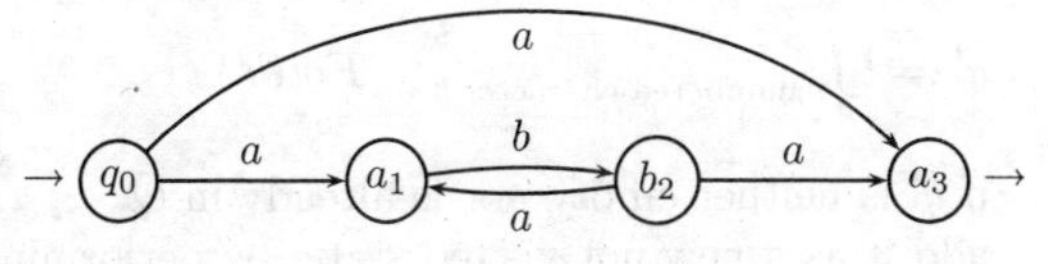


Notice the automaton is indeterministic, devoid of spontaneous moves, and has as many states as the characters of the r.e. plus one.

[11] This is an example of transliteration (homomorphism) defined on p. 80.

### 3.8.3 Deterministic Recognizer by Berry and Sethi Algorithm

Of course the local automaton computed by GMY may be converted to a deterministic one using the known powerset algorithm. But a direct approach, also based on local sets, allows to immediately construct a deterministic machine from the r.e.[12]
Take an r.e. $e$ of alphabet $\Sigma$ and let $e'$ be the numbered expression and $\Sigma_N$ its alphabet. Let the local sets of $e'$ be $Ini$, $Fin$, $Dig$, and $Null$ the nullability function.

For convenience instead of the digrams we use the equivalent notion of *set of followers* of a character in the numbered r.e.:

$$Fol(a_i) = \{b_j \mid a_i b_j \in Dig(e')\}$$

We stipulate that the special character $\dashv$ (string terminator) is a follower of every final character:

$$\dashv \in Fol(a_i) \text{ for every } a_i \in Fin(e')$$

(this is tantamount to working on the r.e. $e' \dashv$ instead of $e'$).
The terminator has no follower, i.e., $Fol(\dashv) = \emptyset$.

*Algorithm.* Algorithm BS (Berry and Sethi)
Each state will be denoted by a subset of $(\Sigma_N \cup \dashv)$. The algorithm examines every state, in order to compute the outgoing arcs and their destination states, by applying a rule similar to the one of the powerset algorithm. After the examination of a state is finished, the state is marked as visited to prevent the algorithm from reexamining it.
The initial state is $Ini(e' \dashv)$. A state is final if it contains the element $\dashv$. When the algorithm begins, the state set $Q$ only contains the initial state.

$Q := \{Ini(e' \dashv)\}$
while a not yet visited state $q$ exists in $Q$ do
    mark $q$ as visited
    for every character $b \in \Sigma$
    do

$$q' := \bigcup_{\forall \text{ numbered character } b' \in q} Fol(b')$$

        if $q'$ is neither empty nor is already in $Q$,
        add it as a new not visited state, by performing the assignment
        $Q := Q \cup \{q'\}$
        add the arc $q \xrightarrow{b} q'$ to the set of arcs
    end do
end do

[12] For a thorough justification of the method we refer to [7].

*Example 3.34.* Number the r.e. $(a \mid bb)^*(ac)^+$ as

$$(a_1 \mid b_2 b_3)^* (a_4 c_5)^+ \dashv$$

Then compute the set $Ini(e') = \{a_1, b_2, a_4\}$ and function $Follow$:

| | *Followers* |
|---|---|
| $a_1$ | $a_1, b_2, a_4$ |
| $b_2$ | $b_3$ |
| $b_3$ | $a_1, b_2, a_4$ |
| $a_4$ | $c_5$ |
| $c_5$ | $a_4, \dashv$ |

The deterministic automaton is shown in Figure 3.18.

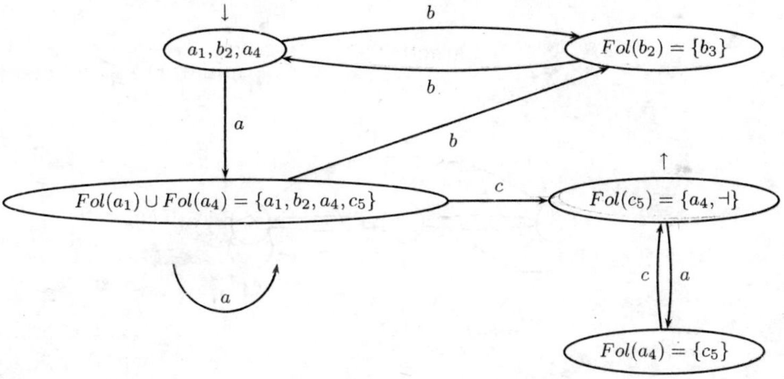


**Fig. 3.18** Direct construction of the deterministic automaton for $(a \mid bb)^*(ac)^+$ (example 3.34).

We mention the automata thus produced often contain more states than necessary, but of course can be minimized by the usual method.

## Use for Determinizing an Automaton

Another use of algorithm BS is as an alternative to the powerset construction, for converting a not deterministic machine $N$ into a deterministic one $M$. This approach is actually more flexible since it applies also to machines having $\varepsilon$-arcs. We proceed as follows.

1. Distinctly number the arc labels of $N$ . The numbered automaton $N'$ thus obtained recognizes a local language.
2. Compute the local sets $Ini$, $Fin$, and $Fol$ for automaton $N'$. Their computation is entirely analogous to the one for r.e. (p. 130).

3. Applying the BS construction produce the deterministic automaton $M$.

It is sufficient to illustrate this application with an example.

*Example 3.35.* Given the nondeterministic automaton $N$ of Figure 3.19 (top), numbering the arc labels we obtain automaton $N'$ (bottom). Its language is

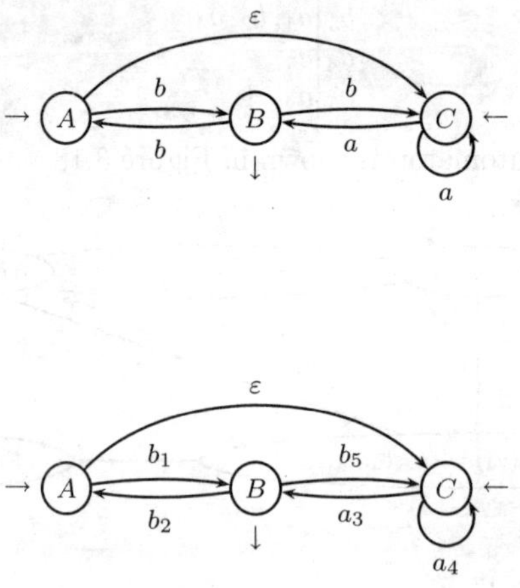


**Fig. 3.19** Automaton $N$ (top) with spontaneous moves and numbered version $N'$ (bottom) (Example 3.35).

local and not nullable. Then compute the initials

$$Ini(L(N') \dashv) = \{b_1, a_3, a_4\}$$

and note that $\varepsilon a_4 = a_4$ and $\varepsilon a_3 = a_3$. Continue with the set of followers

| | *Followers* |
|---|---|
| $b_1$ | $b_2, b_5, \dashv$ |
| $b_2$ | $b_1, a_3, a_4$ |
| $a_3$ | $b_2, b_5, \dashv$ |
| $a_4$ | $a_3, a_4$ |
| $b_5$ | $a_3, a_4$ |

Finally apply algorithm BS to construct the deterministic automaton $M$ of Figure 3.20.

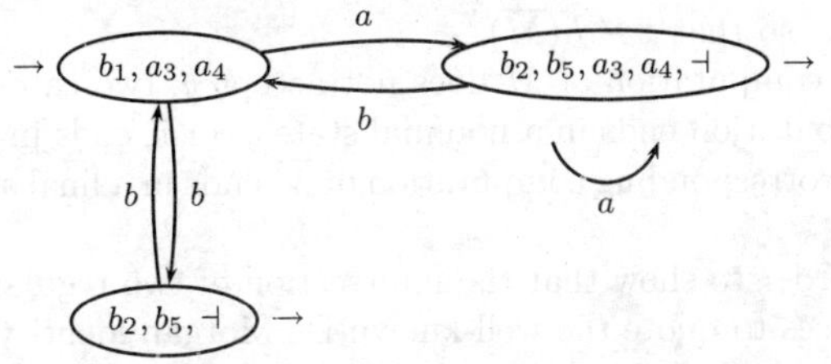


**Fig. 3.20** Deterministic machine constructed by the BS algorithm for example 3.35.

## 3.9 Regular Expressions with Complement and Intersection

We have now all the knowledge for completing the study of those operations that were left suspended in Chapter 2: complement, intersection, and set difference. This will allow us to extend regular expressions with such operations, to the purpose of writing more concise or expressive language specifications. We can now state a property anticipated in Chapter 1.

*Property 3.36.* Closure of *REG* by complement and intersection.
Let $L$ and $L'$ be regular languages. The complement $\neg L$ and the intersection $L \cap L'$ are regular languages.

First we show how to build the recognizer of the complement $\neg L = \Sigma^* \setminus L$. We assume the recognizer $M$ of $L$ is deterministic, with initial state $q_0$, state set $Q$, final state set $F$, and transition function $\delta$.

*Algorithm.* Construction of deterministic recognizer $\overline{M}$ of complement. First we complete the automaton $M$, in order to make its function total, by adding the error or sink state $p$ and the arcs to and from it.

1. Create a new state $p \notin Q$, the *sink*; the states of $\overline{M}$ are $Q \cup \{p\}$
2. the transition function $\overline{\delta}$ is:
   a. $\overline{\delta}(q, a) = \delta(q, a)$, where $\delta(q, a) \in Q$;
   b. $\overline{\delta}(q, a) = p$, where $\delta(q, a)$ is not defined;
   c. $\overline{\delta}(p, a) = p$, for every character $a \in \Sigma$;
3. the final states are $\overline{F} = (Q \setminus F) \cup \{p\}$.

Notice the final and nonfinal states have been interchanged.

To justify the construction, first observe that if a computation of $M$ accepts a string $x \in L(M)$, then the corresponding computation of $\overline{M}$ terminates in a nonfinal state, so that $x \notin L(\overline{M})$.

Second, if a computation of $M$ does not accept $y$, two cases are possible: either the computation ends in a nonfinal state $q$, or it ends in the sink $p$. In both cases the corresponding computation of $\overline{M}$ ends in a final state, meaning $y$ is in $L(\overline{M})$.

At last, in order to show that the intersection of two regular languages is regular, it suffices to quote the well-known De Morgan identity:

$$L \cap L' = \neg(\neg L \cup \neg L')$$

because, knowing that the languages $\neg L$ and $\neg L'$ are regular, their union too is regular as well as its complement.

As a corollary, the *set difference* of two regular languages is regular because of the identity

$$L \setminus L' = L \cap \neg L'$$

*Example 3.37.* Automaton of complement

Figure 3.21 shows three machines: the given one $M$, the intermediate completed with sink, and the recognizer $\overline{M}$ of complement.

For the construction to work the original machine must be deterministic, otherwise the language accepted by the constructed machine may be nondisjoint from the original one, which would violate the characteristic property of complement, $L \cap \neg L = \emptyset$. See the following counterexample where the pseudo-complement machine mistakenly accepts string $a$, which is in the original language.

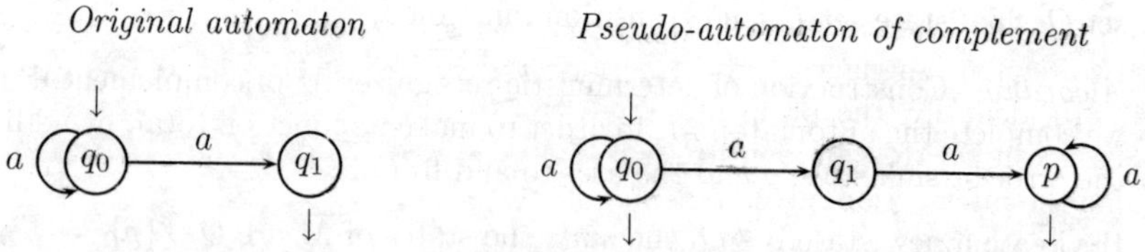


Finally we mention the construction may produce unclean or nonminimal machines.

### 3.9.1 Product of Automata

A frequently used technique consists in simulating two (or more) machines by a single one having as state set the cartesian product of the two state sets.

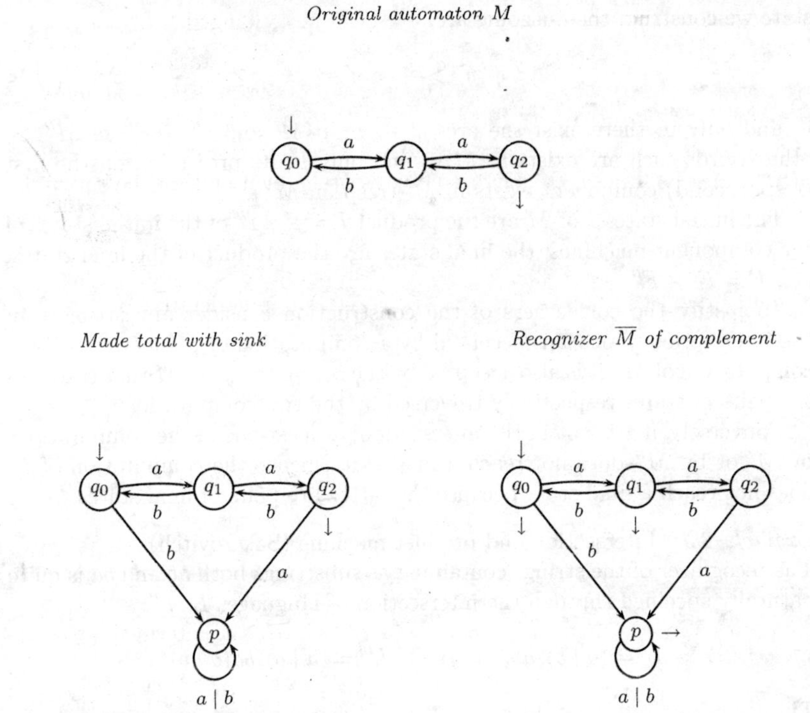


**Fig. 3.21** Construction of recognizer of complement (example 3.37).

We present the technique for the case of the recognizer of the intersection of two regular languages.

Incidentally, the proof of the closure of family *REG* under intersection based on De Morgan identity (p. 138) already gives a procedure for recognizing the intersection: given two finite deterministic recognizers, first construct the recognizers of the complement languages, then the recognizer of their union (by the method of Thompson on p. 124). From the latter (after determinization if needed), construct the complement machine, which is the desired result.

More directly, the intersection of two regular languages is accepted by the cartesian product of the given machines $M'$ and $M''$. We assume the machines to be free from spontaneous moves, but not necessarily deterministic.

The *product machine* $M$ has state set $Q' \times Q''$, the cartesian product of the two state sets. This means each state is a pair $< q', q'' >$, where the first (second) component is a state of the first (second) machine. For such pair or state we construct the outgoing arc

$$< q', q'' > \xrightarrow{a} < r', r'' >$$

if, and only if, there exist the arcs $q' \xrightarrow{a} r'$ in $M'$ and $q'' \xrightarrow{a} r''$ in $M''$. In other words such arc exists in $M$ if, and only if, its projection on the first (resp. second) component exists in $M'$ (resp. in $M''$).

The initial states $I$ of $M$ are the product $I = I' \times I''$ of the initial states of the component machines; the final states are the product of the final states, i.e., $F = F' \times F''$.

To justify the correctness of the construction consider any string $x$ in the intersection. Since $x$ is accepted by a computation of $M'$ as well as by a computation of $M''$ it is also accepted by the computation of $M$ that traverses the pairs of states respectively traversed by the two computations.

Conversely, if $x$ is not in the intersection, at least one of the computations by $M'$ or by $M''$ does not reach a final state, hence the computation of $M$ does not reach a final state because the latter are pairs of final states.

*Example 3.38.* Intersection and product machine (Sakarovitch)
The recognizer of the strings containing as substrings both *ab* and *ba* is quite naturally specified through the intersection of languages $L', L''$:

$$L' = (a \mid b)^* ab(a \mid b)^* \qquad L'' = (a \mid b)^* ba(a \mid b)^*$$

The cartesian product of the recognizers of the component languages is shown in Figure 3.22. As usual the pairs of the cartesian product, which are not accessible from the initial state, can be discarded.

The cartesian product method can be exploited for operations different from intersection; thus, in the case of union, it would be easy to modify the product machine construction in order to accept a string if at least one (instead of both as in the intersection) component machine accepts it. This would give us an alternative method for building the recognizer of the union of two languages. But the product machine may have many more states than the machine obtained with the Thompson method: the product of the cardinalities of the given machines, instead of the sum.

## Extended and Restricted Regular Expressions

A *regular expression* is *extended* if it uses other operators beyond the basic ones (i.e., union, concatenation, star, cross): complement, intersection, and set difference.

For instance, the strings containing one or multiple occurrences of *aa* as substring and not ending with *bb* are defined by the extended r.e.

$$((a \mid b)^* aa(a \mid b)^*) \cap \neg((a \mid b)^* bb)$$

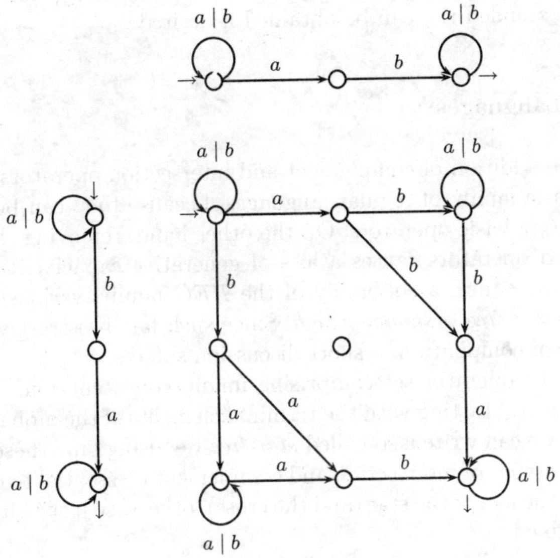


**Fig. 3.22** Recognizers of component languages (top and left) and product machine recognizing their intersection (example 3.38).

The next realistic example shows the practicality of using extended expressions for greater expressivity.

*Example 3.39.* Identifiers
Suppose the valid identifiers may contain letters $a \dots z$, digits $0 \dots 9$ (not in first position) and the dash $'-'$ (neither in first nor in last position). Adjacent dashes are not permitted. A sentence of this language is: $after - 2nd - test$.

The next extended r.e. prescribes that (i) the strings start with a letter, (ii) it does not contain consecutive dashes, and (iii) it does not end with a dash:

$$\underbrace{(a \dots z)^+ (a \dots z \mid 0 \dots 9 \mid -)^*}_{(i)} \cap$$
$$\underbrace{\neg((a \dots z \mid 0 \dots 9 \mid -)^* - -(a \dots z \mid 0 \dots 9 \mid -)^*)}_{(ii)} \cap$$
$$\underbrace{\neg((a \dots z \mid 0 \dots 9 \mid -)^* -)}_{(iii)}$$

When a language is specified by an extended r.e. we can of course construct its recognizer by applying the complement and cartesian product methods. Then a nonextended r.e. can be obtained if desired.

### Star-Free Languages

We know the addition of complement and intersection operators to r.e. does not enlarge the family of regular languages, because they can be eliminated and replaced by basic operators. On the other hand, removing the star from the permitted operators causes a loss of generative capacity: the family of languages shrinks into a subfamily of the *REG* family, variously named as *aperiodic* or *star free* or *noncounting*. Since such family is rarely considered in the realm of compilation, a short discussion suffices.

Consider the operator set comprising union, concatenation, intersection, and complement. Starting with the terminal elements of the alphabet and the empty set $\emptyset$, we can write a so-called *star-free* r.e. using only these operators. Notice the presence of intersection and complement is essential to compensate somehow for the loss of the star (and the cross), otherwise just finite languages would be defined.

A language is called *star-free* if there exists a star-free r.e. that defines it.

First, observe the universal language of alphabet $\Sigma$ is star-free, since it is the complement of the empty set, i.e., it is defined by the star-free r.e. $\Sigma^* = \neg\emptyset$.

Second, a useful subclass of star-free languages has already been studied without even knowing the term: the local languages on p. 127 can indeed be defined without stars or crosses. Recall that a local language is specified by three local sets: initials, finals, and permitted (or forbidden) digrams. Its specification can be directly mapped on the intersection of three star-free languages as next illustrated.

*Example 3.40.* Star-free r.e. of local and nonlocal languages
The sentences of local language $(abc)^+$ (example 3.25 on p. 127) start with $a$, end with $c$, and do not contain any digram from $\{aa \mid ac \mid ba \mid bb \mid cb \mid cc\}$. The language is therefore specified by the star-free r.e.:

$$(a\,\neg\emptyset) \cap (\neg\emptyset\, c) \cap (\neg(\neg\emptyset\,(aa \mid ac \mid ba \mid bb \mid cb \mid cc)\,\neg\emptyset))$$

Second example. The language $L_2 = a^*ba^*$ is star-free because it can be converted to the equivalent star-free r.e.:

$$\overbrace{\neg(\neg\emptyset\, b\,\neg\emptyset)}^{a^*}\quad\overbrace{b}^{b}\quad\overbrace{\neg(\neg\emptyset\, b\,\neg\emptyset)}^{a^*}$$

On the other hand, this language is not local because the local sets do not suffice to eliminate spurious strings. Amidst the strings that, as prescribed by $L_2$, start and end with $a$ or $b$ and may contain the digrams $\{aa \mid ab \mid ba\}$, we find the string, say, $abab$, which does not belong to $L_2$.

The family of star-free languages is strictly included in the family of regular languages. It excludes in particular the languages characterized by certain counting properties that justify the other name "noncounting" of the family. An example is the regular language

$$\{x \in \{a \mid b\}^* \mid |x|_a \text{ is even}\}$$

which is accepted by a machine having in its graph a length two circuit, i.e., a modulo 2 counter (or flip-flop) of the letters $a$ encountered. This language cannot be defined with an r.e not using star or cross.

A philosophical remark is that in the panorama of artificial and human languages the operation of counting letters or substrings modulo some integer constant (in the intuitive sense of the previous example) is rarely if ever needed. In other words, the classification of strings based on the classes of congruences modulo some integer is usually not correlated with their being valid sentences or not. For reasons which may have to do with the organization of the human mind or perhaps with robustness of noisy communication, none of the existing technical languages discriminates sentences from illegal strings on the basis of cyclic counting properties: indeed it would be strange if a computer program were considered valid depending on the number of its instructions being, say, a multiple of three or not!

Therefore in principle it would be enough to deal with the subfamily of aperiodic or noncounting regular languages when modelling compilation and artificial languages. But on one side star-free r.e. are often less readable than basic ones. On the other side, in different fields of computer science, counting is of uttermost importance: for instance, a most common digital component is the flip-flop or modulo 2 counter, which recognizes the language $(11)^*$, obviously not a star-free one.[13]

## 3.10 Summary of Relations between Regular Languages, Grammars, and Automata

As we leave the topic of regular languages and finite automata, it is convenient to recapitulate the relations and transformations between the various formal models associated with this family of languages. Figure 3.23 represents by means of a flow graph the conversion methods back and forth from regular expressions and automata of different types. For instance, we read that algorithm GMY converts an r.e. to an automaton devoid of spontaneous moves.

[13] For the theory of star-free languages we refer to McNaughton and Papert [36].

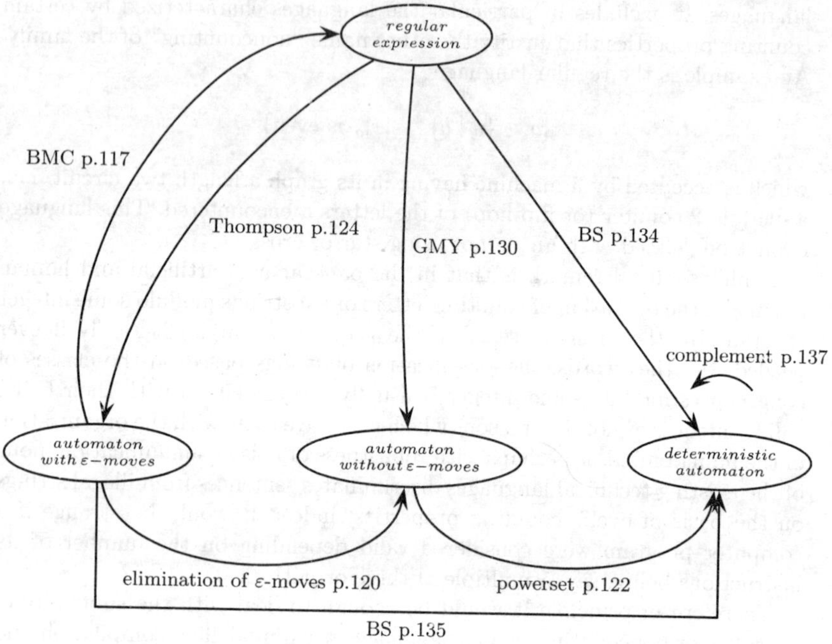


**Fig. 3.23** Conversion methods between r.e. and finite automata deterministic and not.

Figure 3.24 represents the direct correspondence between right-linear grammars and finite automata. The relation between automata and left-linear

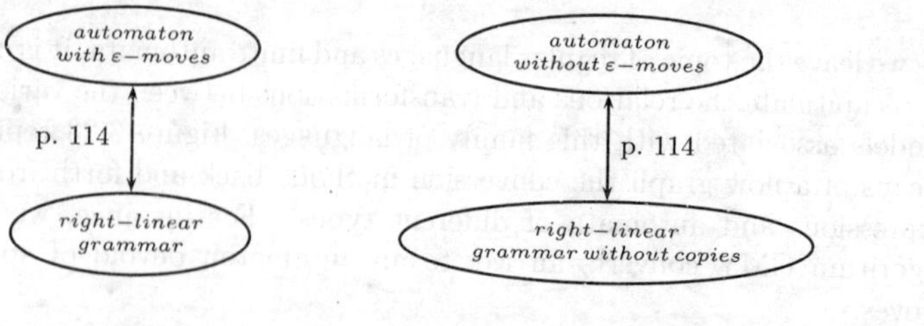


**Fig. 3.24** Correspondence between right-linear grammars and finite automata.

grammars are not listed, because they are essentially identical, thanks to the left/right duality of grammar rules and the arrow reversing transformation of automaton moves.

At last Figure 3.25 lists the relations between regular expressions and grammars.

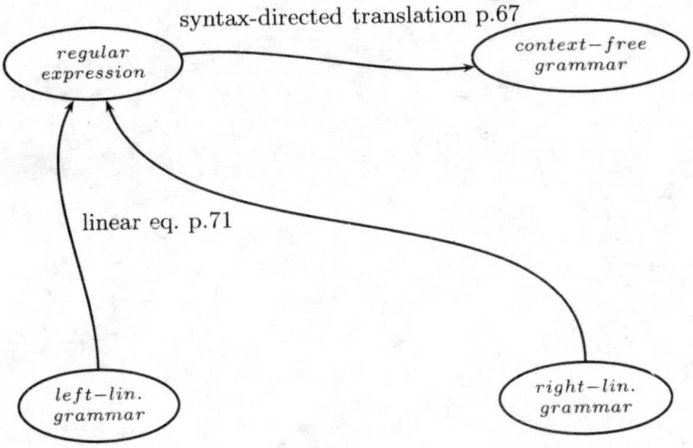


**Fig. 3.25** Correspondence between regular expression and grammars.

The three figures give evidence to the equivalence of the three models used for regular languages: regular expressions, finite automata, and unilinear grammars.

Finally we recall that regular languages are a very restricted subset of the context-free, which are indispensable for defining artificial languages.

# Chapter 4
# Pushdown Automata and Top-down Parsing

## 4.1 Introduction

The algorithms for recognizing if a string is a sentence require more memory resources for context-free than for regular languages. This and the next chapter present several algorithms, first as abstract automata with a pushdown memory stack, then as parsing[1] (or syntax analysis) procedures producing the syntax tree of a sentence. Incidentally, parsing has little interest for regular languages because their syntax structure is predeterminate (left or right-linear) whereas for context-free languages any tree structure is possible.

Similarly to unilinear grammars, also context-free grammar rules can be made to correspond to the moves of an automaton, which is no longer a pure finite-state machine but possesses also a pushdown stack memory. In contrast to the finite case, it is not always possible to obtain a deterministic pushdown machine. Moreover, the presence of two memories, i.e., the states and the stack, introduces a variety of functioning modes that complicate the theoretical study of such machines.
After the presentation of pushdown automata our study specializes on efficient deterministic machines and on the corresponding important family *DET* of deterministic context-free languages.

Several useful parsing algorithms will be described: in this chapter the fast top-down predictive algorithms, in Chapter 5 the bottom-up or shift-reduce algorithms and a general algorithm able to cope with ambiguous and nondeterministic grammars.

The widespread linear-time parsers used in compilers are classified as top-down or predictive ($LL(k)$) and bottom-up ($LR(k)$), depending on the construction order of syntax trees. Both types make the assumption that the language is deterministic context-free and impose specific restrictions on the form of grammar rules.

---

[1] From Latin *pars, partis*, in the sense of dividing a sentence into its parts or constituents.

S.C. Reghizzi, *Formal Languages and Compilation*,
Texts in Computer Science, DOI 10.1007/978-1-84882-050-0_4,

Our presentation of parser construction methods is based on a common representation of a grammar as a network of finite automata, which can invoke each other. This allows a substantial reduction in the number of tediously similar definitions and conditions in comparison to traditional presentations.

After the characterization of top-down parsers, we show their straightforward implementations with recursive procedures which are widely adopted especially in hand-coded compilers.

Table-driven bottom-up parsers and general parsers are left for the next chapter as well as a discussion of choice criteria.

### 4.1.1 Pushdown Automaton

Any compiler includes a recognition algorithm which is essentially a finite automaton enriched with an auxiliary memory organized as a pushdown or LIFO stack of unbounded capacity, storing symbols:

$$\overbrace{A_1}^{\text{bottom symbol}} \quad A_2 \ldots \quad \overbrace{A_k}^{\text{top symbol}}$$

The input or source string, delimited to the right by the terminator, is

$$a_1 a_2 \ldots \quad \overbrace{a_i}^{\text{current character}} \quad \ldots a_n \dashv$$

The following operations apply to a stack:

*pushing*: *push*$(B)$ inserts symbol $B$ on top, i.e., to the right of $A_k$; several push operations can be combined in a single command *push*$(B_1\, B_2 \ldots B_n)$ that inserts $B_n$ on top;

*emptiness test*: *empty*, the predicate is true if, and only if, $k = 0$;

*popping*: *pop*, if the stack is not empty removes the top symbol $A_k$.

It is sometimes convenient to imagine that a special symbol is painted on the bottom of the stack, denoted $Z_0$ and termed the *bottom*. Such symbol may be read but neither pushed nor popped. The presence of $Z_0$ on top of the stack means the stack is empty.

The machine reads from left-to-right the source characters using a reading head. The character under the reading head is termed *current*. At each instant the machine *configuration* is specified by: the current character, the current state, and the stack content. With a move the automaton may

- read the current character and shift the reading head, or perform a spontaneous move without reading;
- read the top symbol and pop it, or read the bottom $Z_0$ if the stack is empty;

- compute the next state from the values of current state, current character, and stack symbol;
- push one or more symbols on the stack (or none).

### 4.1.2 From Grammar to Pushdown Automaton

We show grammar rules can be interpreted as instructions of a not deterministic pushdown machine that recognizes the language. The machine is so simple that it does without any internal state, but only uses the stack for memory. Intuitively, the machine operation is *predictive* or goal oriented: the stack serves as an agenda of predicted future actions. The stack symbols are nonterminal and terminal characters of the grammar. If the stack contains from top to bottom symbols $A_k \dots A_1$, the machine first executes the action prescribed by $A_k$, then the action for $A_{k-1}$, and so on until the last action for $A_1$. The action prescribed by $A_k$ has to recognize if the source string, starting from the current character $a_i$, contains a substring $w$ which derives from $A_k$. If so, the action will eventually shift the reading head of $|w|$ positions. Naturally enough, the goal can recursively spawn subgoals, if, for recognizing the derivation from $A_k$, it is necessary to recognize other terminal or nonterminal symbols. Initially the first goal is the axiom of the grammar: the task of the machine is to recognize if the source string derives from the axiom.

*Algorithm.* From grammar to nondeterministic one-state pushdown machine.

Given a grammar $G = (V, \Sigma, P, S)$ Table 4.1 explicates the correspondence between rules and moves. Letter $b$ denotes a terminal, letters $A, B$ denote nonterminals, and $A_i$ can be any symbol. The form of a rule shapes the move.

**Table 4.1** Correspondence between grammar rules and moves of nondeterministic pushdown machine with one state. The current input character is *cc*.

| | *rule* | *move* | *comment* |
|---|---|---|---|
| 1 | $A \to BA_1 \dots A_n$ $n \geqslant 0$ | if *top* = $A$ then pop; push($A_n \dots A_1 B$) end if | to recognize $A$, first recognize $BA_1 \dots A_n$; |
| 2 | $A \to bA_1 \dots A_n$ $n \geqslant 0$ | if $cc = b \wedge top = A$ then pop; push ($A_n \dots A_1$); shift reading head | $b$ was expected as the next character and has been read; it remains to recognize $A_1 \dots A_n$; |
| 3 | $A \to \varepsilon$ | if *top* = $A$ then pop | the empty string deriving from $A$ has been recognized; |
| 4 | for every character $b \in \Sigma$ | if $cc = b \wedge top = b$ then pop; shift reading head | $b$ was expected as next character and has been read; |
| 5 | — — — | if $cc = \dashv \wedge$ stack is empty then accept; halt | the string has been entirely scanned and the agenda contains no goals; |

For (2) the right-hand side starts with a terminal and the move is triggered by reading it. On the contrary rules (1) and (3) give rise to spontaneous moves that do not check the current character. Move (4) checks that a terminal, when it surfaces on stack top (having been previously pushed by a move of type (1) or (2)), matches the current character. Lastly, move (5) accepts the string if the stack is empty upon reading the terminator.

Initially the stack contains the bottom symbol $Z_0$ and the axiom $S$, and the reading head is on the first input character. At each step the automaton (not deterministically) chooses a move, which is defined in the current configuration, and executes it. The machine recognizes the string if there exists a computation that ends with move (5). Accordingly, we say this machine model recognizes a sentence *by empty stack.*

Surprisingly enough this automaton never changes state and the stack is its only memory. Later on we will be obliged to introduce the states in order to make the behavior of the machine deterministic.

*Example 4.1.* The moves of the recognizer of language

$$L = \{a^n b^m \mid n \geqslant m \geqslant 1\}$$

are listed in Table 4.2 next to the grammar rules. The choice between moves 1 and 2 is not deterministic, since 2 may be taken also when $a$ is the current character; similarly for the choice between 3 and 4.

**Table 4.2** Pushdown machine moves associated with grammar rules of example 4.1.

| | *Rule* | *Move* |
|---|---|---|
| 1 | $S \to aS$ | if $cc = a \quad \wedge \quad top = S$ then pop; push($S$); shift |
| 2 | $S \to A$ | if $top = S$ then pop; push($A$) |
| 3 | $A \to aAb$ | if $cc = a \quad \wedge \quad top = A$ then pop; push($bA$); shift |
| 4 | $A \to ab$ | if $cc = a$ and $top = A$ then pop; push($b$); shift |
| 5 | | if $cc = b \quad \wedge \quad top = b$ then pop; shift |
| 6 | | if $cc = \dashv \quad \wedge$ stack is empty then accept; halt |

It is not difficult to see a string is accepted by this machine if, and only if, it is generated by the grammar. In fact, for each accepting computation there exists a corresponding derivation and conversely; in other words the automaton simulates the leftmost derivations of the grammar. For instance, derivation

$$S \Rightarrow A \Rightarrow aAb \Rightarrow aabb$$

mirrors the successful trace in Figure 4.1 (left). But the algorithm has no a priori information on which, if any among possible derivations, will succeed and it has to explore all possibilities, including the computations ending in

| *Stack* | $x$ |
|---|---|
| $Z_0S$ | $aabb \dashv$ |
| $Z_0A$ | $aabb \dashv$ |
| $Z_0bA$ | $abb \dashv$ |
| $Z_0bb$ | $bb \dashv$ |
| $Z_0b$ | $b \dashv$ |
| $Z_0$ | $\dashv$ |

| *Stack* | $x$ |
|---|---|
| $Z_0S$ | $aabb \dashv$ |
| $Z_0S$ | $abb \dashv$ |
| $Z_0S$ | $bb \dashv$ |
| $Z_0A$ | $bb \dashv$ |
| error | |

**Fig. 4.1** Two computations: accepting (left) and non (right).

error as the one traced (right). Moreover, the source string is accepted by different computations if, and only if, it is generated by diverse left derivations, i.e., if it is ambiguous for the grammar.

With some thought we may see that the mapping of Table 4.1 on p. 149 is bidirectional and can be applied the other way round, to transform the moves of a pushdown machine (of the model considered) into the rules of an equivalent grammar. This remark permits us to state an important theoretical fact.

*Property 4.2.* The family $CF$ of context-free languages coincides with the family of languages accepted, with empty stack, by a nondeterministic pushdown machine having one state.

We stress the mapping from automaton to grammar does not work when the pushdown automaton has a set of states: other methods will be developed in that case.

It may appear that in little space we have already reached the objective of the chapter, to obtain a procedure for building the recognizer of a language defined by a grammar. Unfortunately the automaton is nondeterministic and is forced in the worst case to explore all paths, with a time complexity non-polynomial with respect to the length of the source string: more efficient algorithms are needed.

### Computational Complexity of Pushdown Automata

We compute an upper bound on the number of steps needed to recognize a string with the previous pushdown machine in the worst case. For simplicity we consider a grammar $G$ in Greibach normal form (p. 66), which as we know features rules starting with a terminal and not containing other terminals.

Therefore the machine is free from spontaneous moves (types (1) and (3) of Table 4.1 on p. 149) and it never pushes a terminal character onto the stack.

For a string $x$ of length $n$ the derivation $S \stackrel{+}{\Rightarrow} x$, if it exists, has exactly $n$ steps. The same number of moves is performed by the automaton to recognize $x$. Let $K$ be the maximum number of alternatives $A \rightarrow \alpha_1 \mid \alpha_2 \mid \ldots \mid \alpha_k$, for any nonterminal of the grammar. At each step of a leftmost derivation, the leftmost nonterminal is rewritten choosing one out of $k \leqslant K$ alternatives. It follows the number of possible derivations of length $n$ is at most $K^n$. Since in the worst case the algorithm is forced to compute all derivations before finding the accepting one or declaring failure, the time complexity is exponential in $n$.

However, this result is overly pessimistic; at the end of Chapter 5 a clever algorithm for string recognition in polynomial time, using other data structures instead of a LIFO stack, will be described.

### 4.1.3 Definition of Pushdown Automaton

We are going to define several pushdown machine models. We trust the reader to adapt to the present context the analogous concepts already seen for finite automata in order to expedite the presentation.

A pushdown automaton $M$ is defined by seven items:

1. $Q$, finite *set of states* of control unit;
2. $\Sigma$, *input alphabet*;
3. $\Gamma$, *stack alphabet*;
4. $\delta$, *transition function*;
5. $q_0 \in Q$, *initial state*;
6. $Z_0 \in \Gamma$, *initial stack symbol*;
7. $F \subseteq Q$, *set of final states*.

Such machine is in general nondeterministic. The domain and range of the transition function are made of cartesian products:

| *domain* | *range* |
|---|---|
| $Q \times (\Sigma \cup (\varepsilon)) \times \Gamma$ | the *power set* of the set $Q \times \Gamma^*$ |

The moves, i.e., the values of $\delta$, fall into the following cases.

- reading move:

$$\delta(q, a, Z) = \{(p_1, \gamma_1), (p_2, \gamma_2), \ldots, (p_n, \gamma_n)\}$$

  with $n \geqslant 1, a \in \Sigma, Z \in \Gamma$ and with $p_i \in Q, \gamma_i \in \Gamma^*$.
  The machine in state $q$ with $Z$ on top of the stack, reads $a$ and enters one of states $p_i, 1 \leqslant i \leqslant n$ after performing operations: pop, push($\gamma_i$).

Notes: the choice of the $i$-th action among $n$ possibilities is not deterministic; the reading head automatically shifts forward; the top symbol is always popped; the string pushed onto the stack may be empty.

- spontaneous move:

$$\delta(q, \varepsilon, Z) = \{(p_1, \gamma_1), (p_2, \gamma_2), \ldots, (p_n, \gamma_n)\}$$

with the same stipulations as before.
The machine in state $q$ with $Z$ on top of the stack, without reading an input character, enters one of the states $p_i, 1 \leqslant i \leqslant n$, after performing the operations: pop, push$(\gamma_i)$.

From the definition it is clear the behavior can be nondeterministic for two causes: the range of the transition function comprises a set of alternative actions, and the machine may contain spontaneous moves.

The *instantaneous configuration* of a machine $M$ is a 3-tuple $(q, y, \eta) \in Q \times \Sigma^* \times \Gamma^+$ which specifies:

- $q$, the current state;
- $y$, the remaining portion (suffix) of the source string $x$ to be read;
- $\eta$, the stack content.

The *initial* configuration is $(q_0, x, Z_0)$ or $(q_0, x \dashv, Z_0)$, if the terminator is there.

Applying a move, a transition from a configuration to another occurs, to be denoted as $(q, y, \eta) \mapsto (p, z, \lambda)$. A computation is a chain of zero or more transitions, denoted by $\overset{*}{\mapsto}$. As customary, the cross instead of the star denotes a computation with at least one transition.

Depending on the move the following transitions are possible.

| *Current config.* | *Next config.* | *Applied move* |
|---|---|---|
| $(q, az, \eta Z)$ | $(p, z, \eta\gamma)$ | reading move: $\delta(q, a, Z) = \{(p, \gamma), \ldots\}$ |
| $(q, az, \eta Z)$ | $(p, az, \eta\gamma)$ | spontaneous move: $\delta(q, \varepsilon, Z) = \{(p, \gamma), \ldots\}$ |

Although a move erases the top symbol, the same can be pushed again by the move if the computation needs to keep it on stack.
A string $x$ is *recognized* (or accepted) *with final state* if there exists a computation that entirely reads the string and terminates in a final state:

$$(q_0, x, Z_0) \overset{*}{\mapsto} (q, \varepsilon, \lambda), \qquad q \text{ is a final state}, \lambda \in \Gamma^*$$

The language recognized is the set of accepted strings.

Notice that when the machine recognizes and halts, the stack contains some string $\lambda$, not further specified, since the recognition modality is by final state; in particular, $\lambda$ is not necessarily empty.

### State-Transition Diagram for Pushdown Automata

The transition function as in finite automata can be graphically presented although its readability is somewhat lessened by the need to specify stack operations. This is shown in the next example.

*Example 4.3.* The language $L = \{uu^R \mid u \in \{a, b\}^*\}$ of palindromes (p. 31) of even length is accepted with final state by the next pushdown recognizer:

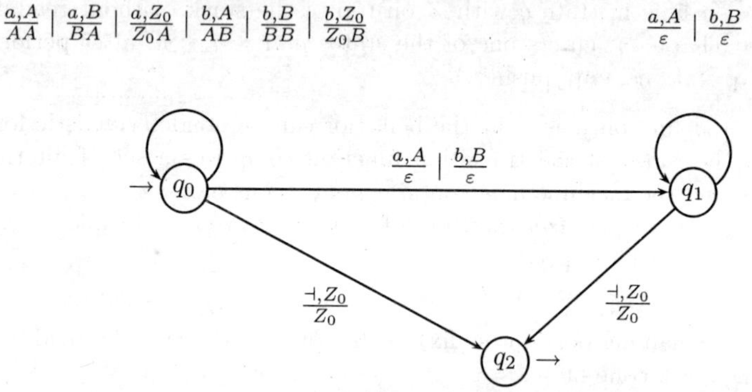


The stack alphabet has three symbols: $Z_0$, the initial symbol, and $A$ and $B$ respectively indicating that $a$ or $b$ has been read. For instance, arc $q_0 \xrightarrow{\frac{a,B}{BA}} q_0$ denotes the reading move $(q_0, BA) \in \delta(q_0, a, B)$.

A nondeterministic behavior occurs in state $q_0$ when reading $a$ from input and $A$ from stack: the machine may remain in $q_0$ pushing $AA$, or go to $q_1$ pushing nothing.

We trace in Figure 4.2 two among other possible computations for string $x = aa$. Since the computation (right) reads entirely the string $aa$ and reaches a final state, the string is accepted. Another example is the empty string, recognized by the move corresponding to the arc from $q_0$ to $q_2$.

| *Stack* | $x$ | *State* | *Comment* |
|---|---|---|---|
| $Z_0$ | $aa \dashv$ | $q_0$ | |
| $Z_0A$ | $a \dashv$ | $q_0$ | |
| $Z_0AA$ | $\dashv$ | $q_0$ | failure: no move is defined for $(q_0, \dashv, A)$ |

| *Stack* | $x$ | *State* | *Comment* |
|---|---|---|---|
| $Z_0$ | $aa \dashv$ | $q_0$ | |
| $Z_0A$ | $a \dashv$ | $q_0$ | |
| $Z_0$ | $\dashv$ | $q_1$ | |
| $Z_0$ | $\dashv$ | $q_2$ | recognition by final state |

**Fig. 4.2** Two computations of example 4.3 for input $x = aa$.

## Varieties of Pushdown Automata

It is worth noticing that the pushdown machine of the definition differs from the one obtained from a grammar by the mapping of Table 4.1 on p. 149, in two aspects: it performs state transitions, and it checks if the current state is final to recognize a string. These and other differences are discussed next.

### Accepting Modes

Two different manners of deciding acceptance when a computation ends have been encountered so far: when the machine enters a final state or when the stack is empty. The former mode *with final state* disregards the stack content; on the other hand, the latter mode with *empty stack* disregards the current state of the machine.

The two modes can also be combined into recognition with *final state and empty stack*. A natural question is whether these, and other, acceptance modes are equivalent.

*Property 4.4.* For the family of nondeterministic pushdown automata the acceptance modes

1. with empty stack
2. with final state
3. combined (empty stack and final state)

have the same capacity with respect to language recognition.

The statement says that any one of the three modes of acceptance can be simulated by any other. In fact, if the automaton recognizes with final state, it is easy to modify it by adding new states, so that it recognizes with empty stack: simply, when the original machine enters a final state, the second machine enters a new state and there remains while it empties the stack by spontaneous moves until the bottom symbol pops up.

Vice versa, to convert an automaton recognizing with empty stack to the final state mode, do the following:

- add a new final state $f$ and a move leading to it whenever the stack becomes empty;
- when, performing a move to state $q$, the stack of the original machine ceases to be empty, the second machine moves from state $f$ to state $q$.

Similar considerations could be made for the third acceptance mode.

### Spontaneous Loops and On-Line Functioning

In principle an automaton can perform an unbounded series of spontaneous moves, i.e., a long computation without reading the input. When this hap-

pens we say the machine has entered a *spontaneous loop*. A spontaneous loop may cause the machine not to read entirely the input, or it may trigger an unbounded computation after the input has been entirely scanned before deciding for acceptance or not. Both situations are in some sense pathological, as it would be for a program to enter a never-ending loop; they can be eliminated from pushdown machines without loss of generality.
The following reasoning[2] outlines how to construct an equivalent machine, free from spontaneous loops. Moreover, such machine will always scan the entire source string and immediately halt after reading the last character.
First, we can easily modify the given machine by introducing a sink state, so that it never stops until the input is entirely read.
Suppose this machine has a spontaneous loop, i.e., a computation that can be repeated forever. By necessity this computation visits a configuration with state $p$ and stack $\gamma A$, such that the automaton can perform unboundedly many spontaneous moves without consuming the top stack symbol $A$. Then we modify the machine adding two new states, as next explained. If during the spontaneous loop the automaton does not enter a final configuration, we add the new error state $p_E$ and the move

$$p \xrightarrow{\frac{\varepsilon, A}{A}} p_E$$

Otherwise we add the new final state $p_F$ and the moves

$$p \xrightarrow{\frac{\varepsilon, A}{A}} p_F, \quad p_F \xrightarrow{\frac{\varepsilon, A}{A}} p_E$$

To complete the conversion, the error state $p_E$ should be programmed to consume the remaining suffix of the input string.

A machine is said to function *on line* if, upon reading the last input character, it decides at once to accept or reject the string without further computation.
Any pushdown machine can always be transformed to work on line. Since we know that spontaneous loops can be removed, the only situation to be considered is when the machine, after reading the last character, enters state $p$ and performs a finite series of moves. Such moves will examine a finite topmost stack segment of maximal length $k$, before accepting or rejecting; the segment is accordingly qualified as accepting or rejecting. Since the stack segment is finite, the corresponding information can be stored in the state memory. This requires to multiply the states, so that in any computation the topmost stack segment of length $k$ is also represented in the current state. Whenever the original machine entered state $p$, the second machine will enter a state that represents the combination of $p$ and the stack segment. If the segment of the original machine is accepting, then the second machine accepts as well, otherwise it rejects the input.

[2] For a thorough discussion of this point and of the next one, we refer to e.g.,[25, 34].

## 4.2 One Family for Context-Free Languages and Pushdown Automata

We are going to show that the language accepted by a pushdown machine using states is context-free. This, combined with the property (p. 151) that a context-free language can be recognized by a pushdown machine, leads to the next central characterization of context-free languages, analogous to the characterization of regular languages by finite automata.

*Property 4.5.* The family $CF$ of context-free languages coincides with the set of languages recognized by pushdown automata.

*Proof.* Let $L = L(M)$ be the language recognized by a pushdown machine $M$ with the following stipulations: it has only one final state, it accepts only if the stack is empty, and each transition has one of the forms

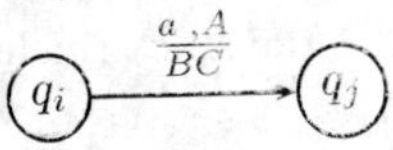


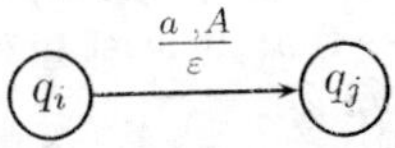


where $a$ is a terminal or the empty string and $A$, $B$, and $C$ are stack symbols. Thus a move either pushes two symbols or none. It turns out that this assumption does not reduce the generality of the machine. The initial stack symbol is $Z$ and $q_0$ the initial state.

We are going to construct a grammar $G$ equivalent to this machine. The construction may produce useless rules that can later be removed by cleaning. In the resulting grammar the axiom is $S$ and all other nonterminal symbols are formed by a 3-tuple containing two states and a stack symbol, written as $\langle q_i, A, q_j \rangle$.

Grammar rules are constructed in such a way that each computation represents a leftmost derivation. The old construction for stateless automata (Table 4.1, p. 149) created a nonterminal for each stack symbol. But now we have to take care of the states as well. To this end, each stack symbol $A$ is associated with multiple nonterminals, marked with two states having the following meaning. From nonterminal $\langle q_i, A, q_j \rangle$ string $z$ derives if, and only if, the automaton starting in state $q_i$ with $A$ on top of the stack performs a computation that reads string $z$ enters state $q_j$ and deletes $A$ from stack. According to this principle, the axiom rewriting rules of the grammar have the form

$$S \to \langle q_0, Z, q_f \rangle$$

where $Z$ is the initial stack symbol, $q_0$ is the initial state, and $q_f$ is a final state.

The other grammar rules are obtained as next specified.

1. Moves of the form 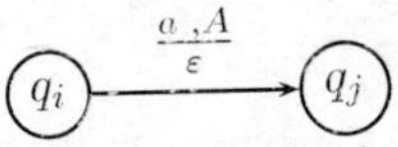 where the two states may coincide and $a$ may be empty, are converted to rule $\langle q_i, A, q_j \rangle \to a$.

2. Moves of the form 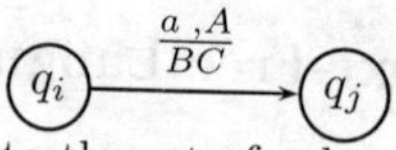

where the two states may coincide, are converted to the set of rules

$$\{\langle q_i, A, q_x\rangle \to a\langle q_j, B, q_x\rangle\langle q_y, C, q_x\rangle \mid \text{for all states } q_x \text{ and } q_y \text{ of } M\}$$

Notice the nonempty grammar rules obtained by 1. and 2. are in Greibach normal form.

We omit the correctness proof [3] of the construction and move to an example.

*Example 4.6.* Grammar equivalent to pushdown machine[4]
The language

$$L = \{a^n b^m \mid n > m \geqslant 1\}$$

is accepted by the pushdown automaton on top of Figure 4.3. The automaton reads $a$ and stores it as $A$ on the stack. Then for each $b$ it pops a symbol. At last it checks that at least one $A$ is left and empties the stack (including the initial symbol $Z$).

The grammar rules are listed under the automaton: notice the axiom is $\langle q_0, Z, q_3\rangle$. Useless rules created by step 2. such as

$$\langle q_0, A, q_1\rangle \to a\langle q_0, A, q_3\rangle\langle q_3, A, q_1\rangle$$

which contains the undefined nonterminal $\langle q_0, A, q_3\rangle$, are not listed.
To understand the mapping between the two models, it helps to compare the computation

$$\langle 0, aab, Z\rangle \overset{5}{\mapsto} \langle 3, \varepsilon, \varepsilon\rangle$$

and the leftmost derivation

$$\langle q_0, Z, q_3\rangle \overset{5}{\Rightarrow} aab$$

The computation and the corresponding derivation tree with steps numbered are in Figure 4.4 where nonterminal names are simplified to, say, $0Z3$. Observe the following properties hold at each step of computation and derivation:

- the string prefixes read by the machine and generated by the derivation are identical;
- the stack content is the mirror of the string obtained by concatenating the middle symbols $(A, Z)$ of each 3-tuple occurring in the derived string;
- any two consecutive 3-tuples in the derived string are chained together by the identity of the states, which are marked by the same arrow style in the next line

---

[3] See for instance [25, 28, 29, 47].

[4] This example has been prepared using JFLAP, the formal language and automata package of Rodger and Finley[44].

*Pushdown automaton M*

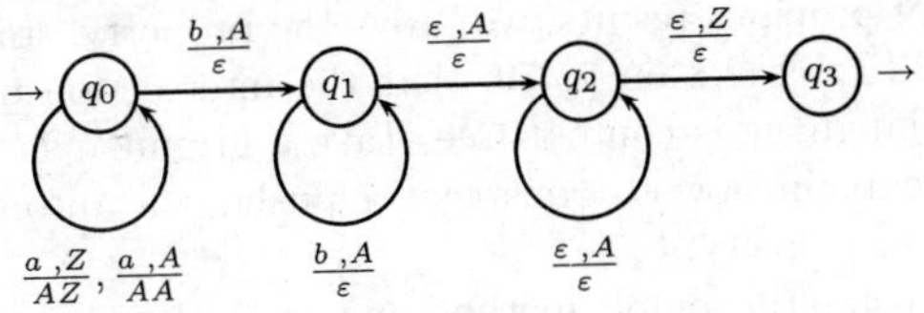


*Grammar G*

$$
\begin{aligned}
\langle q_0, Z, q_3\rangle &\to a\langle q_0, A, q_2\rangle\langle q_2, Z, q_3\rangle \\
\langle q_0, A, q_1\rangle &\to a\langle q_0, A, q_1\rangle\langle q_1, A, q_1\rangle \\
\langle q_0, A, q_1\rangle &\to b \\
\langle q_0, A, q_2\rangle &\to a\langle q_0, A, q_1\rangle\langle q_1, A, q_2\rangle \\
\langle q_0, A, q_2\rangle &\to a\langle q_0, A, q_2\rangle\langle q_2, A, q_2\rangle \\
\langle q_0, A, q_2\rangle &\to \varepsilon \\
\langle q_2, Z, q_3\rangle &\to \varepsilon \\
\langle q_1, A, q_1\rangle &\to b \\
\langle q_1, A, q_2\rangle &\to \varepsilon
\end{aligned}
$$

**Fig. 4.3** Pushdown automaton and grammar for example 4.6.

$$0Z3 \stackrel{+}{\Rightarrow} aa \quad 0A\overset{\downarrow}{1} \quad \overset{\downarrow}{1}A\overset{\Downarrow}{2} \quad \overset{\Downarrow}{2}Z3$$

Such step-by-step correspondence between transitions and derivation steps ensure the two models define the same language.

$$
\begin{aligned}
\langle 0, aab, Z\rangle &\mapsto \langle 0, ab, ZA\rangle \\
&\mapsto \langle 0, b, ZAA\rangle \\
&\mapsto \langle 1, \varepsilon, ZA\rangle \\
&\mapsto \langle 2, \varepsilon, Z\rangle \\
&\mapsto \langle 3, \varepsilon, \varepsilon\rangle
\end{aligned}
$$

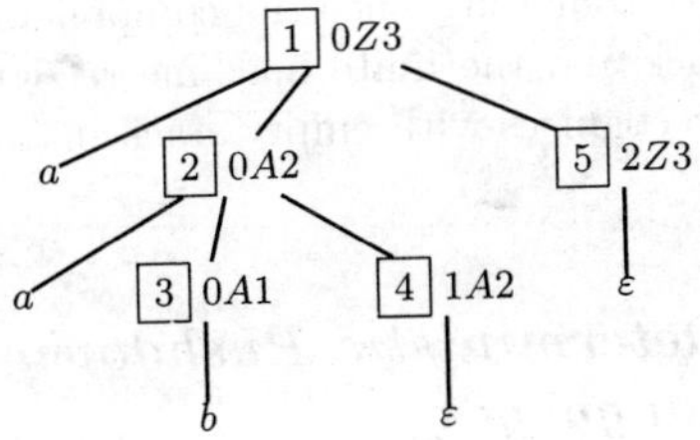


**Fig. 4.4** A computation of machine $M$ (left) and the corresponding derivation tree for example 4.6.

### 4.2.1 Intersection of Regular and Context-Free Languages

As an illustration of previous results, we prove the property, stated without proof in Chapter 2, Table 2.8 on p. 79, that the intersection of a context-free and a regular language is context-free. Take a grammar $G$ and a finite automaton $A$; we explain how to construct a pushdown automaton $M$ to recognize the language $L(G) \cap L(A)$.
First we construct, using the simple method on p. 149, the one-state automaton $N$ that recognizes the language $L(G)$ with empty stack.
Then, to simulate the respective computations of machines $N$ and $A$, we construct the cartesian product machine $M$. The construction is essentially the same explained for two finite machines (p. 138), with the difference of the presence of a stack. The state set is the cartesian product of the state sets of the component machines. The product machine $M$ performs on the stack the same operations as component machine $N$. Recognition is with final state and empty stack; the final states of $M$ are those containing a final state of finite machine $A$.
The product machine is deterministic if both component machines are so.
It is easy to see that a computation of $M$ empties the stack and enters a final state, i.e., recognizes a string, if, and only if, the string is accepted with empty stack by $N$ and is accepted also by $A$ which reaches a final state. It follows that machine $M$ accepts the intersection of the two languages.

*Example 4.7.* We want (as in example 2.81, p. 80) the intersection of the Dyck language with alphabet $\Sigma = \{a, a'\}$ and the regular language $a^*a'^+$. The result is the language $\{a^n a'^n \mid n \geqslant 1\}$.
It is straightforward to imagine a pushdown machine with one state, accepting the Dyck language with empty stack. This, the finite automaton, and the product machine are depicted in Figure 4.5. Clearly the resulting machine simulates both component machines step-by-step. For instance, the arc from $\{q, s\}$ to $\{r, s\}$ associated with a reading move of $a'$ operates on the stack exactly as automaton $N$: it pops $A$ and goes from state $q$ to state $r$ exactly as the finite automaton. Since the component pushdown machine accepts with empty stack and the finite machine recognizes in final state $r$, the product machine recognizes with empty stack in final state $(r, s)$.

### 4.2.2 Deterministic Pushdown Automata and Languages

It is important to further the study of deterministic recognizers and corresponding languages because they are widely adopted in compilers thanks to

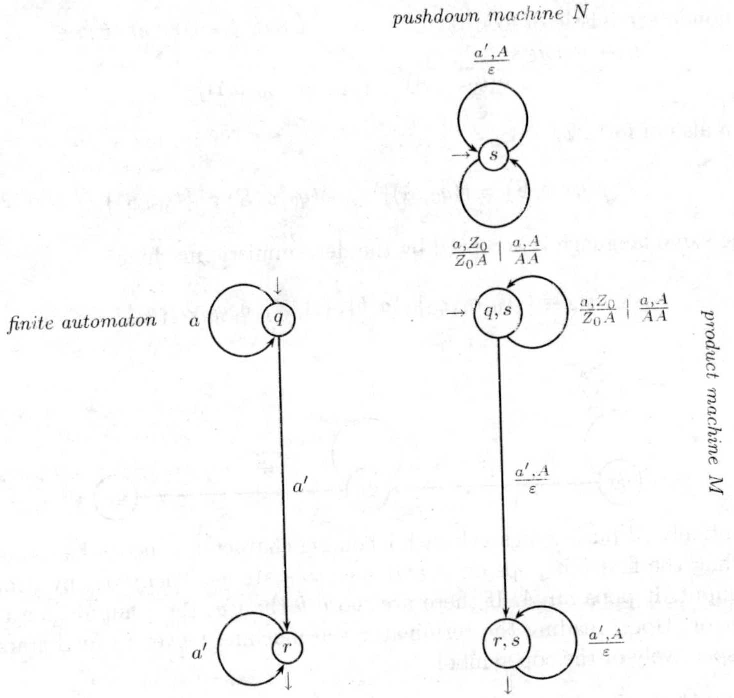


**Fig. 4.5** Product machine for intersection of a Dyck language and $a^* a'^+$ (example 4.7).

their computational efficiency. Observing a pushdown machine (as defined on p. 152), we may find three forms of indeterminism.

1. Uncertainty between reading moves, if, for a state $q$, character $a$ and stack symbol $A$, the transition function has two or more values: $|\delta(q, a, A)| > 1$.
2. Uncertainty between a spontaneous move and a reading move, if both moves $\delta(q, \varepsilon, A)$ and $\delta(q, a, A)$ are defined.
3. Uncertainty between spontaneous moves, if for some state $q$ and symbol $A$, the function $\delta(q, \varepsilon, A)$ takes multiple values: $|\delta(q, \varepsilon, A)| > 1$ .

If none of the three forms occurs in the transition function, the pushdown machine is *deterministic*. The language recognized by a deterministic pushdown machine is called (context-free) *deterministic*, and the family of such languages is named *DET*.

*Example 4.8.* Forms of nondeterminism
The one state recognizer (p. 150) of the language $L = \{a^n b^m \mid n \geqslant m > 0\}$

is nondeterministic of form 1

$$\delta(q_0, a, A) = \{(q_0, b), (q_0, bA)\}$$

and also of form 2

$$\delta(q_0, \varepsilon, S) = \{(q_0, A)\} \qquad \delta(q_0, a, S) = \{(q_0, S)\}$$

The same language is accepted by the deterministic machine

$$M_2 = (\{q_0, q_1, q_2\}, \{a, b\}, \{A, Z\}, \delta, q_0, Z, \{q_2\})$$

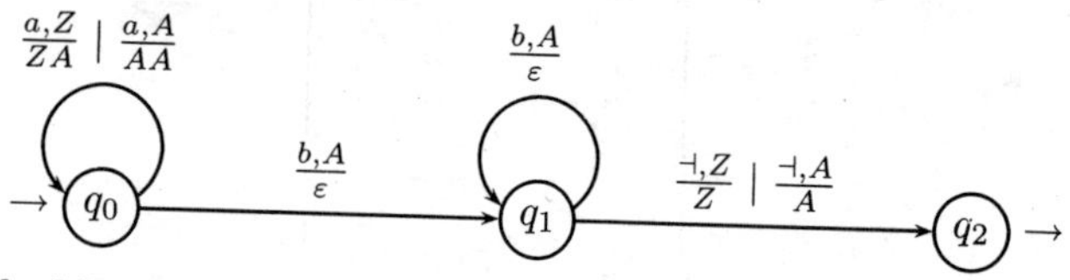


Intuitively $M$ pushes on stack each incoming character $a$ encoded as $A$; upon reading the first $b$ it pops an $A$ and goes to state $q_1$. Then, for any $b$ found on input, it pops an $A$. If there are more $b$ than $a$, the computation ends in error. Upon reading the terminator the machine moves to final state $q_2$ irrespectively of the top symbol.

Although we have been able to find a deterministic pushdown machine for the language of the example, this is not possible for other context-free languages: in other words $DET$ is a subfamily of $CF$ as we shall see.

### Closure Properties of Deterministic Languages

Deterministic languages are a subclass of context-free languages and have specific properties. Starting from the known properties (Table 2.8 on p. 79), we list in Table 4.3 the properties of deterministic languages. We symbolize with $L$, $D$, and $R$ a language respectively belonging to the family $LIB$, $DET$, and $REG$. Next we argue for the listed properties and support them by examples.[5]

Reflection: the language

$$L_1 = \{a^n b^n e\} \cup \{a^n b^{2n} d\}, \quad n \geqslant 1$$

satisfies the equality $|x|_a = |x|_b$ when the sentence ends with $e$, and the equality $2|x|_a = |x|_b$ if it ends with $d$. The language is not deterministic,

[5] It may be superfluous to recall that a statement such as $D^R \notin DET$ means there exists some language $D$ such that $D^R$ is not deterministic.

**Table 4.3** Closure properties of $DET$, $REG$, and $CF$.

| *Operation* | *Property* | *(Already known property)* |
|---|---|---|
| *Reflection* | $D^R \notin DET$ | $D^R \in CF$ |
| *Star* | $D^* \notin DET$ | $D^* \in CF$ |
| *Complement* | $\neg D \in DET$ | $\neg L \notin CF$ |
| *Union* | $D_1 \cup D_2 \notin DET$, $D \cup R \in DET$ | $D_1 \cup D_2 \in CF$ |
| *Concatenation* | $D_1.D_2 \notin DET$ , $D.R \in DET$ | $D_1.D_2 \in CF$ |
| *Intersection* | $D \cap R \in DET$ | $D_1 \cap D_2 \notin CF$ |

but the reflected language is so. In fact, it suffices to read the first character to decide which one of the equalities has to be checked.

Complement: the complement of a deterministic language is deterministic; the proof (similar to the proof for regular languages on p. 137) constructs the recognizer of the complement by creating a new sink state and interchanging the final and nonfinal states.[6] It follows that if a context-free language has as complement a noncontext-free language, it cannot be deterministic.

Union: example 4.11 on p. 165 shows the union of deterministic languages (as $L'$ and $L''$ obviously are) is in general nondeterministic. From De Morgan identity it follows that $D \cup R = \neg(\neg D \cap \neg R)$, which is a deterministic language, for the following reasons: the complement of a deterministic language (regular) is deterministic (regular); the intersection of a deterministic language and a regular one is deterministic (discussed next).

Intersection $D \cap R$: the cartesian product of a deterministic pushdown machine and a deterministic finite automaton is deterministic. To show that the intersection of two deterministic languages may go out of $DET$, recall the language with three equal exponents (p. 76) is not context-free; but it can be defined by the intersection of two languages, both deterministic:

$$\{a^n b^n c^n \mid n \geqslant 0\} = \{a^n b^n c^* \mid n \geqslant 0\} \cap \{a^* b^n c^n \mid n \geqslant 0\}$$

Concatenation and star: when two deterministic languages are concatenated, it may happen that a deterministic pushdown machine cannot localize the frontier between the strings of the first and second language. Therefore it is unable to decide the point for switching from the first to the second transition function. Example: starting with the languages

6 See for instance [25, 28]. Alternatively there is a method [27] for transforming the grammar of a deterministic language to the grammar of its complement.

$$L_0 = \{a^i b^i a^j \mid i, j \geqslant 1\} \qquad L_1 = \{a^i b^j a^j \mid i, j \geqslant 1\} \qquad R = \{c, c^2\}$$

the language $L = cL_0 \cup L_1$ is deterministic, but the concatenation $RL$ is not.[7] In fact, the presence of a prefix $cc$ can be alternatively interpreted as coming either from $c.cL_0$ or from $c^2.L_1$.

The situation for the star of a deterministic language is similar.

Concatenation with a regular language : the recognizer of $D.R$ can be constructed by *cascade composition* of a deterministic pushdown machine and a deterministic finite automaton. More precisely, when the pushdown machine enters the final state that recognizes a sentence of $D$, the new machine moves to the initial state of the finite recognizers of $R$ and simulates its computation until the end.

Table 4.3 witnesses that the basic operations of regular expressions may spoil determinism when applied to a deterministic language. This creates some difficulty for language designers: when two existing technical languages are united, there is no guarantee the result will be deterministic (it may even be ambiguous). The same danger threatens the concatenation and the star or cross of deterministic languages. In practice, the designer must check that after any transformation of the language under development the property of determinism is preserved.

It is worth mentioning that the families $DET$ and $CF$ have another important difference. While the equivalence of two $CF$ grammars or pushdown automata is undecidable, an algorithm exists for checking if two deterministic automata are equivalent.[8]

## Nondeterministic Languages

Unlike regular languages, there exist context-free languages which cannot be accepted by a deterministic automaton.

*Property 4.9.* The family $DET$ of deterministic languages is strictly included in the family $CF$ of context-free languages.

The statement follows from two known facts: first, the inclusion $DET \subseteq CF$ is obvious since a deterministic pushdown automaton is a special case of the nondeterministic one; second, it is $DET \neq CF$ because certain closure properties (Table 4.3) differentiate a family from the other.

This completes the proof but it is worthwhile to exhibit typical nondeterministic context-free languages in order to evidence some language paradigms that ought to be carefully avoided by language designers.

---

[7] The proof can be found in [25].

[8] The algorithm is fairly complex, see [48].

Lemma of Double Service

A valuable technique for proving that a context-free language is not deterministic is based on the analysis of the sentences that are the prefix of each other.

Let $D$ be a deterministic language, $x \in D$ a sentence, and suppose there exists another sentence $y \in D$ which is a prefix of $x$, i.e., $x = yz$, where all the strings can be empty.

Now we define another language called the *double service* of $D$ obtained by inserting a new terminal, the sharp sign $\sharp$, between strings $y$ and $z$:

$$ds(D) = \{y\sharp z \mid y \in D \land z \in \Sigma^* \land yz \in D\}$$

For instance, for language $F = \{a, ab, bb\}$ the double service language is

$$ds(F) = \{a\sharp b, a\sharp, ab\sharp, bb\sharp\}$$

Notice the original sentences are terminated by $\sharp$ and may be followed or not by a suffix.

**Lemma 4.10.** *If $D$ is a deterministic language, then also the double service language $ds(D)$ is deterministic.*

Proof.[9] We are going to transform the deterministic recognizer $M$ of $D$ into a deterministic recognizer $M'$ of the double service language. To simplify the construction, we assume the automaton $M$ functions *on line* (p. 155); this means that, as it scans the input string, the machine can at once decide if the scanned string is a sentence. Now consider the computation of $M$ accepting string $y$. If $y$ is followed by a sharp sign the new machine $M'$ reads the sharp and accepts, if the input is finished (because $y\sharp \in ds(D)$ if $y \in D$). Otherwise the computation of $M'$ proceeds deterministically, scanning the string $z$ exactly as $M$ would do in order to recognize string $yz$.

The reason for the curious name of the language is now clear: the automaton simultaneously performs two services inasmuch as it has to recognize a prefix and a longer string.

The lemma has the practical implication that if the double service of a $CF$ language $L$ is not $CF$, then $L$ is not deterministic.

*Example 4.11.* Nondeterministic union of deterministic languages
The language

$$L = \{a^n b^n \mid n \geqslant 1\} \cup \{a^n b^{2n} \mid n \geqslant 1\} = L' \cup L"$$

union of two deterministic languages, is not deterministic.

Intuitively the automaton has to read and store on the stack one or more characters $a$. Then, if the string (e.g., $aabb$) is in the first set, it must pop an

[9] See Floyd and Beigel [20] for further reading.

$a$ upon reading a $b$; but if the string is in the second set (e.g.,$aabbbb$), it must read two letters $b$ before popping one $a$. Since the machine does not know which is the correct choice (for that it should count the number of $b$ examining an unbounded substring), it is obliged to carry on nondeterministically both computations.

More rigorously, assume by contradiction that $L$ is deterministic. Then also its double service language $ds(L)$ would be deterministic and, from the closure property of $DET$ (p. 162) under intersection with regular languages, the language

$$L_R = ds(L) \cap (a^+ b^+ \sharp b^+)$$

is deterministic. But $L_R$ is not a context-free language hence certainly not a deterministic one because the sentences have the form $a^i b^i \sharp b^i$, $i \geqslant 1$, with three equal exponents (p. 76), a well-known non-context-free case.

The next example applies the same method to the basic paradigm of palindromes.

*Example 4.12.* Palindromes
The language of palindromes $L$ is defined by grammar

$$S \rightarrow aSa \mid bSb \mid a \mid b \mid \varepsilon$$

To prove that it is not deterministic, we intersect the language of double service with a regular language with the aim of obtaining a language that is not in $CF$. Consider the language

$$L_R = ds(L) \cap (a^* b a^* \sharp b a^*)$$

A string of form $a^i b a^j \sharp b a^k$ is in $L_R$ if, and only if, condition $j = i \wedge k = i$ holds. But this language is again the non-$CF$ language with three equal exponents.

## Determinism and Unambiguity of Language

If a language is accepted by a deterministic automaton, each sentence is recognized with exactly one computation and it is possible to prove that the language is generated by a nonambiguous grammar.

The construction of p. 157 produces a grammar equivalent to a pushdown automaton, which simulates computations by derivations: the grammar generates a sentence with a leftmost derivation if, and only if, the machine performs a computation that accepts the sentence. It follows that two distinct derivations (of the same sentence) correspond to distinct computations, which on a deterministic machine necessarily scan different strings.

*Property 4.13.* Let $M$ be a deterministic pushdown machine; then the corresponding grammar of $L(M)$ obtained by the construction on p. 157 is nonambiguous.

But of course other grammars of $L(M)$ may be ambiguous.

A consequence is that any inherently ambiguous context-free language is nondeterministic: suppose by contradiction it is deterministic, then the preceding property states a nonambiguous equivalent grammar does exist. This contradicts the very definition of inherent ambiguity (p. 56) that every grammar of the language is ambiguous. In other words, an inherently ambiguous language cannot be recognized by a deterministic pushdown machine. The discussion confirms what has been already said on the irrelevance of inherently ambiguous languages for technical applications.

*Example 4.14.* Inherently ambiguous language and indeterminism
The inherently ambiguous language of example 2.56 (p. 56) is the union of two languages

$$L_A = \{a^i b^i c^* \mid i \geqslant 0\} \cup \{a^* b^i c^i \mid i \geqslant 0\} = L_1 \cup L_2$$

both deterministic (by the way another proof that family $DET$ is not closed by union).

Intuitively, to recognize the language two different strategies must be adopted for the strings of each language. In the former the letters $a$ are pushed on the stack and popped upon reading $b$; the same happens in the latter case but for the letters $b$ and $c$. Therefore any sentence belonging to both languages is accepted by two different computations and the automaton is nondeterministic.

The notion of ambiguity applies to any kind of automata. An *automaton* is *ambiguous* if a sentence exists such that it is recognized by two distinct computations.

We observe the condition of determinism is more stringent than absence of ambiguity: the family of deterministic pushdown automata is strictly contained in the family of nonambiguous pushdown automata. To clarify the statement we show two examples.

*Example 4.15.* The language $L_A$ of the previous example is nondeterministic and also ambiguous because certain sentences are necessarily accepted by different computations.

On the other hand, the language of example 4.11 on p. 165

$$L_I = \{a^n b^n \mid n \geqslant 1\} \cup \{a^n b^{2n} \mid n \geqslant 1\} = L' \cup L''$$

although nondeterministic (as argued there), is unambiguous. In fact, each of the two sublanguages $L', L''$ is easily defined by an unambiguous grammar and the union remains unambiguous because the components are disjoint. The two recognition strategies described on p. 165 are implemented by distinct computations but one at most of them may succeed for any given string.

## Subclasses of Deterministic Pushdown Automata

The family $DET$ is by definition associated with the most general type of deterministic pushdown machine, the one featuring several states and using final states for acceptance. Various limitations on internal states and on acceptance modes having no consequence in the indeterministic case cause a restriction of the language family recognized by a deterministic machine. The main cases are briefly mentioned.[10]

Automaton having one state only: acceptance is necessarily with empty stack and it is less powerful than recognition with final state.

Limitation on the number of states: the family of languages is more restricted than $DET$; a similar loss is caused if a limit is imposed on just the number of final states; or, more generally, on the number of final configurations of the machine.

Real-time functioning, i.e., without spontaneous moves: it restricts the family of recognizable languages.

## Some Simple Deterministic Subfamilies

In many practical situations, technical languages are designed so that they are deterministic. For instance, this is the case for almost all programming languages and for the family XML of mark-up languages of the Net. Different approaches exist for ensuring that a language is deterministic by imposing some conditions on the language or on its grammar. Depending on the conditions, one obtains different subfamilies of $DET$. Two simple cases are next described to introduce the topic; others, much more important for applications, will be obtained with the $LL(k)$ and $LR(k)$ conditions to be respectively studied in this and the next chapter.

### Simple Deterministic Languages

A grammar is called *simple deterministic* if it satisfies the next conditions.

1. Every right part of a rule starts with a terminal character (hence there are no empty rules);
2. for any nonterminal $A$, alternatives do not exist starting with the same character, i.e.:

$$\nexists\ A \to a\alpha \mid a\beta \text{ with } a \in \Sigma,\ \alpha, \beta \in (\Sigma \cup V)^*,\ \alpha \neq \beta$$

An example is the simple deterministic grammar $S \to aSb \mid c$.

---

[10] For further reading, see [25, 49].

Clearly, if we construct the pushdown machine from a simple deterministic grammar using the method of Table 4.1 on p. 149, the result is a deterministic machine. Moreover, this machine consumes a character with each move, i.e., it works in real-time, which follows from the fact that such grammars are (almost) in Greibach normal form.
We hasten to say the simple deterministic condition is too inconvenient for practical use.

### Parenthesis Languages

It is easy to check that parenthesized structures and languages, introduced in Chapter 2 on p. 44, are deterministic. Any sentence generated by a parenthesized grammar has a bracketed structure that marks the start and end of the right part of each rule used in the derivation. We assume the grammar is *distinctly parenthesized* (p. 45); otherwise, if just one type of parentheses is used, we assume rules do not exist with identical right-hand sides. Either assumption ensures that the grammar is unambiguous.

A simple recognition algorithm scans the string to localize a substring not containing parentheses and enclosed between a matching pair of parentheses. Then the relevant set of the right parts of the grammar rules are searched for the parenthesized substring. If none matches, the source string is rejected. Otherwise the parenthesized substring is reduced to the corresponding nonterminal (the left part of the matching rule) thus producing a shorter string to be recognized. The algorithm then resumes scanning the new string in the same way and at last recognizes when the string is reduced to the axiom. It is not difficult to encode the algorithm by means of a deterministic pushdown machine.

If a grammar defines a nondeterministic language or if it is ambiguous, the transformation to a parenthesized grammar removes both defects. For instance, the language of palindromes ($S \to aSa \mid bSb \mid a \mid b \mid \varepsilon$ on p. 166) is changed to a deterministic one when every right part of a rule is parenthesized:

$$S \to (aSa) \mid (bSb) \mid (a) \mid (b) \mid ()$$

Web documents and semistructured databases are often encoded in the mark-up language XML. Distinct opening and closing marks are used to delimit the parts of a document in order to allow efficient recognition and transformation. Therefore the XML language family is deterministic. The XML grammar model[11] (technically known as Document Type Definition) is similar to the case of parenthesized grammars, but has as distinguishing feature the use of various regular expression operators in the grammar rules.

---

[11] Such grammars generate context-free languages but differ from context-free grammars in several ways, see [9] for an initial comparison.

## 4.3 Syntax Analysis

The rest of the chapter introduces the distinction between top-down and bottom-up sentence recognition and covers the classical fast parsing algorithms used in top-down compilers, also for grammars extended with regular expressions.

Consider a grammar $G$. The syntax analyzer or parser scans the source string and computes a derivation or syntax tree if the string is in the language $L(G)$; otherwise it stops indicating the configuration where the error was detected (diagnosis); it may preferably resume parsing, skipping the substrings contaminated by the error (error recovering), in order to offer as much diagnostic help as possible with a single scan of the source string.

Disregarding error treatment, an analyzer is simply a recognizer capable of recording the derivation of the string. To this end, the pushdown machine has to save in some data structure the label of the grammar rule when it performs a corresponding move. Upon termination, the data structure will represent the derivation or syntax tree.

If the source string is ambiguous, the result is a set of trees. In that case the parser may decide to stop when the first derivation has been found or to exhaustively produce all of them.

### *4.3.1 Top-Down and Bottom-Up Analysis*

We know the same (syntax) tree corresponds to many derivations notably leftmost and rightmost ones and less relevant others proceeding in zigzaging orders. Depending on the derivation being leftmost or rightmost and on the order it is constructed, we obtain the two most important classes of parsers.

*Top-down* analysis: constructs the leftmost derivation starting from the axiom i.e., the root of the tree, and growing the tree towards the leaves; each step of the algorithm corresponds to a derivation step.

*Bottom-up* analysis: constructs the rightmost derivation but in reflected order, i.e., from the leaves to the root of the tree; each step corresponds to a reduction. The algorithms are described in the next chapter.

This is best explained by an example.

*Example 4.16.* Orders of visit of a tree
Consider grammar

| | |
|---|---|
| 1. $S \to aSAB$ | 2. $S \to b$ |
| 3. $A \to bA$ | 4. $A \to a$ |
| 5. $B \to cB$ | 6. $B \to a$ |

and sentence $a^2b^3a^4$. The orderings corresponding to top-down and bottom-up visits are shown in Figure 4.6. In each node the framed number gives the order of visit and the subscript indicates the grammar rule applied. A top-down analyzer grafts under the left part of a rule the corresponding right part. If the latter contains terminal characters, they must match with the characters of the source string. The procedure terminates when all nonterminal symbols have been transformed to terminal characters (or to empty strings).

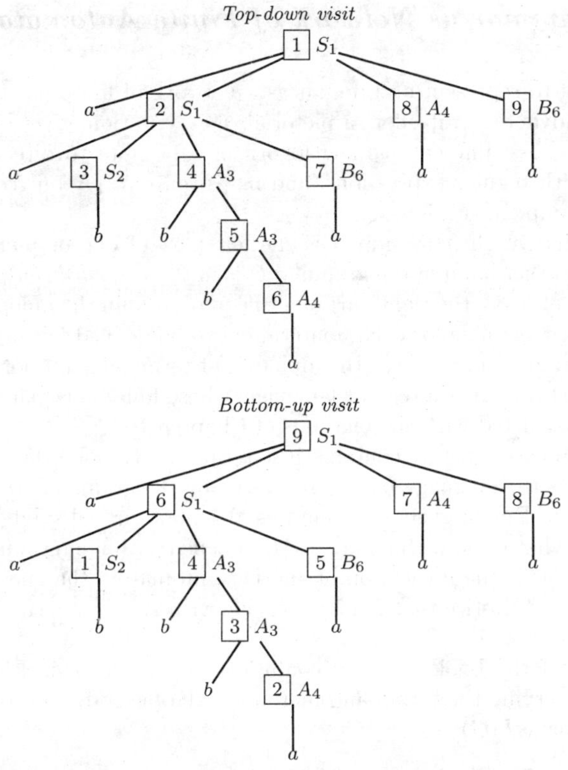


**Fig. 4.6** Orders of visit of a tree for example 4.16.

On the other hand, starting with the source text a bottom-up analyzer reduces to a nonterminal the substrings matching the right part of a rule, as they are encountered in a left-to-right scan. After each reduction, the modified text is again scanned to find the next reduction until the text is reduced to the axiom.
In both cases the process is interrupted when an error is found.

In principle both approaches to analysis also work from right to left, scanning the reflected source string. In practice all existing languages are designed for left-to-right processing as it happens in natural language where the natural reading direction corresponds to the order a sentence is uttered by a speaker. Incidentally, reversing the scanning direction may damage the determinism of the language because the $DET$ family is not closed by mirror reflection (p. 163).

### 4.3.2 Grammar as Network of Finite Automata

We are going to represent a grammar as a network of finite machines. This has several advantages: it offers a pictorial representation, gives evidence to similarities across different parsing algorithms, permits to directly handle grammars with regular expressions, and maps quite nicely on recursive descent parser implementation.

For a grammar, each nonterminal is the left part of one or more alternatives. On the other hand, if the grammar $G$ is in the *extended context-free* (or EBNF) form of p. 83, the right part of a rule may contain the union operator, which makes it possible for each nonterminal to be defined by just one rule, $A \to \alpha$, where $\alpha$ is an r.e. over the alphabet of terminals and nonterminals. The right part $\alpha$ defines a regular language, whose finite automaton $M_A$ can be easily constructed with the methods of Chapter 3.

In the simple case when $\alpha$ contains just terminal symbols, the automaton $M_A$ recognizes the language $L_A(G)$ generated by the grammar starting from nonterminal $A$. But in general $\alpha$ contains also nonterminal symbols and we next discuss what to do with an arc of $M_A$ labelled with nonterminal $B$. This can be thought as the invocation of another automaton, the one associated with rule $B \to \beta$. Notice that $B$ may coincide with $A$, causing the invocation to be recursive.

In this part of the book to avoid confusion we call "machines" the finite automata, reserving the term "automaton" to the pushdown automaton accepting language $L(G)$.

**Definition 4.17.** Recursive net of finite machines

All the finite machines considered are deterministic.

- Let $\Sigma$ be the terminal alphabet, $V = \{S, A, B, \ldots\}$ the nonterminal set, and $S$ the axiom of the extended context-free grammar $G$.
- For each nonterminal $A$ there is one rule $A \to \alpha$ and the right part $\alpha$ is an r.e. of alphabet $\Sigma \cup V$.
- Let the rules be denoted by $S \to \sigma, A \to \alpha, B \to \beta, \ldots$.
  Then symbols $R_S, R_A, R_B, \ldots$ denote the regular languages, with alphabet $\Sigma \cup V$, defined by r.e. $\sigma, \alpha, \beta, \ldots$.

- Symbols $M_S, M_A, M_B, \ldots$ are the names of the (finite deterministic) machines accepting the corresponding regular languages $R_S, R_A, \ldots$. The set of all machines, i.e., the *net* is denoted by $\mathcal{M}$.
- In order to avoid confusion, we assume that the names of the states of any two machines are disjoint. The state set of machine $M_A$ is denoted $Q_A$, the initial state is $q_{A,0}$, and the final states are $F_A$. The transition function of all machines will be denoted with the same name $\delta$ at no risk of confusion, since the state sets are disjoint.
- For a state $q$ of machine $M_A$, $R(M_A, q)$ (or $R(q)$ if the machine name is understood) denotes the regular language of alphabet $\Sigma \cup V$ accepted by the machine starting in state $q$. If $q$ is the initial state, we have $R(M_A, q_{A,0}) \equiv R_A$.

We observe a rule $A \to \alpha$ is perfectly represented by machine $M_A$, due to the bijective correspondence between the strings defined by $\alpha$ and the paths in the graph going from the initial state to a final state. Therefore the machine net $\mathcal{M} = \{M_S, M_A, \ldots\}$ is essentially a notational variant of a grammar and we may go on using the usual concepts such as derivation. In particular, the terminal language (with alphabet $\Sigma$) $L(\mathcal{M})$ defined (or recognized) by the machine net coincides with the language generated by the grammar, $L(G)$.

We need to consider also the terminal language defined by a generic machine $M_A$, starting from a state possibly other than the initial one. For state $q$ of machine $M_A$ we write

$$L(M_A, q) = \{y \in \Sigma^* \mid \eta \in R(M_A, q) \wedge \eta \overset{*}{\Rightarrow} y\}$$

To simplify notation, we write $L(q)$ if the machine is understood. The formula above contains a string $\eta$ over terminals and nonterminals, accepted by machine $M_A$, starting in state $q$. The derivations originating from $\eta$ produce all the terminal strings of language $L(q)$.

In particular, from previous stipulations it follows that

$$L(M_A, q_{A,0}) \equiv L(q_{A,0}) \equiv L_A(G)$$

and for the axiom it is

$$L(M_S, q_{S,0}) \equiv L(q_{S,0}) \equiv L(\mathcal{M}) = L(G)$$

*Example 4.18.* Machine nets for arithmetic expressions
The grammar has three nonterminals ($E$ is the axiom), therefore also three rules:

$$E \to [+ \mid -]T\ ((+ \mid -)T)^* \qquad T \to F\,((\times \mid /)F)^* \qquad F \to (a \mid '('\,E\,')')$$

Figure 4.7 shows the machines of net $\mathcal{M}$. We list some languages defined by the net and by component machines, in order to illustrate the definitions.

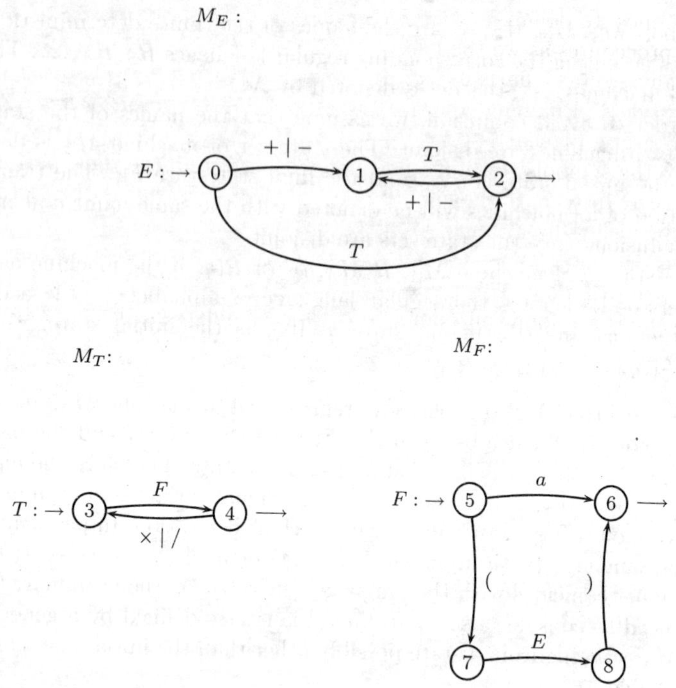


**Fig. 4.7** Machine net of example 4.18.

$$
\begin{aligned}
&R(M_E,0) = R(M_E) = [+ \mid -]T\ ((+ \mid -)T)^* \\
&R(M_T,4) = R(4) = ((\times \mid /)F)^* \\
&L(M_E,0) = L(0) = L_E(G) = L(G) = L(\mathcal{M}) = \{a, a+a, a\times(a-a), \ldots\} \\
&L(M_F,5) = L(5) = L_F(G) = \{a, (a), (-a+a), \ldots\} \\
&L(M_F,8) = L(8) = \{')'\}
\end{aligned}
$$

## Syntax Charts

As a short intermission we cite the use of machine nets for the documentation of technical languages. In many branches of engineering it is customary to use graphics for technical documentation in addition to textual documents, which in our case are grammars and regular expressions. The so-called *syntax charts* are frequently included in language reference manuals, as a pictorial representation of extended context-free grammars; under the name of transition networks they are used in computational linguistics to represent the grammars of natural languages. The popularity of syntax charts derives from their readability as well as from the fact this representation serves two purposes at once: to document the language and to describe the control flow of parsing procedures as we shall see.

Actually syntax charts differ from machine nets only with respect to graphic style and naming. First, every finite machine graph is converted to the dual graph or chart by interchanging arcs and nodes. The nodes of a chart are the symbols (terminal and non-) occurring in the right part of the rule $A \to \alpha$. In a chart the arcs are not labelled; this means the states are not distinguished by a name, but only by their position in the graph. The chart has one entry point indicated by an arrow with the chart nonterminal $A$, and one exit point corresponding to one or more final states. Different graphic styles are found in manuals to visually differentiate the two classes of symbols.

*Example 4.19.* Syntax charts of arithmetic expressions (example 4.18)
The machines (Figure 4.7) of the net are redrawn as syntax charts in Figure 4.8. The nodes are grammar symbols with dashed boxes for nonterminals and with solid boxes for terminals. Machine states are not drawn as graph nodes nor do they carry a label.

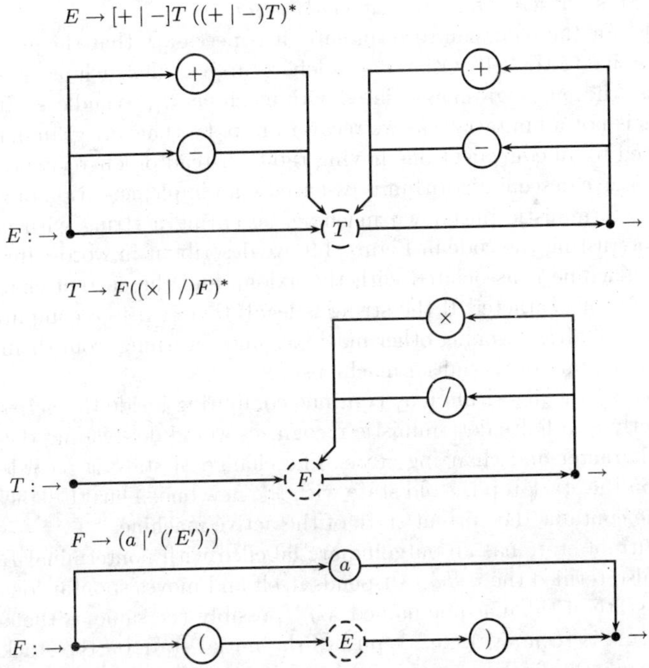


**Fig. 4.8** Syntax charts equivalent to the machine net of Figure 4.7.

Traversing a chart from entry to exit, we obtain any possible right part of the corresponding syntax rule. For instance, some traversing paths in the chart of nonterminal $E$ are:

$$T, \quad +T, \quad T+T, \ldots$$

It should be clear how to construct the syntax charts of a given EBNF grammar: construct, by means of known methods, the finite recognizer of each r.e. occurring as right part of a grammar rule, then adjust the machine graphic representation to the desired convention.

### 4.3.3 Nondeterministic Recognition Algorithm

It is straightforward to interpret a machine net as the control flow graph of a nondeterministic algorithm that accepts the sentences of the language. Each machine is viewed as a subprogram and the jump from a machine to another is then the invocation of a second subprogram, which after termination returns to the calling machine. Since the machines can be recursively linked, this type of algorithm is termed a *recursive descent parser*.

Actually, for the recursion to terminate, it is necessary that the grammar is not recursive to the left. Otherwise a left-recursive rule, such as $A \to A\gamma$, would cause the subprogram associated with machine $M_A$ to endlessly invoke itself. This is not a limitation, as we recall from p. 63 that any grammar can be converted to an equivalent one having right- instead of left-recursions.

The recursive descent algorithm is essentially an implementation of a generally nondeterministic pushdown machine, accepting a string with empty stack. Before listing the code in Figure 4.9, we describe it in words. Initially, the active machine is associated with the axiom, and the current character is the first input character. If the string is legal, there exists a computation which, possibly after invoking other machines and returning from them, will enter the final state of the initial machine.

At each step the algorithm may continue computing inside the *active machine*, exactly as a finite deterministic recognizer would do, reading the next terminal character and changing state. The change of state is recorded by replacing on the stack top the old state with the new one. Thus the stack top at any time contains the current state of the active machine.

If the current state has an outgoing arc labelled with nonterminal $B$, the machine (also termed the *caller*) suspends itself and moves spontaneously to the initial state of the machine named $M_B$ (possibly the same as the active one if the rule is recursive), i.e., it pushes the initial state on the stack and covers the caller state.

When a computation enters the final state of a machine, we say the machine has terminated the current activation. Then the machine returns control to the caller machine, which had been suspended. The return action consists of two steps: first, the algorithm pops the state of the active machine, thus allowing the state of the most recently suspended machine to surface and the machine to be reactivated. Second, the machine executes the transition labelled with the name of the terminating machine. The operation of the

*Algorithm.* The pushdown machine:
*begin*

1. source string $x$; current terminal character $cc$;
2. stack symbols are the (disjoint) union $Q = Q_A \cup Q_B \cup \ldots$ of the states of all machines;
3. the pushdown automaton has one state, to be left understood;
4. the stack initially contains the initial state $q_{S,0}$;
5. transitions are next specified; let $s \in Q_A$ be the top symbol, i.e., the state of the active machine $M_A$;

   a. (scanning move) if the move $s \xrightarrow{cc} s'$ is defined (for the active machine $M_A$), scan the current character and replace the stack top $s$ with $s'$;
   b. (invocation move) if the move $s \xrightarrow{B} s'$ is defined for some nonterminal $B$, perform a spontaneous move that pushes on the stack the initial state $q_{B,0}$ of machine $M_B$, thus making it the active one;
   c. (return move) if $s$ is a final state of machine $M_B$, pop it then perform from the state $r$ that has surfaced, the move $r \xrightarrow{B} s'$ and replace the stack top $r$ with $s'$;
   d. (recognition move) if $s$ is a final state of $M_S$ (the axiom machine ) and $cc = \dashv$, accept and halt;
   e. in any other case reject the string and halt.

*end*

**Fig. 4.9** Nondeterministic recursive descent algorithm for a machine net.

nondeterministic algorithm is illustrated in the next example.

*Example 4.20.* List of odd palindromes
The two EBNF rules and the corresponding net are shown in Figure 4.10. Taking state 0 as initial, we obtain the language $L(0) \equiv L(G)$, the lists of odd length palindromes. Taking state 2 as initial, we have instead the language $L(2)$ of odd palindromes.

To parse string $a, b \dashv$, start with state 0 on top of the stack. Machine $M_S$ pushes 2 on the stack thus invoking machine $M_P$, which reads $a$ and replaces 2 with 3 on the stack. Then $M_P$ has a choice: to terminate or to perform self-invocation, but the latter choice would end in failure. Suppose $M_P$ decides to terminate; it pops 3 and the computation resumes in state 0. Next, machine $M_S$ replaces 0 by 1 on the stack top then reads a comma, replaces 1 with 0 on stack top, and calls again $M_P$, and so on. The computation ends in state 1 upon reading the terminator character.

$$S \rightarrow P(,P)^*$$

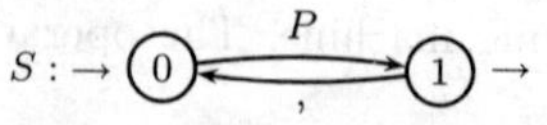


$$P \rightarrow aPa \mid bPb \mid a \mid b$$

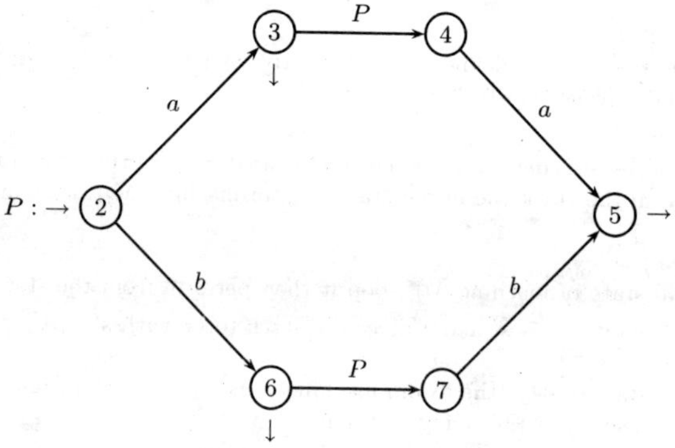


**Fig. 4.10** Grammar and machine net for example 4.20 (list of palindromes).

The next section presents a deterministic version of the algorithm and the enabling conditions on the machine net.

## 4.4 Top-Down Deterministic Syntax Analysis

A majority of technical grammars are especially designed to allow fast deterministic parsing. The next method termed $LL(k)$[12] for constructing deterministic recursive descent pushdown automata is intuitive and practical. It allows the construction of flexible and efficient syntax-directed translators.

After discussing the conditions enabling $LL(k)$ processing, two different implementations will be considered: a classical pushdown machine and a re-

[12] The acronym $LL(1)$ is historical. The first $L$ says scanning is from left-to-right; the second $L$ says the derivation is leftmost; the number $k \geqslant 1$ gives the length in characters of the look-ahead exploration.

cursive descent program comprising a set of recursive procedures. In the second case, the pushdown stack is automatically provided by the stack of the activation records of invoked procedures. At last we discuss how to adjust a grammar to make this method applicable.

### 4.4.1 Condition for LL(1) Parsing

Given grammar $G$, consider the equivalent machine net, with rule $A \to \alpha$ specified by a deterministic finite machine $M_A$, that recognizes the regular language defined by r.e. $\alpha$.
Recall a language is *nullable* if it contains the empty string.
Moving from similar concepts introduced for finite automata (algorithms GMY 3.8.2 and BS 3.8.3 p. 130 and following), we define some useful sets.

*Set of initials of a state* $q$: take the initials of the strings recognized starting from the state, $Ini(q) = Ini(L(q))$.

*Follow set*: the set of followers $Fol(A)$ of a nonterminal $A$ contains the terminals that may follow $A$ in some derivation. Moreover, the terminator $\dashv$ is in the follow set of the axiom.

In order to compute the initials and followers, we give a set of logical clauses. Let $a$ be a terminal, $A, B$ nonterminals, and $q, r$ machine states.

*Algorithm.* Set of initials of language $L(q)$.

1. $a \in Ini(q)$ if $\exists$ arc 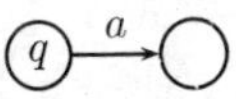


2. $a \in Ini(q)$ if $\exists$ arc 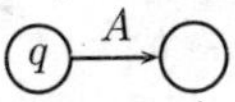

   $\wedge\ a \in Ini(q_{A,0})$, where $q_{A,0}$ is the initial state of machine $M_A$.

3. $a \in Ini(q)$ if $\exists$ arc 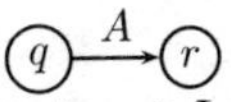

   $\wedge\ L(q_{A,0})$ is nullable $\wedge\ a \in Ini(r)$

Cases 1. and 2. are self-explanatory. For case 3., since $\varepsilon \in L(q_{A,0})$, a transition from state $q$ to state $r$ may read nothing; therefore the first character encountered is the one read from state $r$.

*Algorithm.* Follow set of a nonterminal $A$.

1. $\dashv \in Fol(S)$

2. $a \in Fol(A)$ if $\exists$ arc 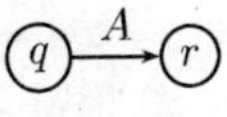

   $\wedge\ a \in Ini(r)$

3. $a \in Fol(A)$ if $\exists$ arc $(q) \xrightarrow{A} (r)$ for machine $M_B, B \neq A$
 $\wedge$ the language $L(r)$ is nullable
 $\wedge\ a \in Fol(B)$

4. $a \in Fol(A)$ if $\exists$ arc $(q) \xrightarrow{A} (r) \rightarrow$
 $\wedge\ r$ is a final state of machine $M_B$, with $B \neq A$
 $\wedge\ a \in Fol(B)$

Case 1. clause says the axiom, consistently with the fact it derives a sentence, is followed by the terminator.
Case 2. adds to the followers of $A$ the initials of the language recognized starting from any state entered by an arc labelled $A$.
For case 4., after reading a string of language $L_A(G)$, the automaton is in the final state of machine $M_B$, meaning it has finished reading a string of language $L_B(G)$. Therefore the following character belongs to the follow set of $B$ and of $A$.
Case 3. generalizes case 4., in the sense that state $r$ is not directly final, but is connected to a final state of machine $M_B$ via a path that may read the empty string.

The clauses are applied in any order (as in a logical program) to compute the sets of initials and followers. First initialize all the sets to empty. Then repeatedly apply the clauses in any order until the sets of initials and followers cease to grow (i.e., a fixed point has been reached).

*Example 4.21.* Initials and followers
Some computations are listed for grammar

$$S \rightarrow Aa \qquad A \rightarrow BC \qquad B \rightarrow b \mid \varepsilon \qquad C \rightarrow c \mid \varepsilon$$

represented as a net in Figure 4.11. The languages derived from $A, B, C$ are nullable.

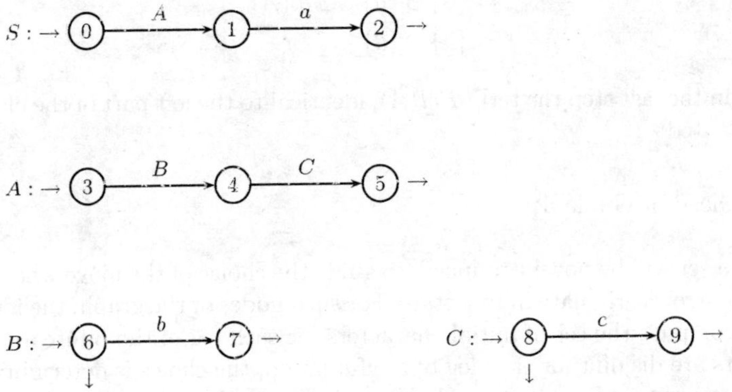


**Fig. 4.11** Example 4.21 for computations of initials and followers.

Computation of initials

$$
\begin{aligned}
Ini(0) &= Ini(3) \cup Ini(1) \\
&= Ini(6) \cup Ini(4) \cup Ini(1) \\
&= Ini(6) \cup Ini(8) \cup Ini(5) \cup Ini(1) \\
&= \{b\} \cup \{c\} \cup \emptyset \cup \{a\}
\end{aligned}
$$

Computation of followers

$$
\begin{aligned}
Fol(S) &= \{\dashv\} \\
Fol(A) &= Ini(1) \\
&= \{a\} \\
Fol(B) &= Ini(4) \cup Fol(A) \\
&= Ini(8) \cup Fol(A) \\
&= \{c\} \cup \{a\} \\
Fol(C) &= Fol(A) \\
&= \{a\}
\end{aligned}
$$

Observe that, if in the net a nonterminal occurs many times, the followers of each occurrence must be united. To illustrate we modify machine $M_C$ of the net:

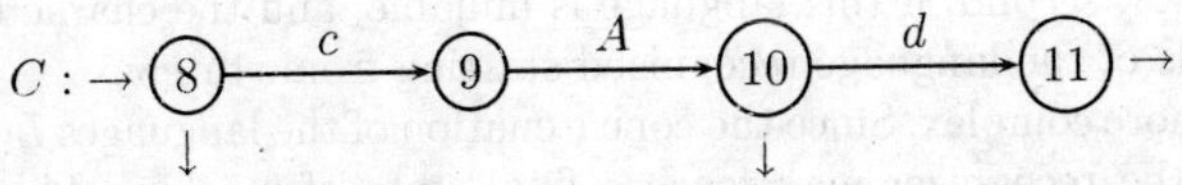

Then we recompute the followers of $A$:

$$\begin{aligned} Fol(A) &= Ini(1) \cup Ini(10) \cup Fol(C) \\ &= \{a\} \cup \{d\} \cup Fol(A) \\ &= \{a\} \cup \{d\} \end{aligned}$$

Notice in the last step the term $Fol(A)$, identical to the left part of the clause, is eliminated.

### Look-Ahead or Guide Set

At last a set will be now introduced, to guide the choice of the move when two or more arrows originate from a state. For such nodes of the graph, the idea is to pre-compute the set of initial characters for each leg of the bifurcation. If such sets are disjoint for each leg of a bifurcation, the choice is deterministic: take the leg having the current character in the guide set.

**Definition 4.22.** *Guide* (or Look-ahead) *set.*
The guide set $Gui(q \to \ldots) \subseteq \Sigma \cup \{\dashv\}$ is defined for every arrow (i.e., an arc or a final state arrow) of the net. Depending on the type of arrow and on its label, several cases occur.

1. For an arc $q \xrightarrow{b} r$ with terminal label $b \in \Sigma$:

$$Gui(q \xrightarrow{b} r) = \{b\}$$

2. For an arc $q \xrightarrow{A} r$ of machine $M_B$ with nonterminal label $A$:

   a. $Gui(q \xrightarrow{A} r) = Ini\left(L\left(q_{A,0}\right)\, L(r)\right)$, if the concatenation $L(q_{A,0})\, L(r)$ is not nullable;

   b. $Gui(q \xrightarrow{A} r) = Ini\left(L\left(q_{A,0}\right)\, L(r)\right) \cup Fol(B)$, otherwise.

3. For an arrow $q \to$ of a final state $q$ of machine $M_B$:

$$Gui(q \to) = Fol(B)$$

Case 1. is obvious: the first character is the terminal arc label.
In 2.a the move labelled with nonterminal $A$ will be chosen under two conditions. First, if the character is an initial one of the language defined by nonterminal $A$; second, if this language is nullable, and the character is one of the initials of the language recognized starting from state $r$.
Case 2.b is more complex. Since the concatenation of the languages $L(q_{A,0})L(r)$ is nullable, the recognizer may reach a final state of machine $M_B$ without

reading any character. Then the first character to be encountered is any character following nonterminal $B$.
Last, in case 3. the computation on machine $M_B$ can terminate when the current character is in the follow set of $B$.

*Example 4.23.* Cases of guide set definition
To illustrate consider the following grammar and the net in Figure 4.12. State 3 of machine $M_A$ is a bifurcation and, since the concatenation

$$L(6)L(8) = L(6)L(4) = \{\varepsilon, b\}\{\varepsilon, c\}$$

is nullable, the guide sets of the two legs are

$$\begin{aligned} Gui(3 \xrightarrow{B} 4) &= Ini(L(6)L(8)) \cup Fol(A) \\ &= Ini(\{\varepsilon, b, c, bc\}) \cup \{a\} \\ &= \{b, c, a\} \\ Gui(3 \xrightarrow{d} 10) &= \{d\} \end{aligned}$$

$$S \to Aa \qquad A \to BC \mid d \qquad B \to b \mid \varepsilon \qquad C \to c \mid \varepsilon$$

In bifurcation 6 we have

$$\begin{aligned} Gui(6 \to) &= Fol(B) \\ &= \{a, c\} \\ Gui(6 \xrightarrow{b} 7) &= \{b\} \end{aligned}$$

The last bifurcation is 8, where we have

$$\begin{aligned} Gui(8 \to) &= Fol(C) \\ &= Fol(A) \\ &= \{a\} \\ Gui(8 \xrightarrow{c} 9) &= \{c\} \end{aligned}$$

We have determined that in every bifurcation point the guide sets of outgoing arrows are disjoint. This allows us to state that the grammar satisfies condition $LL(1)$.

The preceding result is essentially a sufficient condition for the pushdown machine of algorithm 4.3.3 to be deterministic.

**Definition 4.24.** Condition $LL(1)$
A machine $M_A$ of the net satisfies condition $LL(1)$ in state $q$ if, for every pair of outgoing arrows from state $q$, the guide sets are disjoint.
A rule satisfies condition $LL(1)$ if every state of the corresponding machine meets the condition.

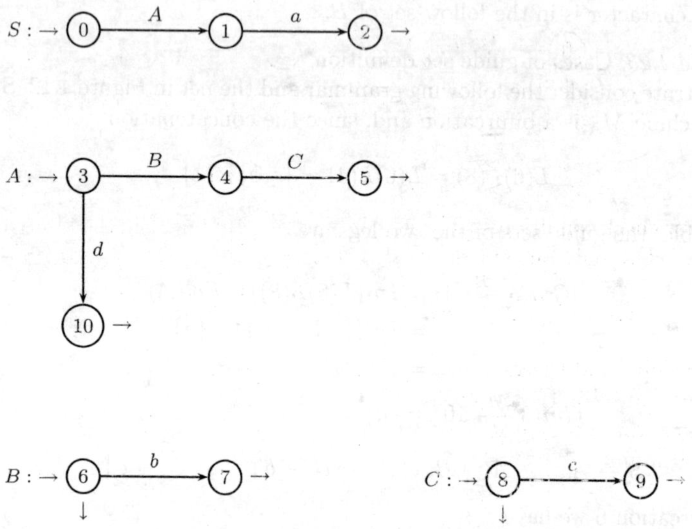


**Fig. 4.12** Net for illustrating guide set definition (example 4.23).

A grammar has property $LL(1)$ if every state of the machine net satisfies the condition.

An obvious remark is that a nondeterministic state always violates the condition because it has two outgoing arcs with the same label. This remark motivates our obligation to use deterministic machines for the construction of $LL(1)$ parsers.[13]
Several examples of computation of guide sets and $LL(1)$ condition checking come next.

*Example 4.25.* Grammars and condition $LL(1)$

1. The grammar

$$G_1: \qquad S \to aSb \mid \varepsilon$$

generates the language $\{a^n b^n \mid n \geqslant 0\}$. On the equivalent deterministic machine

[13] In Chapter 5 this assumption is not needed for bottom-up parsers.

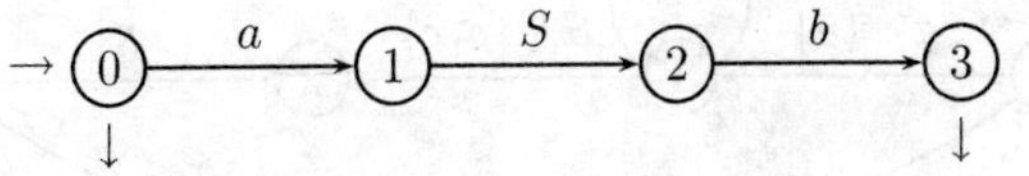


we now check condition $LL(1)$: we compute the guide sets in the bifurcation nodes. Here only one exists, state 0. The sets

$$Gui(0 \xrightarrow{a} 1) = \{a\}, \qquad Gui(0 \rightarrow) = Fol(S) = \{b, \dashv\}$$

are disjoint and the grammar is $LL(1)$.
Notice the second set contains $b$ because $S$ in state 2 is followed by $b$; it contains the terminator because $S$ is the axiom.

2. The grammar

$$G_2 : \qquad S \rightarrow aSb \mid aSc \mid \varepsilon$$

generates language $\{a^n(b \mid c)^n \mid n \geqslant 0\}$. The machine is $LL(1)$ because in bifurcations 0 and 2 the lookahead sets of outgoing arrows, enclosed between braces, are disjoint.

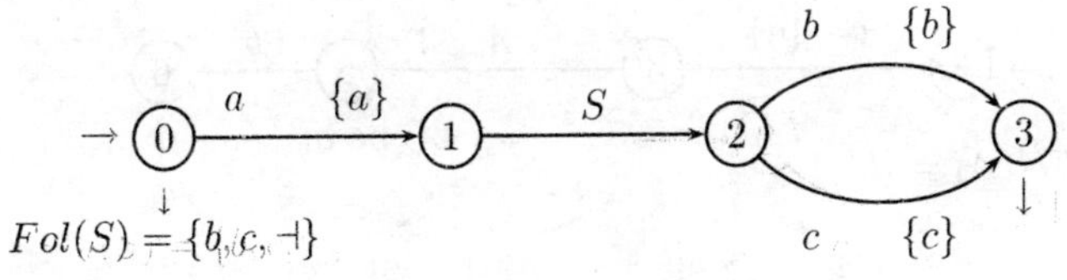


3. The grammar (ambiguous)

$$G_3 : \qquad S \rightarrow a^+Sb \mid c$$

generates the language $\{a^*a^ncb^n \mid n \geqslant 0\}$. The machine graph contains a circuit (self-loop) corresponding to the cross operation of the r.e.

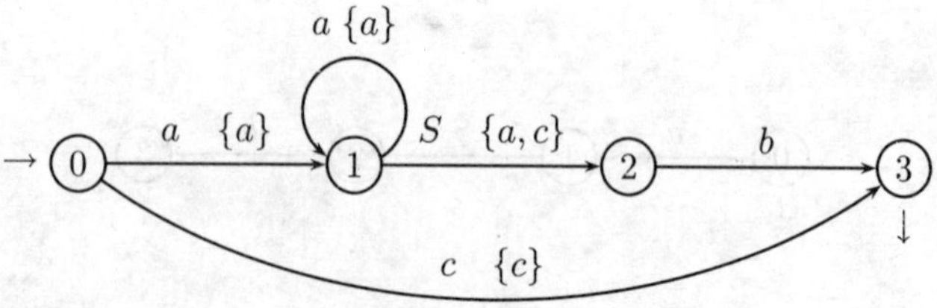


State 1 violates condition $LL(1)$ because $Ini(S) = \{a, c\}$ contains $a$. On the other hand, at bifurcation 0 the condition is satisfied.

4. The grammar

$$G_4: \qquad S \to Ab^+ \qquad A \to aAb \mid \varepsilon$$

generates language $\{a^n b^n b^+ \mid n \geqslant 0\}$.

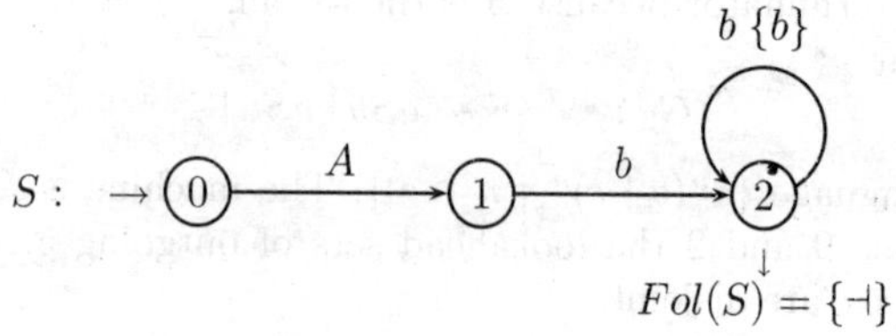


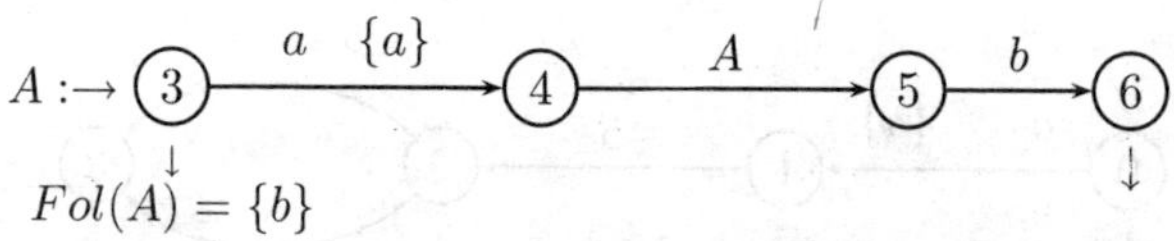


Both machines satisfy the condition at bifurcations 2 and 3.

5. The grammar of the lists of palindromes (example 4.20 on p. 177) reproduced in Figure 4.13 is not $LL(1)$ in state 3, where the final arrow has the set

$$Gui(3 \to) = Fol(P) = \{,\} \cup Fol(S) \cup \{a\} \cup \{b\} = \{, \dashv a\, b\}$$

computed combining the three occurrences of $P$ in the net. The set overlaps the set

$$Gui(3 \xrightarrow{P} 4) = Ini(L_P(G)) = Ini(2) = \{a, b\}$$

The same conflict is found in state 6.
On the other hand, bifurcation 1 of the first machine satisfies the condition, because the comma is not in the set $Gui(1 \to) = Fol(S) = \{\dashv\}$.

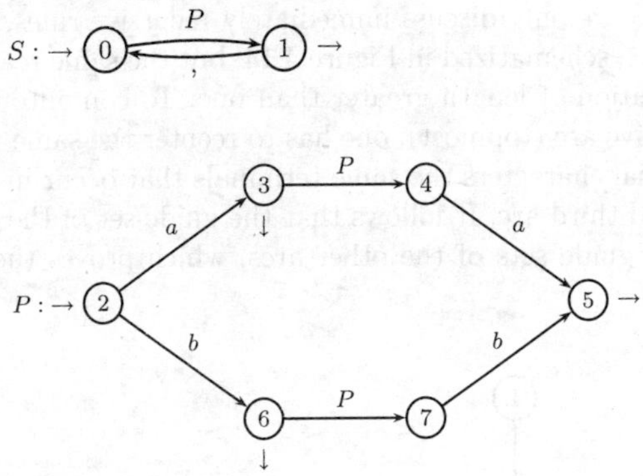


**Fig. 4.13** Machine net of the language of lists of palindromes (example 4.25), with guide sets in braces.

## Simplified Computation of Guide Sets

The computation of guide sets is simpler when the grammar is not extended with regular expressions, and then it is better done on grammar rules rather than on the machine net. The definitions will be restated for this simpler case.

Let $A \to \alpha$ be a rule of grammar $G$, with axiom $S$.

$$\begin{cases} Gui(A \to \alpha) = Ini(\alpha), & \text{if } \alpha \text{ is not nullable;} \\ Gui(A \to \alpha) = Ini(\alpha) \cup Fol(A), & \text{otherwise.} \end{cases}$$

The terms occurring in the definition are redefined on grammar rules:

$$Ini(\alpha) = \{a \in \Sigma \mid \alpha \overset{*}{\Rightarrow} ay \wedge y \in \Sigma^*\}$$
$$Fol(A) = \{a \in \Sigma \cup \{\dashv\} \mid S \dashv \overset{*}{\Rightarrow} yAaz \wedge y, z \in \Sigma^*\}$$

In words, condition $LL(1)$ imposes that the guide sets be disjoint for every pair of alternative rules $A \to \alpha$, $A \to \alpha'$ of the grammar.

## Left Recursion

The next property, an immediate consequence of the definitions, excludes from $LL(1)$ analysis any grammar with left-recursive derivations.

*Property 4.26.* A left-recursive rule violates condition $LL(1)$.

*Proof.* For brevity we only discuss immediately recursive rules, such as $A \rightarrow A \ldots \mid a \ldots \mid B \ldots$, schematized in Figure 4.14, but the same reasoning would apply to a derivation of length greater than one. To compute the guide set of the left-recursive arc (topmost), one has to reenter the same machine thus obtaining as initial characters the same terminals that occur in the guide set of the second and third arc. It follows that the guide set of the left-recursive arc contains the guide sets of the other arcs, which proves the violation of condition $LL(1)$.

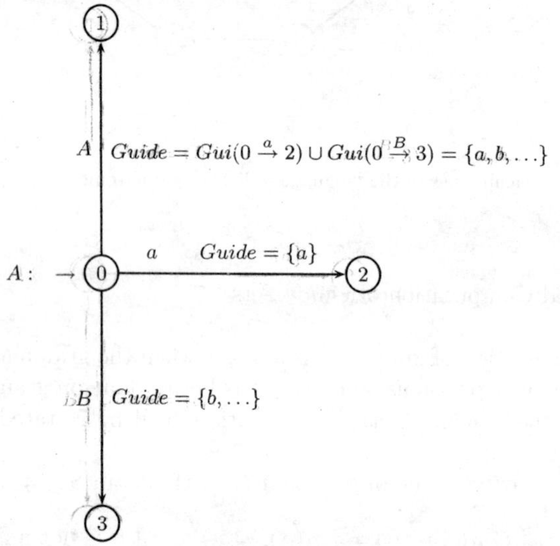


**Fig. 4.14** Illustration of property 4.26: a left-recursive rule infringes condition $LL(1)$.

Actually we have already observed that left-recursion causes a recursive descent algorithm (p. 177) to fall into an endless loop. The practical implication is that every left-recursion present in a grammar must be converted to a right recursion (as explained on p. 63), if one intends to use $LL(1)$ parsing. If the conversion effort is deemed too high, the designer has the option to use the parsing methods of the next chapter.

## $LL(1)$ Recognizer

The point of arrival of the preceding discussions can now be stated.

*Property 4.27.* If a grammar has property $LL(1)$, the recursive descent string recognition algorithm (Figure 4.9 on p. 177) becomes deterministic.

In Figure 4.15 we specialize the algorithm under the $LL(1)$ assumption and we argue that indeterministic choices vanish. At step 5., since the guide sets

*Algorithm.* Recursive descent deterministic recognizer

The pushdown machine:
*begin*

1. source string $x$; current terminal character $cc$;
2. stack symbols are the (disjoint) union $Q = Q_A \cup Q_B \cup \ldots$ of the states of all machines;
3. the pushdown automaton has one state, to be left understood;
4. the stack initially contains the initial state $q_{S,0}$;
5. transitions are next specified; let $s \in Q_A$ be the top symbol, i.e., the state of the active machine $M_A$;

   a. (scanning move)
   if the move $s \xrightarrow{cc} s'$ is defined (for the active machine $M_A$), scan the current character and replace the stack top $s$ with $s'$;
   b. (invocation move)
   if the move $s \xrightarrow{B} s'$ is defined for some nonterminal $B$ and $cc \in Gui(s \xrightarrow{B} s')$, perform the spontaneous move that pushes on stack the initial state $q_{B,0}$ of machine $M_B$, thus making it the active one;
   c. (return move)
   if $s$ is a final state of machine $M_B$ and $cc \in Gui(s \rightarrow)$, pop it then perform from the state $r$ that has surfaced the spontaneous move $r \xrightarrow{B} s'$, that replaces the stack top $r$ with $s'$;
   d. (recognition move)
   if $s$ is a final state of $M_S$ (axiom machine) and $cc = \dashv$, accept and halt;
   e. in any other case reject the string and halt.

*end*

**Fig. 4.15** Deterministic recursive descent algorithm for an $LL(1)$ compliant machine net.

of the arrows outgoing from state $s$ are disjoint due to $LL(1)$ hypothesis, the conditions a), b), c), and d) are mutually exclusive and the choice of the move becomes deterministic.

The time complexity is linear in the string length $n$. In fact, the automaton either reads and consumes an input character or performs a spontaneous move in cases b) and c). But the number of spontaneous moves between any two successive reading moves is bounded from above by a constant, as next argued. A spontaneous move invokes a machine, which in turn may immediately (i.e., without reading a character) invoke another machine, and so on. Since the grammar does not contain left-recursive rules (more generally derivations), the length of the chain of invocations is bounded by the number of nonterminals of the grammar. Therefore the number of spontaneous moves between two reading moves cannot exceed a constant, independent from the source string length, and the complexity of the algorithm is $O(n)$. In particular, the number of steps executed by the algorithm is exactly equal to the length of the string, when the grammar is $LL(1)$ and in Greibach normal form (p. 66), that for this reason is also called in real-time .

## Parser Implementation by Recursive Procedures

An elegant and practical implementation relies on a set of procedures, sometimes called *syntactic*, in one-to-one correspondence with the machines of the net, i.e., with the nonterminal symbols of the grammar. We show an example of this implementation.

*Example 4.28.* Syntactic procedures for lists of palindromes with center
The grammar

$$S \to P(,P)^* \qquad\qquad P \to aPa \mid bPb \mid c$$

and the equivalent machine net (Figure 4.16) have property $LL(1)$ as apparent from the guide sets listed in the drawing. The syntactic procedures

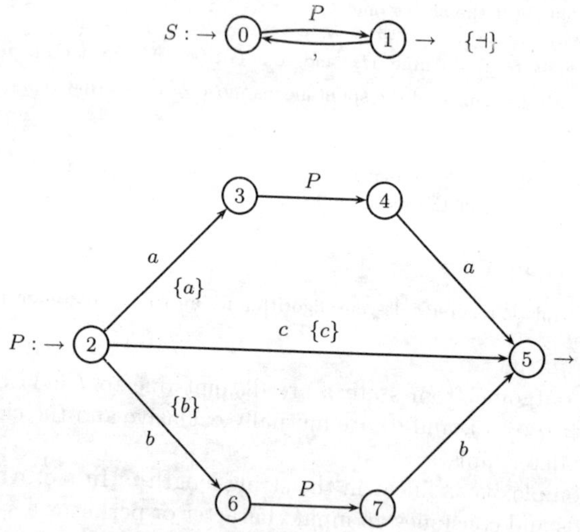


**Fig. 4.16** Machine net for lists of palindromes with center (example 4.28).

corresponding to the nonterminal symbols of the grammar are listed in Figure 4.17. It is interesting to observe that the flowchart of a syntactic procedure is represented (details apart) by the state-transition graph of the corresponding machine. The procedure examines the current character and decides, depending on the guide set it belongs to, which arrow or arc to take in the graph. If the arc label is terminal, the next current character is returned by function Next (which is the main interface of the lexical analyzer or scanner to be

```
procedure S
begin
 1. call P;
 2. if cc='⊣' then accept and halt;
 3. else if cc=',' then cc := Next; go to 1;
 4. else Error;
end

procedure P
begin
 1. if cc='a' then
    begin
    cc:=Next; call P; if cc='a' then
    cc:=Next else Error
    end
 2. else if cc='b' then
    begin
    cc:=Next; call P; if cc='b' then
    cc:=Next else Error
    end
 3. else if cc='c' then
    begin
    cc:=Next
    end
 4. else Error
end
```

**Fig. 4.17** Syntactic procedures of recursive descent parser (example 4.28).

discussed in Chapter 6). If the label is nonterminal, the corresponding procedure is invoked. At last, if the current character is not present in any of the bifurcation guide sets, an error occurs and the source string is rejected. Parsing starts in the axiom procedure $S$, scanning the first character of the string.

For a programmer it should not be difficult to imagine several manners of improving the procedure code of Figure 4.17. For instance, in procedure $S$, the iteration denoted by the star in the r.e. $P(,P)^*$, can be directly coded by means of a *while ... do* loop.

### Error Treatment

In case of an error the above parser terminates without giving explanations, but compiler users expect a parser to provide diagnostic messages. Actually they are straightforward to automatically produce by comparing the characters awaited in the active state (the union of the guide sets of outgoing arrows) with the current character, and writing: "the expected characters are ..., instead of ...".

Another improvement concerns the time an error is detected: clearly early detection simplifies program correction. To anticipate detection, the parser can perform the test on the guide set not just at bifurcation points, but also when there is only one outgoing arc labelled with a nonterminal. If the current character is not present in the guide set, there is an error. Notice that the error would have been detected by the parser, but some steps later.

Last but not least, a production quality parser should perform error recovery, i.e., it should go on parsing after the first error in order to examine the whole source text in a single compilation, thus avoiding the annoyance of recompiling as many times as there are errors.[14]

### 4.4.2 How to Obtain $LL(1)$ Grammars

A majority of grammars from language reference manuals, as such, do not satisfy the condition on guide set disjointedness and need modification. But as a preliminary caution, observe that it would be wasteful to spend time computing the guide set for an ambiguous or left-recursive grammar: both defects should be eliminated (as discussed on p. 49 and p. 63, respectively) before proceeding further. After that, the guide sets are computed and the causes of any violation are examined. To this end, it helps to introduce another more synthetical formulation of condition $LL(1)$. At the same time we take the opportunity to moderately generalize the concept, by considering the look-ahead length as a parameter possibly greater than one (anticipating the discussion on p. 196).

*Property 4.29.* A nonterminal $A$ of the grammar violates the $LL(k)$, $k \geqslant 1$, condition if, and only if, two derivations exists:

$$S \overset{*}{\Rightarrow} uAv \Rightarrow u\alpha v \overset{*}{\Rightarrow} uzv \qquad S \overset{*}{\Rightarrow} uAv \Rightarrow u\alpha' v' \overset{*}{\Rightarrow} uz'v'$$

where $\alpha, \alpha'$ are strings of terminals and nonterminals; the strings $u, v, z, z', v'$ are possibly empty terminal strings complying with the following condition. Let $m = \min(k, |zv|, |z'v'|)$ be the minimum among $k$ and the lengths of strings $zv$ and $z'v'$. Then the prefixes of length $m$ of $zv$ and of $z'v'$ are identical.

The purpose of specifying the minimal length is to rule out the absurdity of having a prefix longer than the string it comes from.

Consider the basic case $k = 1$. To persuade oneself that the formulation is equivalent to the preceding condition 4.24 on p. 183, observe that:

[14] For error treatment in parsers see e.g.,[24].

1. if two such derivations exist, examination of the next $k = 1$ characters, i.e., of the guide sets of the alternative rules $A \to \alpha$ and $A \to \alpha'$, would not be enough for choosing between the two;
2. conversely, if the guide sets, in the state of machine $M_A$ where the bifurcation with legs $\alpha$ and $\alpha'$ occurs, are disjoint, then the two prefixes considered in the statement are different.

### Left Factoring

A basic transformation to remedy $LL(1)$ conflicts, termed *left factoring*, is described by means of an example.

*Example 4.30.* Left factoring
The grammar

$$S \to \langle IT \rangle \mid \langle ITE \rangle$$

$$\langle IT \rangle \to if\ C\ then\ A \qquad \langle ITE \rangle \to if\ C\ then\ A\ else\ A$$

$$C \to \dots \qquad A \to \dots$$

abstractly represents the conditional instructions with or without the *else* leg; the nonterminals $C$ and $A$, left to be defined, denote a boolean condition and an assignment statement.
We apply condition 4.29 to the derivations

$$S \Rightarrow \underbrace{\langle IT \rangle}_{A} \Rightarrow \underbrace{if\ C\ then\ A}_{\alpha} \stackrel{+}{\Rightarrow} \underbrace{if\ x \geqslant 3\ then\ x = 5}_{z}$$

$$S \Rightarrow \underbrace{\langle ITE \rangle}_{A} \Rightarrow \underbrace{if\ C\ then\ A\ else\ A}_{\alpha'} \stackrel{+}{\Rightarrow} \underbrace{if\ x \geqslant 3\ then\ x = 5\ else\ x = 7}_{z'}$$

Since the prefixes of length 1 (i.e., the initials) of the strings $z$ and $z'$ are identical to $if$, nonterminal $S$ violates condition $LL(1)$. The same conclusion is obtained computing the guide sets of the first machine of the net in Figure 4.18. Clearly the guide sets of the arcs leaving 0 coincide.
Notice that increasing the look-ahead length would not help, because the prefixes of $z$ and of $z'$ remain identical:

$$if\ x, \quad if\ x \geqslant, \quad if\ x \geqslant 3, \quad \text{etc.}$$

To differentiate the prefixes of the example, the parameter should take the value $k = 11$. But such unpractically large value would not suffice for other sentences. It should be evident that, for any fixed value of $k$, we can find a string (a boolean condition) deriving from $C$ and a string (an assignment) deriving from $A$, such that the prefixes of length $k$ are identical. The implication is that, with this grammar, it is impossible to construct a deterministic top-down parser, no matter how large the look-ahead parameter is.

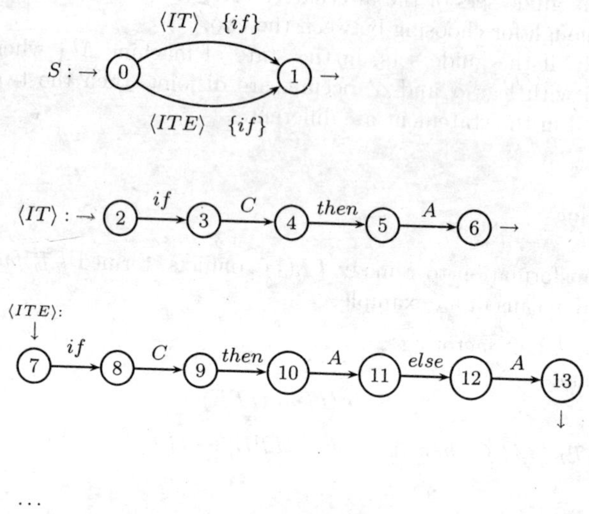


**Fig. 4.18** Machine net of conditional instructions before left factoring (example 4.30).

The cause of the conflict is quite simple: the one-leg conditional is a prefix of the two-legs conditional. The remedy is to defer the choice between the two conditional constructs to the moment when the presence or absence of *else* manifests the right decision. A simple change to the grammar implements the idea, shown in the machine net of Figure 4.19 and in the grammar

$$S \to \langle IT \rangle (\varepsilon \mid \textit{else } A) \qquad\qquad \langle IT \rangle \to \textit{if } C \textit{ then } A$$

Now the only bifurcation is in state 1 where the guide sets are disjoint.

Left factoring transformations often succeed in curing a non-$LL(1)$ grammar, by exposing the longest common prefix of the languages starting from the bifurcating arcs. In essence, the machine graph is modified in order to assign just one path to the common prefixes. The common path is upstream of the node where the two derivations start differentiating. The final effect is then to displace downstream the original bifurcation, i.e., to defer the choice. One may notice a conceptual similarity with the powerset construction for making a finite machine deterministic.

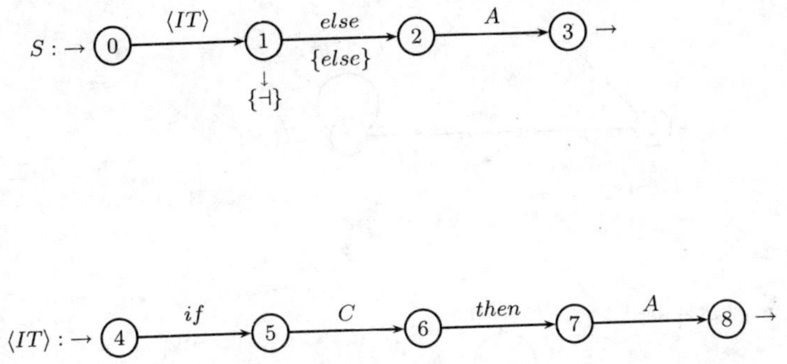


**Fig. 4.19** Machine net of conditional instructions after left factoring (example 4.30).

## Other Transformations

Other cases of infringement of condition $LL(1)$ exist such as the next one, to be remedied by a different transformation.

*Example 4.31.* Extracting a construct from a recursion
The language $\{a^n b^* b^n \mid n \geqslant 0\}$ is defined by the grammar

$$S \rightarrow aSb \mid b^*$$

The machine net is in Figure 4.20 (top). In the original net the guide sets of bifurcations overlap in both states 0 and 4. Moving the term $b^*$ out of the recursion, we obtain the equivalent $LL(1)$ grammar

$$S \rightarrow Ab^* \qquad A \rightarrow aAb \mid \varepsilon$$

also depicted in the bottom net.

We finish with a very particular case. If the given non-$LL(1)$ grammar generates a regular language, another radical method always permits to obtain an equivalent suitable grammar. It suffices to construct the finite deterministic automaton that recognizes the language: its graph contains terminal labels only and, by the very definition of determinism, satisfies condition $LL(1)$ (more of that on p. 241, property 5.32).

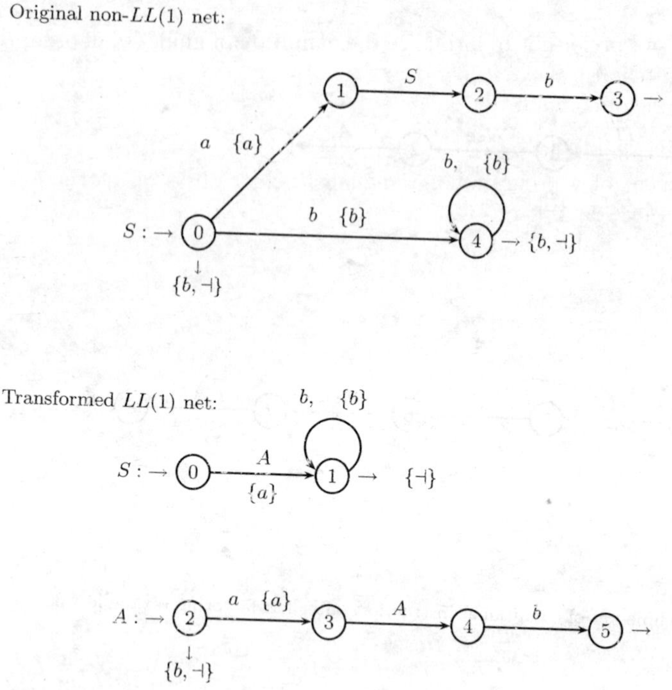


**Fig. 4.20** Example 4.31. Adjusting a grammar (top) to $LL(1)$ condition by extracting a construct from a recursion (bottom).

### 4.4.3 Increasing Look-ahead

A pragmatic approach for obtaining a deterministic top-down parser when the grammar does not comply with condition $LL(1)$ is to look ahead of the current character to examine the following ones. This often allows to make a deterministic choice between alternatives and has the advantage of not requiring annoying modifications of the original grammar.

The algorithm has to be slightly modified, in order to examine in a bifurcation state the input characters $k > 1$ positions ahead of the current one before deciding the move. If such test succeeds in reducing the choice to one, we say the state satisfies condition $LL(k)$.

A grammar has the $LL(k)$ property if there exists an integer $k \geqslant 1$ such that, for every machine of the net and for every state, at most one choice between outgoing arrows is compatible with the characters that may occur at a look-ahead distance $\leqslant k$.

For brevity we prefer not to formalize the definition of guide set of order $k$ since it is a quite natural extension of the basic case, and we directly proceed with an example of computation of look-ahead sets of length $k = 2$.

*Example 4.32.* Conflict between instruction labels and variable names
A small fragment of a programming language includes lists of instructions (assignments, *for* statements, *if* statements, etc.) with or without a label. Both labels and variable names are *identifiers*. The EBNF grammar is:

$$
\begin{aligned}
\text{progr} &\rightarrow [\text{label} :]\text{stat}(; \text{stat})^* \\
\text{stat} &\rightarrow \text{assign\_stat} \mid \text{for\_stat} \mid \ldots \\
\text{assign\_stat} &\rightarrow \text{id} = \text{expr} \\
\text{for\_stat} &\rightarrow \textit{for}\ \text{id}\ \ldots \\
\text{label} &\rightarrow \text{id} \\
\text{expr} &\rightarrow \ldots
\end{aligned}
$$

The machines are depicted in Figure 4.21 with the relevant guide sets of length 1 and 2, the latter framed. Clearly state 0 is not $LL(1)$, since the guide sets (between not framed braces) contain the terminal character id. Refining the analysis, we observe that if the identifier is an instruction label, it is followed by a colon. On the other hand, in the case of arc stat, the identifier is the left part of an assignment statement, and is followed by an equal sign.[15] We have thus ascertained that inspecting the second next character suffices to determine the choice of the move in state 0, which therefore satisfies condition $LL(2)$. In the graph the arrows leaving state 0 are decorated with the guide sets of length two (framed). Such pre-computed sets will be used at run-time by the parser. Notice that in state 3 length $k = 1$ suffices to make the choice: it would be wasteful to use everywhere in the parser the maximal look-ahead length.

Formally the elements of an $LL(k)$ guide set are strings of length up to $k$.[16] In practice parsers use different look-ahead lengths with an obvious criterion of economy: in each bifurcation state, the minimum length $m \leqslant k$ needed to arbitrate the choice of the legs should be used.

More powerful though computationally less efficient, top-down deterministic parsers have been designed,[17] which use a variable and unbounded look-ahead length in different states. Other parsers, if the choice in a bifurcation remains uncertain, take into consideration other cues. One possibility is to

---

[15] In the cases of *for* and *if* statements, for simplicity we assume that the lexemes *for* and *if* are reserved key-words, which may not be used as variable or label identifier.

[16] They may be shorter than $k$ only when they end with terminator $\dashv$.

[17] A well-known example is ANTLR [42].

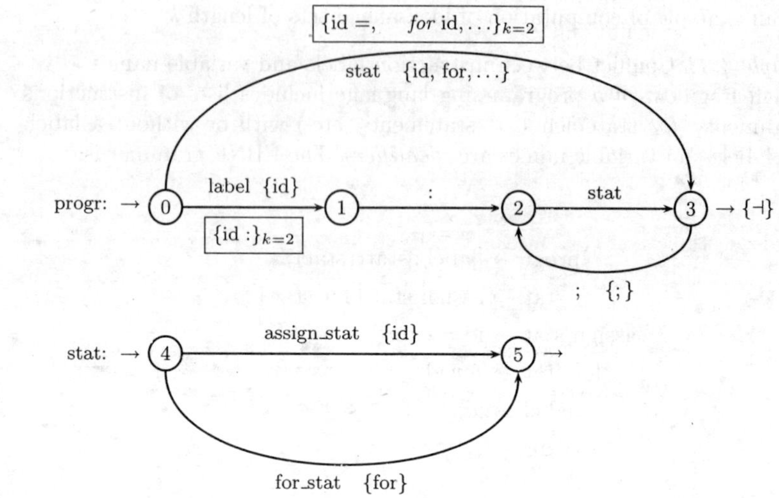


**Fig. 4.21** Machine net of example 4.32. Guide sets are between braces and are framed for $k = 2$.

compute some semantic condition, an idea to be worked out in the last chapter.
Such approaches are often preferred by compiler designers, because they eliminate the problem of managing different versions of the grammar, one for reference, the other for driving the parser.

## Family $LL(k)$ and Its Limits

The $LL(k)$ *family* contains the languages that can be generated by an $LL(k)$ grammar, for some finite integer $k \geqslant 1$. We have chiefly studied the basic case $LL(1)$ and occasionally moved to $LL(2)$, when for a given grammar condition $LL(1)$ was insufficient for designing a deterministic parser. It should be clear that, for any value of $k \geqslant 2$, if a grammar satisfies the $LL(k-1)$ condition, it also satisfies the $LL(k)$ condition. On the other hand, one could find, for any integer $k \geqslant 2$, a grammar satisfying the condition for $k$ but not for $k-1$ (an example for $k = 2$ is the grammar in Figure 4.21).

The question then comes to mind: if we have a grammar which satisfies the $LL(k)$ condition for some $k \geqslant 2$, is it possible to construct an equivalent grammar that satisfies the $LL(k-1)$ condition? In other words, can we define the same language with a grammar that would produce a deterministic top-down parser with shorter look-ahead? Clearly this would be a desirable technical simplification. But a theoretical result says that in general this is not possible.

*Property 4.33.* For any value $k \geqslant 2$ there exist languages that can be defined by an $LL(k)$, but not by an $LL(k-1)$ grammar.

The statement says that one can find formal languages such that they need a look-ahead of any arbitrary length. We do not spend time on it,[18] because it has little relevance for practical technical languages, where, if a finite value of $k$ suffices, it is typically very small.

We briefly discuss the relation of this language family to the others. A serious limitation is that not all deterministic languages can be generated by an $LL(k)$ grammar, no matter how large a parameter we take.

*Property 4.34.* The language family $LL(k)$ is strictly included in the family $DET$ of deterministic languages.

A simple example follows.

*Example 4.35.* A deterministic but not $LL(k)$ language
It is straightforward to construct a deterministic pushdown automaton for the language

$$L_1 = \{a^* a^n b^n \mid n \geqslant 0\}$$

The automaton pushes symbol $A$ on the stack upon reading character $a$; upon reading the first $b$, the automaton changes state and pops a symbol ($A$); then, for any subsequent character $b$, it pops a symbol; it recognizes the string if at the end the stack contains zero or more symbols. Notice that the stack is used as a unary counter. A grammar of the language is $G_1$:

$$S \to a^* A \qquad\qquad A \to aAb \mid \varepsilon$$

[18] For a deeper presentation of the $LL(k)$ family see [51].

The machines with relevant guide sets are shown in Figure 4.22. The $k = 1$ guide sets in state 0 overlap. Stepping up to $k = 2$ does not help because the

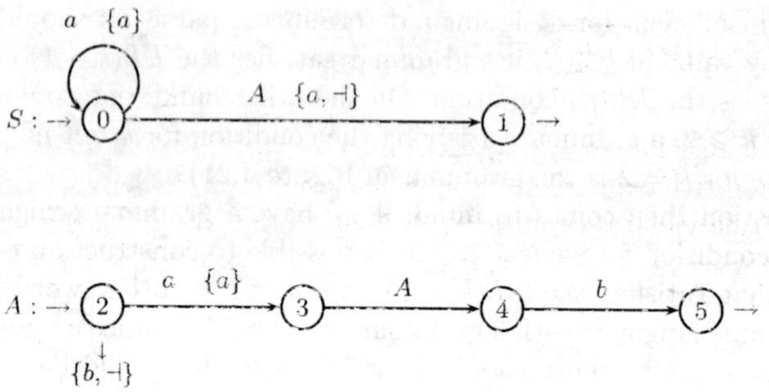


**Fig. 4.22** Machine net of example 4.35.

guide sets below still share string $aa$:

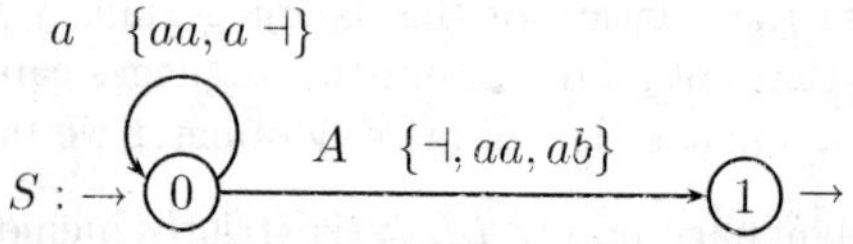


In general, for arbitrary large $k$ we find that both arcs leaving state 0 are compatible with the look-ahead string $a^k$. It follows that grammar $G_1$ does not have property $LL(k)$ for any finite value of parameter $k$.

A natural question is: can we find an equivalent $LL(k)$ grammar for this language? The answer is negative.[19]

This simple example has shown a weakness of the $LL(k)$ language family. The next case teaches us that sometimes the design decision to operate with $LL(k)$ grammars imposes caution in the choice of the terminal symbols of the language, in order to make guide sets disjoint.

*Example 4.36.* Relations and expressions
The grammar $G$:

$$S \to R \mid (S) \qquad R \to E = E \qquad E \to a \mid (E + E)$$

[19] The proof is based on the pumping lemma of $LL(k)$ languages [6].

defines certain equality relations between additive arithmetic expressions, such as

$$\overbrace{\overbrace{(\overbrace{a=a}^{R})}^{S}}^{S} \qquad \overbrace{\overbrace{\overbrace{(\overbrace{(a+a)}^{E}+a)}^{E}=a}^{R}}^{S}$$

Notice that a relation, say $a = a$, may be parenthesized as $(a = a)$, but a nonatomic additive expression must be enclosed between parentheses.

The first rule violates condition $LL(1)$ as seen in the following machine:

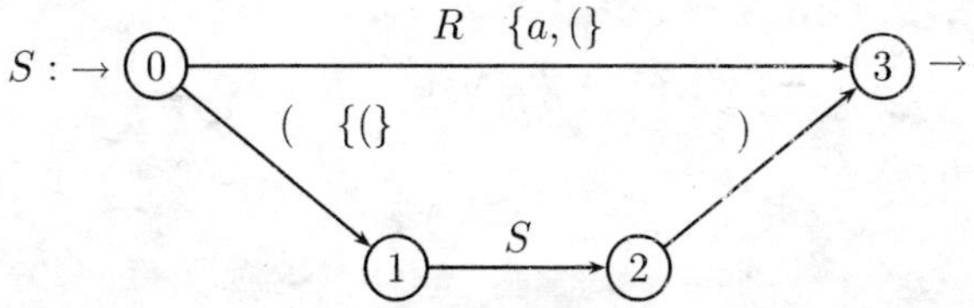


In fact, a string starting with character '(' can be a parenthesized relation $R$ or an expression $E$.

The same reasoning proves that no finite value $k$ exists, such that grammar $G$ is $LL(k)$. This is because one can always find two strings, similar to the preceding ones, such that: both start with $k+1$ open parentheses, the first string is derived with rule $S \to R$, and the second string is generated with rule $S \to (S)$. Since, no matter how the grammar is written, it must present a choice between the two structures of relations and expressions, one could prove that this language is not in the $LL(k)$ family. On the other hand, the language $L(G)$ is deterministic, as the reader may check after studying the next chapter.

The only option left to the designer stubbornly wanting to use the $LL(1)$ approach, is to modify the language. A possibility is to differentiate the parentheses, using, say, brackets for relations and parentheses for arithmetic expressions.

The last two examples should not lead the reader into believing that $LL(k)$ grammars have poor usability. On the contrary, they are widely adopted in compilers on a par with the bottom-up parsers to be studied in next chapter. A discussion of their relative merits is postponed to that moment.

Chapter 5
# Bottom-Up and General Parsing

## 5.1 Introduction

This chapter continues the description of practical parsing algorithms, adding to the previous top-down methods two other interesting approaches, which altogether cover current design practice. The first and primary objective is to present the deterministic bottom-up algorithms, also called shift-reduce, generally applied for automatically implementing parsers starting from a grammar. The formal condition allowing such parser to work is called $LR(k)$. Several variants will be introduced, including historical ones used in popular parser construction tools and a version suitable for grammars extended with regular expressions. We will see that the language family accepted by $LR(k)$ parsers is exactly the family $DET$ of deterministic context-free languages.

The second and last approach to parser construction is no longer based on a pushdown automaton but uses a more flexible data structure for efficiently representing different attempts at constructing a derivation. The algorithm, termed after Earley, is thus able to parse any context-free language including nondeterministic and ambiguous cases. Such generality is needed when the source language has a rather free syntax, and cannot be constrained to be deterministic. Its cost is a slower than linear time algorithm. The chapter ends with a discussion of choice criteria for parsers.

## 5.2 Bottom-Up Deterministic Syntax Analysis

In order to motivate the new approach it is convenient to resume from the discussion of the shortcomings of $LL(k)$ methods. The grammar is represented by a network of finite machines as on p. 172. We recall an $LL(1)$ parser becomes indeterministic, if from a machine state two arrows originate such that the guide sets overlap. Since every machine is deterministic by hypothesis, at least one arrow is either a state transition arc, with nonterminal label $A$, or a final state exit. In the former case, when the current character is in both guide sets (p. 182), the parser is uncertain what to do: to invoke machine $A$ or to perform the other move. In such uncertain situation, it is wise to defer the choice, and proceed with parsing, keeping all options open, until the moment when sufficient evidence will be available for a decision. However, this tactic requires that, in the time interval between the first sight of uncertainty and its resolution, the algorithm preserve the intermediate information that may be needed to make the final decision.

This is the idea underlying the shift-reduce deterministic syntax analyzers, known as $LR(k)$[1] (as well as the general Earley analyzer). Such parser is modelled by a deterministic pushdown automaton endowed with a set of states and scanning the input up to $k$ characters ahead of the current one. Unlike top-down parsers, now it makes sense to set $k$ to zero, because in the simplest cases the choice of the move is solely determined by the current state of the automaton. For graduality, we start from this case and we consider grammar rules without regular expressions.

### *5.2.1 LR(0) Method*

It is convenient to introduce the method with a grammar that is not acceptable for $LL(1)$ parsing.

*Example 5.1.* Introduction to $LR(0)$
A not empty list of constructs $a^n b^n, n \geqslant 1$, is defined by the grammar

$$S \to SA \mid A \qquad\qquad A \to aAb \mid ab$$

represented as a machine net in Figure 5.1. We assume the strings end with the terminator character $\dashv$. Notice that in drawing the graphs we have deliberately kept separate the final states corresponding to alternative rules (a precaution that was not needed in the $LL(k)$ approach).
Condition $LL(k)$ fails in state 0 since both $S$ and $A$ have $a$ as initial because the grammar is left-recursive.
We introduce now the operation of the deterministic pushdown automaton constructed with the $LR(0)$ approach. Initially the automaton is in a state $I_0 = \{0, 4\}$, to be called a *macro-state*, expressing uncertainty between the initial state 0 (of the axiom machine) and state 4; the latter is the initial state of machine $M_A$ (for brevity denoted as $A$), which can be invoked from 0. We can imagine at this moment there are two active copies of a deterministic pushdown automaton: automaton $S$ and automaton $A$, that proceed synchronously. There is some similarity with the behavior of a cartesian product

[1] The acronym, coined by Donald Knuth, has "L" for left-to-right scanning, "R" because the derivation is rightmost, and the parameter $k \geqslant 0$ is the look-ahead length.

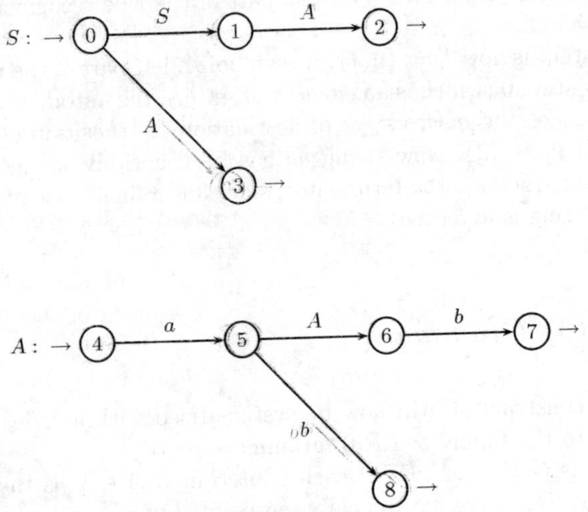


**Fig. 5.1** Machine net of example 5.1.

machine simulating two machines at once. But now the combined machine must also update the pushdown stacks. Clearly it would be impossible to simulate two pushdown automata with one machine of the same type, if the two stacks grow and shrink in totally unrelated ways. Here comes the neat central idea of the $LR(k)$ approach: to simulate with one stack all currently active pushdown machines, but only until one of them performs a pop operation. At that moment a test must be available for arbitrating one out of the active computations and discarding the rest.

The initial stack symbol is $I_0$. To illustrate, take string $ab$. Reading and consuming $a$, the parser moves from macro-state $I_0 = \{0, 4\}$ to the next macro-state $I_2$, performing a a *shift* move. To compute the next macro-state, we take the union of the next states of 0 and 4

$$\delta(0, a) \cup \delta(4, a) = \emptyset \cup \{5\} = \{5\}$$

But since in 5 we can invoke $A$, we add initial state 4, obtaining macro-state $I_2 = \{4,5\}$.
The shift move pushes $I_2$ over $I_0$ in the stack, and terminates.
The next character is $b$, and among the states belonging to macro-state $I_2$, just state 5 can read $b$, and then shift to 8; the automaton pushes macro-state $I_3 = \{8\}$.

Now 8 is a final state of machine $A$, and the time has come to choose the grammar rule to apply, $A \to ab$, thus reducing the string $ab$ to nonterminal $A$. The operation, called a *reduction*, pops $I_2\, I_3$, i.e., a number of symbols equal to the length $|ab| = 2$ of the right part of the rule recognized in state 8.

The stack content is now $I_0 = \{0, 4\}$. As symbol $A$, left part of the rule, labels an arc leaving state 0 (which is an element of set $I_0$), the automaton performs a shift and pushes the macro-state of destination of transition $\delta(0, A) = 3$, to be denoted $I_4 = \{3\}$. Now string $ab$ has been entirely scanned i.e., the current input character is the terminator; since 3 is a final state of the axiom machine the string is accepted.

### 5.2.2 *LR*(0) *Grammars*

The previous construction will now be systematized with a series of definitions, leading to the family of $LR(0)$ grammars.

The grammar is $G = (V, \Sigma, P, S)$; each nonterminal $A \in V$ is the left part of one or more alternatives, graphically represented in a machine named $M_A$ (or simply $A$). We uphold the hypothesis that the machines are deterministic, although this is not strictly necessary. The initial state of machine $A$ is $q_{A,0}$ and the final state set is $F_A$. More precisely the final state associated with alternative $A \to \alpha$ is $q_{A,\alpha}$. Thus we have the transition $\delta(q_{A,0}, \alpha) = q_{A,\alpha}$. Moreover, we stipulate that each alternative $A \to \beta$ has a separate final state, $q_{A,\beta} \in F_A$; this provision will enable the parser to select the alternative within the set of reduction moves.

To make presentation simpler, we add to the grammar the starting rule $S_0 \to S \dashv$, which says every sentence is terminated by the terminator. Symbol $S_0$ is now the axiom and $S$ becomes a plain nonterminal. In the grammar thus modified a sentence cannot be a prefix of another one, a property making the test for reduction more direct.

The initial and final states of the axiom machine are respectively $q_{ini(tial)}$ and $q_{term(inal)}$.

The next function computes the states reachable from another state through a chain of zero or more machine invocations (spontaneous moves).

**Definition 5.2.** $LR(0)$ closure function

Let $q \in Q$ be a state of some machine. The *closure* of $q$ is:

$C := \{q\}$;
*repeat*
$C := C \cup \{q_{A,0} \mid \text{for some } p \in C \text{ and } A \in V, \exists \text{ an arc } ⓟ \xrightarrow{A} ◯$;
*until* no new state is added to $C$;
$closure(q) := C$

For a set $R \subseteq Q$ of states, the closure is

$$closure(R) := \bigcup_{r \in R} closure(r)$$

This function is instrumental for building an abstract finite machine, to be later used as control unit of the bottom-up parser.

**Definition 5.3.** *Pilot machine* for $LR(0)$ analysis.
We define a new deterministic finite automaton

$$N = (R, \Sigma \cup V, \vartheta, I_0, R)$$

that will act as control unit of the parser. To prevent terminological confusion, we reserve the term *machine* for the network machines, the term *automaton* for the pushdown parser, and we refer to the new finite machine as the *pilot* (or *driver*).
The set of states of the pilot, to be termed *macro-states*, is

$$R \subseteq \text{power set of } Q$$

There are no specific final states because the pilot is not used for recognizing strings but as control unit of the pushdown automaton. The alphabet is the union of the terminal and nonterminal sets of the grammar. The macro-states $R = \{I_0, \ldots\}$ and transition function $\vartheta$ (theta, to avoid confusion with the transition function delta of the net machines) are computed, starting from the initial macro-state, with the following procedure:

$I_0 = closure(q_{ini})$;
$R := \{I_0\}$;
*repeat* for all $I_j \in R$ and for all $X \in \Sigma \cup V$
$\vartheta(I_j, X) :=$ closure$(\{r \mid r \in \delta(q, X),$ for some $q \in I_j\})$;
if $\vartheta(I_j, X) \notin R$ then $R := R \cup \vartheta(I_j, X)$;
*until* no new macro-state has been created by current iteration.

Function $\vartheta$ produces a macro-state to be added to the set $R$ (if not present). The function is applied over and over producing new macro-states until nothing new is computed by the last iteration step; then the loop terminates.

A machine state is qualified as *shift* state if in the corresponding machine there is an arrow from the state to another one. A final state of some machine is qualified as *reduction* state.

If a macro-state contains one or more reduction states, the corresponding grammar rules are referred to as the *reductions* associated with the macro-state:

$$reductions(I_j) = \{A \to \alpha \mid q_{A,\alpha} \in I_j\}$$

where $\delta(q_{A,0}, \alpha) = q_{A,\alpha}$. Actually a final state of a machine can be at the same time a shift state: this happens if a labelled arc goes out of it. Combining the above terminology, a macro-state is classified as:

*reduction*: if it uniquely contains reduction states;
*shift*: if it uniquely contains shift states;
*mixed*: if it contains both shift and reduction states.

We can now state the simplest condition for the shift-reduce pushdown automaton to be deterministic.

**Definition 5.4.** $LR(0)$ condition and $LR(0)$ family.
A grammar meets the $LR(0)$ condition if every macro-state of the pilot satisfies both conditions:

1. the macro-state is not mixed;
2. if it is a reduction macro-state, it contains exactly one state.

The $LR(0)$ *family of languages* is the collection of languages that can be generated by grammars satisfying condition $LR(0)$.

Condition 1. forbids a final and a not final state to be in the same macro-state. Condition 2. rules out the presence of two final states in the same macro-state.

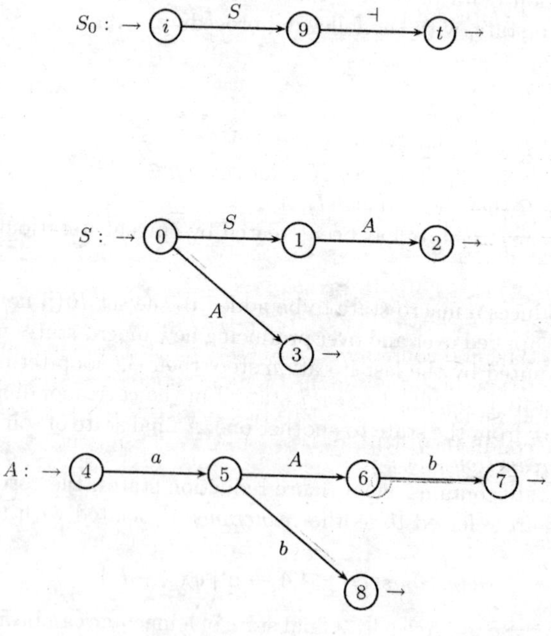


**Fig. 5.2** Machine net of example 5.5.

*Example 5.5.* Pilot construction for grammar of example 5.1
The grammar, with the new axiom $S_0$ added, has rules

$$S_0 \to S \dashv \qquad S \to SA \mid A \qquad A \to aAb \mid ab$$

represented by the net in Figure 5.2. The steps for computing the macro-states and transition function of the pilot are traced in Table 5.1. The state transition graph of the pilot is in Figure 5.3. Macro-states $I_2, I_4, I_5, I_7, I_8$

**Table 5.1** Computing macro-states and transition function of example 5.5, Figure 5.2.

| | *Set of macro-states* | *Macro-state created* | *Move created* |
|---|---|---|---|
| 0 | $\emptyset$ | $closure(i) = \{i, 0, 4\} = I_0$ | |
| 1 | $I_0 = \{i, 0, 4\}$ | $closure(\delta(i, S) \cup \delta(0, S) \cup \delta(4, S)) =$ $closure(\{9, 1\}) = \{9, 1, 4\} = I_1$ | $\vartheta(I_0, S) = I_1$ |
| 2 | $I_0 = \{i, 0, 4\}, I_1$ | $closure(\delta(i, A) \cup \delta(0, A) \cup \delta(4, A)) =$ $closure(3) = \{3\} = I_2$ | $\vartheta(I_0, A) = I_2$ |
| 3 | $I_0 = \{i, 0, 4\}, I_1, I_2$ | $closure(\delta(i, a) \cup \delta(0, a) \cup \delta(4, a)) =$ $closure(5) = \{4, 5\} = I_3$ | $\vartheta(I_0, a) = I_3$ |
| 4 | $I_0, I_1 = \{9, 1, 4\}, I_2, I_3$ | $closure(\delta(9, A) \cup \delta(1, A) \cup \delta(4, A)) =$ $closure(2) = \{2\} = I_4$ | $\vartheta(I_1, A) = I_4$ |
| 5 | $I_0, I_1 = \{9, 1, 4\}, I_2, I_3, I_4$ | $closure(\delta(9, a) \cup \delta(1, a) \cup \delta(4, a)) =$ $closure(5) = \{4, 5\} = I_3$ | $\vartheta(I_1, a) = I_3$ |
| 6 | $I_0, I_1 = \{9, 1, 4\}, I_2, I_3, I_4$ | $closure(\delta(9, \dashv) \cup \delta(1, \dashv) \cup \delta(4, \dashv)) =$ $closure(t) = \{t\} = I_5$ | $\vartheta(I_1, \dashv) = I_5$ |
| 7 | $I_0, I_1, I_2, I_3 = \{4, 5\}, I_4, I_5$ | $closure(\delta(4, A) \cup \delta(5, A)) = closure(6) =$ $\{6\} = I_6$ | $\vartheta(I_3, A) = I_6$ |
| 8 | $I_0, I_1, I_2, I_3 = \{4, 5\}, I_4, I_5, I_6$ | $closure(\delta(4, a) \cup \delta(5, a)) = closure(5) =$ $\{4, 5\} = I_3$ | $\vartheta(I_3, a) = I_3$ |
| 9 | $I_0, I_1, I_2, I_3 = \{4, 5\}, I_4, I_5, I_6$ | $closure(\delta(4, b) \cup \delta(5, b)) = closure(8) =$ $\{8\} = I_7$ | $\vartheta(I_3, b) = I_7$ |
| 10 | $I_0, I_1, I_2, I_3, I_4, I_5, I_6 = \{6\}, I_7$ | $closure(\delta(6, b)) = closure(7) = \{7\} = I_8$ | $\vartheta(I_6, b) = I_8$ |
| 11 | $I_0, I_1, I_2, I_3, I_4, I_5, I_6, I_7, I_8$ | | halt |

are of reduction type and contain one final state each. The remaining macro-states are of shift type because they just contain nonfinal states. No macro-state is mixed and we never find two or more reductions in the same macro-state. Therefore condition $LR(0)$ is satisfied by the grammar.

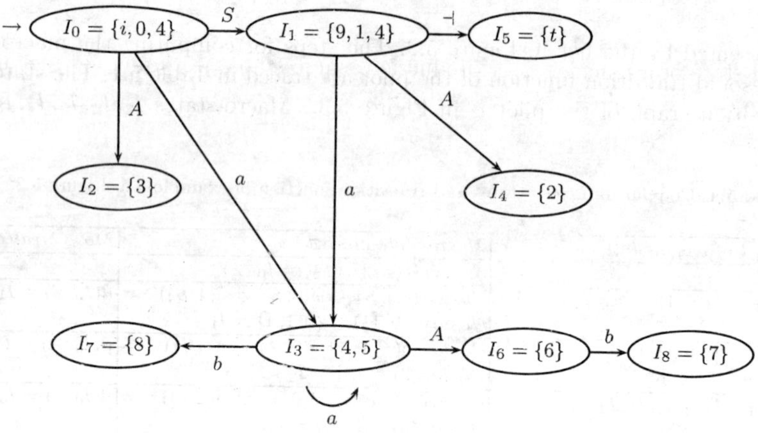


**Fig. 5.3** Pilot of example 5.5, Figure 5.2.

## Properties of Pilot

Observing the graph in Figure 5.3, it is easy to discover the special properties an $LR(0)$ pilot has when viewed as a finite automaton:

1. all the arrows entering a macro-state carry the same label (e.g., see $I_3$);
2. every reduction macro-state has no successor;
3. every shift macro-state has one or more successors.

Since the pilot is an automaton, the question naturally comes: what language does it accept, supposing every macro-state is final. For the example the following strings are recognized:

$$S, A, a, S \dashv, SA, Sa, aA, aa, ab, SaA, Saa, aAb, aaa, aab, aaAb, \ldots$$

Their characteristic is to be a prefix of some string (technically a sentential form, p. 36) produced from the axiom of grammar $G$ by means of a rightmost derivation. For instance, in derivation

$$S_0 \Rightarrow S \dashv \Rightarrow A \dashv \Rightarrow aAb \dashv \Rightarrow aaAbb \dashv \Rightarrow aaabbb \dashv$$

the following prefixes are accepted by the pilot:

$$S, S \dashv, A, A \dashv, a, aA, aAb, aa, aaA, aaAb, aaab$$

On the other hand, some prefixes are not accepted, such as $aaAbb$ and $aaabb$. The explanation of this property comes from the reasoning we have applied in constructing the pilot. Recall that it simultaneously carries on several possible bottom-up parsing attempts until the moment when one of them enters the final state of a machine i.e., a reduction macro-state. More precisely, let us follow in the graph the backwards paths from a reduction macro-state. Let $A \to \beta$ be the (unique) reduction associated with the reduction macro-state $I$; then the pilot graph surely contains a backwards path labelled $\beta^R$, going from node $I$ to a macro-state such that it contains the initial state of machine $A$.

To illustrate, start in macro-state $I_8 = \{7\}$ and make three backwards steps labelled $b, A, a$. There are two backward paths with such labels. One ends in macro-state $I_0$ that contains the initial state 4 of machine $A$; the other ends in macro-state $I_3$ also containing 4.

But why is it that some prefixes of rightmost sentential forms are recognized and others are not? A recognized prefix such as $aaab$ contains as substring the right part of a grammar rule; moreover the substring is in final position, i.e., it is a suffix:

$$aa \underbrace{ab}_{A \to ab}$$

On the other hand, a nonrecognized prefix such as $aaabb$ also contains as substring the right part of the rule, but the substring is internal not a suffix:

$$aa \underbrace{ab}_{A \to ab} b$$

In this case the reduction of $ab$ to nonterminal $A$ should have already taken place during parsing, resulting in the string $aaA$, which indeed is accepted by the pilot.

### *5.2.3 Shift-Reduce Parser*

Given the pilot of a grammar meeting $LR(0)$ condition, it is immediate to obtain a deterministic pushdown automaton that recognizes the strings and produces their syntax tree. The parser uses as stack symbols the pilot macro-states; actually, to ease readability we may also list grammar symbols next to macro-states. Upon reading the current character, with a shift macro-state $I$ on stack top, the automaton performs the move prescribed by the pilot and pushes the new macro-state on stack; the operation is termed a *shift*.
If the type of the macro-state on stack top is a reduction, from condition $LR(0)$ a unique grammar alternative is selected; the automaton then performs

*Algorithm.* Let $G$ be an $LR(0)$ grammar and $N = (R, \Sigma \cup V, \vartheta, I_0, R)$ its pilot.

Stack alphabet: $R \cup \Sigma \cup V$;
Set of states of $A$: irrelevant as it contains just one state;
Initial configuration: the stack contains the initial macro-state $I_0$;
Moves: there are two types, shift and reduce moves. Let $I$ be the macro-state on stack top and $a$ the current character:

*Shift* move: if for pilot macro-state $I$ move $\vartheta(I, a) = I'$ is defined, the automaton reads $a \in \Sigma$, moves ahead the reading head, and pushes string $aI'$ on stack;
*Reduction* move: if macro-state $I$, to be here denoted $I_n$, contains reduction state $q$, with

$$reductions(q) = \{B \rightarrow X_1 X_2 \dots X_n\}$$

where $n \geqslant 0$ is the length of right part, perform the following action.
On stack top there is necessarily (due to the pilot control logic) a string $\beta'$

$$\dots I' \overbrace{X_1 I_1 X_2 I_2 \dots X_n I_n}^{\beta'}$$

containing $n$ macro-states, pushed by preceding moves.
A reduction is a spontaneous move that first pops from stack string $\beta'$ (i.e., $2n$ symbols from top), then pushes string $BI''$, where $I''$ is the macro-state entered by the pilot transition reading (so to speak) nonterminal $B$: $I'' = \vartheta(I', B)$.

Final configuration: stack $= I_0$, input entirely scanned.

**Fig. 5.4** Shift-reduce parser without look-ahead, as pushdown automaton $A$.

a series of actions to simulate a *reduction* occurring in a grammar derivation. First a topmost segment is deleted from stack and then a symbol is pushed. When the source string has been scanned to end, the automaton accepts if the stack is empty (or if it just contains the initial macro-state).

The operations are more precisely specified by the algorithm in Figure 5.4. It goes without saying that the pushdown automaton, reaching a configuration where no move is possible, rejects the string.

The essential property of the algorithm is that, due to $LR(0)$ hypothesis, the macro-state on stack top uniquely determines the move, acceptance, shift, or reduction; in the latter, it also determines the reduction to perform. As a consequence, parser operations are deterministic.

Closer observation reveals that some stacked information is redundant. A shift pushes a terminal $a$ and the macro-state $I'$, but the former is uniquely determined by the latter, because in the pilot all arcs entering a macro-state have the same label. The only reason for storing the terminal is to ease reading the step by step parsing simulations.

A more subtle question concerns the states of the pushdown automaton. Is indeed correct our previous statement that the automaton does not use states? Not quite: a reduction is more complex than the standard elementary operations permitted to pushdown machines. But a reduction can be decomposed into a series of elementary machine operations, provided we use a finite memory to count how many symbols should be removed from the stack, and to remember the name of the nonterminal $B$ of the left part of reduction rule. Indeed, $LR(0)$ pushdown automata use some hidden states inside reduction moves. Moreover, when we shall introduce general $LR(k), k \geqslant 1$, parsers, another use of states will occur: to store $k$ incoming look-ahead characters (exactly as in $LL(k)$ parsers).

To conclude the discussion, all the models of deterministic parsers use some finite memory, i.e., some states, in addition to the unlimited stack, although our presentation tries to hide the existence of states in order to avoid low-level details. The contrary would be absurd, because we know the $DET$ family (p. 161) is characterized by having as recognizer a deterministic pushdown automaton making use of states.

### Reflected Right Derivation

The actual operation of such pushdown automaton is illustrated in Table 5.2 in order to show the sequence of reductions and the corresponding order of construction of the syntax tree through a reverse rightmost derivation.

*Example 5.6.* Trace of parsing steps (example 5.5)
The syntax tree in Figure 5.5 has been constructed by a series of reduction moves in the order of framed numbers. The following rules are applied:

$$A \to ab,\ A \to aAb,\ S \to A,\ A \to ab,\ S \to SA,\ S_0 \to S \dashv$$

They correspond to the sequence of reductions:

**Table 5.2** Trace of parsing for string $aabbab$ (example 5.5).

| *Stack* | $x$ | *Comment* |
|---|---|---|
| $I_0$ | $a\ a\ b\ b\ a\ b\ \dashv$ | shift |
| $I_0\ aI_3$ | $a\ b\ b\ a\ b\ \dashv$ | shift |
| $I_0\ aI_3\ aI_3$ | $b\ b\ a\ b\ \dashv$ | shift |
| $I_0\ aI_3\ aI_3\ bI_7$ | $b\ a\ b\ \dashv$ | reduce with $A \to ab$ |
| $I_0\ aI_3\ AI_6$ | $b\ a\ b\ \dashv$ | shift |
| $I_0\ aI_3\ AI_6\ bI_8$ | $a\ b\ \dashv$ | reduce with $A \to aAb$ |
| $I_0\ AI_2$ | $a\ b\ \dashv$ | reduce with $S \to A$ |
| $I_0\ SI_1$ | $a\ b\ \dashv$ | shift |
| $I_0\ SI_1\ aI_3$ | $b\ \dashv$ | shift |
| $I_0\ SI_1\ aI_3\ bI_7$ | $\dashv$ | reduce with $A \to ab$ |
| $I_0\ SI_1\ AI_4$ | $\dashv$ | reduce with $S \to SA$ |
| $I_0\ SI_1$ | $\dashv$ | shift |
| $I_0\ SI_1\ \dashv I_5$ | | reduce with $S_0 \to S \dashv$ |
| $I_0$ | | accept |

$$aabbab \dashv \Rightarrow aAbab \dashv \Rightarrow Aab \dashv \Rightarrow Sab \dashv \Rightarrow SA \dashv \Rightarrow S \dashv \Rightarrow S_0$$

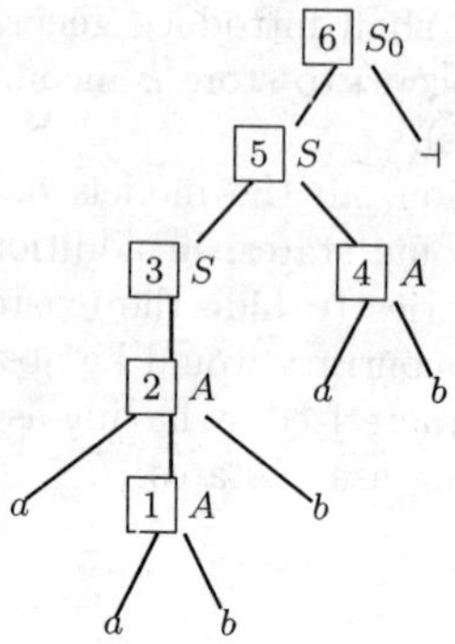


**Fig. 5.5** Syntax tree with order of reductions (example 5.5).

The construction order of tree nodes justifies the name bottom-up of this parsing method. Looking now at the reduction sequence and specularly reversing it, we obtain sequence 654321. The corresponding derivation $S_0 \overset{+}{\Rightarrow} aabbab \dashv$ is rightmost, as already noticed on p. 170.

## *5.2.4 Syntax Analysis with LR(k) Look-Ahead*

The next refinement yields the most general and efficient deterministic parser by combining two successful devices: the use of look-ahead and the deferment tactic of shift-reduce $LR(0)$ parsers. Starting from the limitations of $LR(0)$ analysis, we proceed with the introduction of look-ahead for the $LR(k)$ pilot and we set parameter $k$ to one. The choice of value one is not an oversimplification for the sake of the reader, because, unlike the case of top-down parsers, the family of $LR(1)$ grammars and languages exactly match the family of deterministic languages.

### Limitations of $LR(0)$ Languages

In the real world it seldom happens that an $LR(0)$ parser can be used because very few technical languages meet the condition. A serious weakness of $LR(0)$ languages can be formulated as a property of prefixes. Consider the strings generated by a nonterminal other than the axiom $S$. If one of them is a prefix of another one, a conflict between reduction and shift occurs and condition $LR(0)$ is violated. In other words, the language generated by every nonterminal must be *prefix-free.* The case of the axiom is different, because we assume that sentences are terminated by special character *dashv*, so that no sentence can be a prefix of another. The conflict introduced by prefixes is next illustrated.

*Example 5.7.* A finite yet not $LR(0)$ language
Grammar $\{S \to Xc, X \to a \mid ab\}$ is not $LR(0)$ because nonterminal $X$ generates a language with prefixes, $\{a, ab\}$. Observe in Figure 5.6 the grammar, machine net, and pilot. Macro-state $I_1$ contains final state 4 hence is mixed: reduction with rule $X \to a$ and shift with the arc to $I_5$, therefore condition $LR(0)$ is violated. Intuitively this implies the parser is left with the uncertainty as to reducing with $a \Rightarrow X$ or shifting. Such uncertainty can be easily removed by examining the next character ($c$ for reducing and $b$ for shifting) in the same manner an $LL(1)$ parser would do.

$$S \to Xc \qquad X \to a \mid ab$$

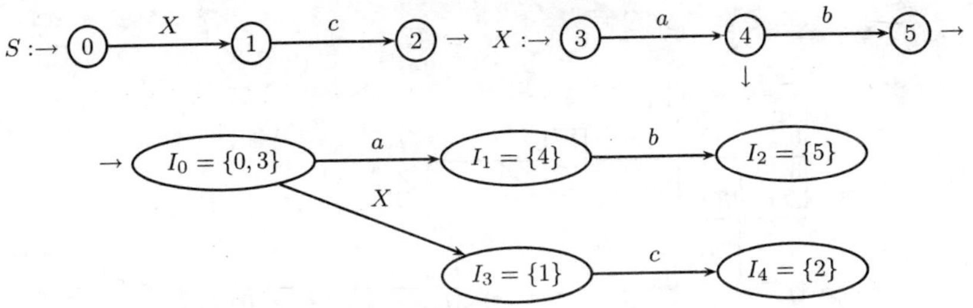


**Fig. 5.6** A finite language (example 5.7) violating the prefix-free property: grammar, machine, and pilot.

A second example containing prefixes is the fundamental construct of lists with separators defined by regular expression $e(se)^*$. It contains for example $e$ and $ese$. From the previous observation condition $LR(0)$ prevents lists with separators from occurring as construct of a language: this would preclude lists of parameters, lists of statements, etc. Very simple regular languages trespass the $LR(0)$ family!

Continuing with similar limitations, it is easily seen that an empty grammar rule violates the condition. Consider two alternatives $A \to \varepsilon \mid \beta$, one of them empty. Then in machine $M_A$ the initial state $q_{A,0}$ is also final. But since the not empty arc $\beta$ originates from the state, the macro-state containing state $q_{A,0}$ is mixed.

*Example 5.8.* Dyck grammar is not $LR(0)$.
The familiar grammar and machine net are shown in Figure 5.7. Computing the $LR(0)$ pilot, we obtain the graph in Figure 5.8. Every macro-state frame

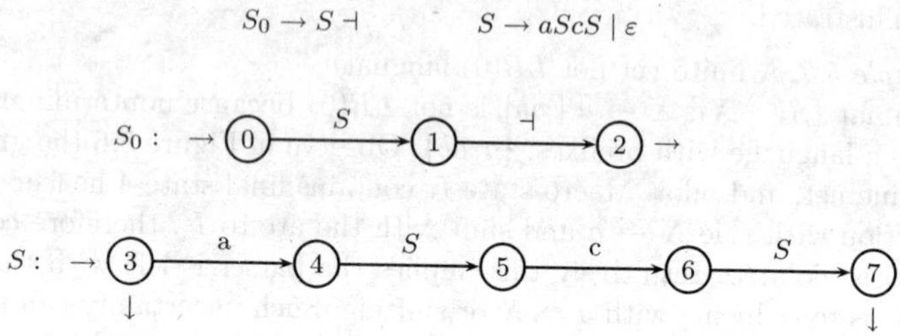


**Fig. 5.7** Dyck grammar and machine net (example 5.8).

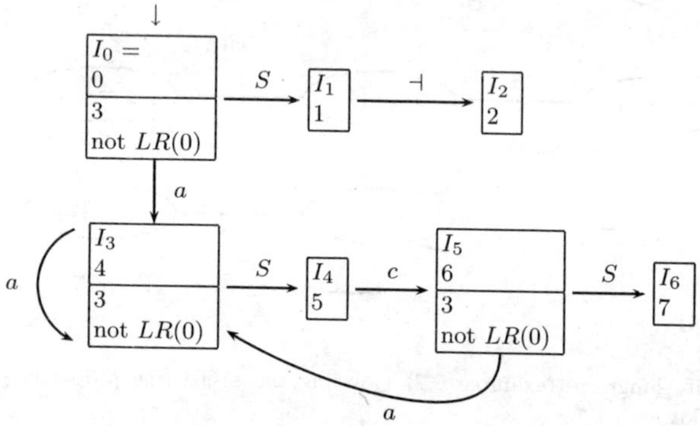


**Fig. 5.8** $LR(0)$ pilot of Dyck grammar (example 5.8).

is horizontally divided into the subsets computed by successive applications of the closure function. Notice that the macro-states containing state 3 are all mixed because 3 is the final state of reduction $S \to \varepsilon$ and arc $3 \xrightarrow{a} 4$ performs a shift. Therefore condition $LR(0)$ is violated.

## Adding Look-ahead to Pilot

We are going to add look-ahead information to every macro-state in order to gain in selectivity and thus make the method practical.
As a macro-state contains multiple states, the set of look-ahead characters has to be individually computed for each one and for each outgoing arrow. Intuitively, a macro-state satisfies condition $LR(1)$ if the next move of the pushdown automaton is uniquely determined from the macro-state on stack top and from the look-ahead set which contains the current character,

**Definition 5.9.** Components of $LR(1)$ pilot machine.
A macro-state $I$ of the $LR(1)$ pilot is a set of pairs, to be termed *candidates*, of the form

$$\langle q, a \rangle \in Q \times (\Sigma \cup \{\dashv\})$$

where $Q$ is a set of states of the machine network and $a$ is the look-ahead character.
It is convenient to group together the candidates having the same state (first component):

$$\langle q, \{a_1, a_2, \ldots, a_k\} \rangle \equiv \{\langle q, a_1 \rangle, \langle q, a_2 \rangle, \ldots, \langle q, a_k \rangle\}$$

The set $\{a_1, a_2, \ldots, a_k\}$ is termed *look-ahead set* of state $q$ in macro-state $I$.
The closure function, introduced in the $LR(0)$ case (p. 206) to find the states reachable with machine invocations, is next refined in order to compute also the look-ahead sets.

**Definition 5.10.** $LR(1)$ closure function.
Let $c = \langle q, \pi \rangle$ be a candidate, where $\pi$ is the look-ahead set of state $q$ in the current macro-state. The $LR(1)$ *closure* of $c$, denoted as $closure_1(c)$, is computed as follows:

$C := \{\langle q, \pi \rangle\};$
*repeat*

$C := C \cup \{\langle q_{A,0}, \rho \rangle\}$ where:

$q_{A,0}$ is the initial state of a machine $M_A$ such that:
there exists a candidate $\langle p, \pi \rangle \in C \ \wedge$ with the outgoing arc $(p) \xrightarrow{A} (r)$.
The look-ahead $\rho$ is computed as:

$$\begin{cases} \rho = Ini(L(r)) & \text{if } L(r) \text{ is not nullable,} \\ \rho = Ini(L(r)) \cup \pi & \text{otherwise} \end{cases}$$

*until* no new element has been added to $C$;
$closure_1(c) := C$

Remark: if the current set $C$ contains a state $p$ with look-ahead $\pi$ and the net has an arc $ⓟ \xrightarrow{A} ⓡ$, then the algorithm inserts into $C$ the initial state $q_{A,0}$ (as in the $LR(0)$ construction). For computing the look-ahead set $\rho$ of $q_{A,0}$, we collect the characters that may follow a string deriving from $A$. Such characters arise in two different situations. First as initial characters of language $L(r)$ recognized starting from state $r$. Second, if state $r$ is final or more generally if $L(r)$ is nullable, set $\rho$ contains also the characters already present in set $\pi$.

For a set $I$ of candidates, the closure is the union of the closures of the candidates present in $I$.

The $LR(1)$ pilot is computed similarly to the $LR(0)$ case paying attention that components of macro-states are now candidates, i.e., records instead of simple states.

**Definition 5.11.** Construction of the $LR(1)$ pilot.
The pilot that will act as control unit of the parser is the deterministic finite automaton

$$N = (R, \Sigma \cup V, \vartheta, I_0, R)$$

defined by:

- the set of macro-states, $R$;
- the alphabet is the union of the terminal $\Sigma$ and nonterminal $V$ sets of the grammar;
- macro-state $I_0$ contains at construction start time the pair $\langle q_{ini}, \dashv\rangle \equiv$(initial state of net, terminator);
- the macro-state set $R = \{I_0, \ldots\}$ and the transition function $\vartheta$ are computed starting from the initial macro-state with the following procedure:

$I_0 = \text{closure}_1(\langle q_{ini}, \dashv\rangle)$;
$R := \{I_0\}$;
*repeat* for all macro-state $I \in R$ and for all symbol $X \in \Sigma \cup V$

$\vartheta(I, X) := \text{closure}_1(\{\langle r, \pi\rangle\}) = \bigcup_{\langle q,\rho\rangle \in I} \text{closure}_1(\langle \delta(q, X), \rho\rangle)$
where the set of candidates $\langle r, \pi\rangle$ is defined as:
in macro-state $I$ there exists a candidate $\langle q, \rho\rangle$ such that
in the net there is an arc $ⓠ \xrightarrow{X} ⓡ$;
the look-ahead set $\pi$ is copied from $\rho$, i.e., $\pi := \rho$;

if $\vartheta(I, X) \notin R$ then $R := R \cup \vartheta(I, X)$;

*until* no new macro-state has been produced by the iteration.

*Example 5.12.* Dyck language (example 5.8) from $LR(1)$ standpoint
The grammar and net are reproduced in Figure 5.9. The graph of the $LR(1)$

pilot is drawn in Figure 5.10. The right column of a macro-state contains look-ahead sets. To make cross-reference easier, we have reproduced in the macro-states some grammar rules with a bullet marking the current state. Such items are termed *marked rules*. For instance, the marked rule $S \to a \bullet ScS$ denotes state 4 of machine $M_S$. Clearly it is redundant to include both states and marked rules since the latter are just a different encoding of states. A macro-state frame contains the identifier and a set of candidates.

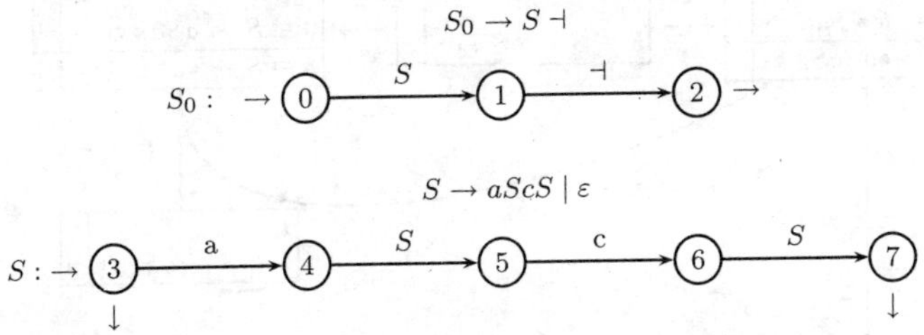


**Fig. 5.9** Grammar and machine net of Dyck language (example 5.12).

Thus the candidates of macro-state $I_3$ are $\langle 4, \{\dashv\}\rangle$ and$\langle 3, \{c\}\rangle$. The separation of candidates by horizontal lines is only meant to facilitate checking their computation by the closure function but the order of candidates in a macro-state is irrelevant. Some candidates are special, in that they do not need a look-ahead set: they are associated with the conventional axiom $S_0 \to S \dashv$ (within macro-states $I_0, I_1, I_2$)

We illustrate look-ahead computation for $I_3$. The pair $\langle 4, \dashv\rangle$ has the same look-ahead as state 3 of $I_0$, from which it comes because of arc $3 \xrightarrow{a} 4$. The closure function applied to pair $\langle 4, \dashv\rangle$, returns state 3 with look-ahead $\{c\}$ since $Ini(L(5)) = \{c\}$ and $L(5)$ is not nullable. We observe that state 3 is commented by two different marked rules, $S \to \bullet aScS$ and $S \to \bullet\varepsilon$; the latter may also be written as $S \to \varepsilon\bullet$.

Comparing this pilot with the $LR(0)$ one (Figure 5.8), the number of macro-states has increased because of the diversification brought by look-ahead sets. In fact, two macro-states such as $I_3$ and $I_7$ differing only in their look-ahead are merged in one $LR(0)$ macro-state.

### *LR*(1) Condition

A marked rule is said to be *completed* if the bullet is at the right end, e.g.,

$$S \to \varepsilon \bullet \qquad S \to aScS \bullet \qquad S_0 \to S \dashv \bullet$$

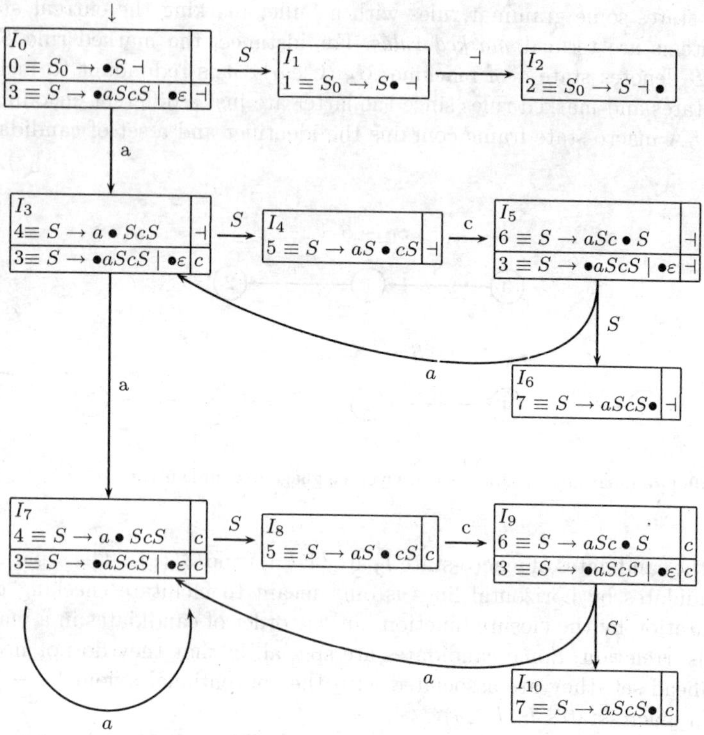


**Fig. 5.10** $LR(1)$ pilot of Dyck language grammar (example 5.12, Figure 5.9).

We recall and extend to case $k = 1$ the previous classification of $LR(0)$ macro-states. A candidate is a *reduction candidate* if its state is final for some machine of the net; this means the state is associated with a completed marked rule. A candidate is a *shift candidate* if its state is the origin of an arc labelled with a terminal or nonterminal symbol; this means in the associated marked rule the bullet is followed by a symbol.

Now the drastic $LR(0)$ condition, that prevented any macro-state from containing reductions and shifts or from containing multiple reductions, will be replaced by a finer control on look-ahead sets.

**Definition 5.13.** $LR(1)$ condition.
A pilot macro-state satisfies condition $LR(1)$ if both clauses hold:

1. *no reduction-shift conflict*: every reduction candidate has a look-ahead set disjoint from the set of terminal symbols of shift moves (i.e., from the set of terminal labels of arcs outgoing from the macro-state);

2. *no reduction-reduction conflict*: if the macro-state contains multiple reduction candidates, their look-ahead sets are disjoint.

A grammar has the $LR(1)$ property if every macro-state satisfies condition $LR(1)$.

*Example 5.14.* Dyck language (example 5.12) and $LR(1)$ condition
We examine the pilot in Figure 5.10. Macro-states $I_1, I_2, I_4, I_6, I_8, I_{10}$ are singleton sets, therefore they trivially satisfy condition $LR(1)$. Each of the macro-states $I_0, I_3, I_5, I_7, I_9$ contains reduction candidate $S \to \bullet\varepsilon$ and shift candidate $S \to \bullet aScS$ (both associated with state 3), plus another shift candidate. We check disjunction of look-ahead sets:

| *macro-state* | *look-ahead of* $S \to \varepsilon$ | *outgoing labels* | *condition* |
|---|---|---|---|
| $I_0$ | $\dashv$ | $a$ | $\{\dashv\} \cap \{a\} = \emptyset$ |
| $I_3$ | $c$ | $a$ | $\{c\} \cap \{a\} = \emptyset$ |
| $I_5$ | $\dashv$ | $a$ | $\{\dashv\} \cap \{a\} = \emptyset$ |
| $I_7$ | $c$ | $a$ | $\{c\} \cap \{a\} = \emptyset$ |
| $I_9$ | $c$ | $a$ | $\{c\} \cap \{a\} = \emptyset$ |

Every macro-state satisfies the condition, therefore the grammar is $LR(1)$.

We need the next example to illustrate the second clause of the condition.

*Example 5.15.* Multiple reductions in an $LR(1)$ macro-state
The grammar (of a finite language)

$$S \to A \mid Ba \mid bAa \mid bB \qquad A \to a \qquad B \to a$$

is represented by the machines in Figure 5.11. We omit the starting rule $S_0 \to S$ which is irrelevant to the point considered. The $LR(1)$ pilot is de-

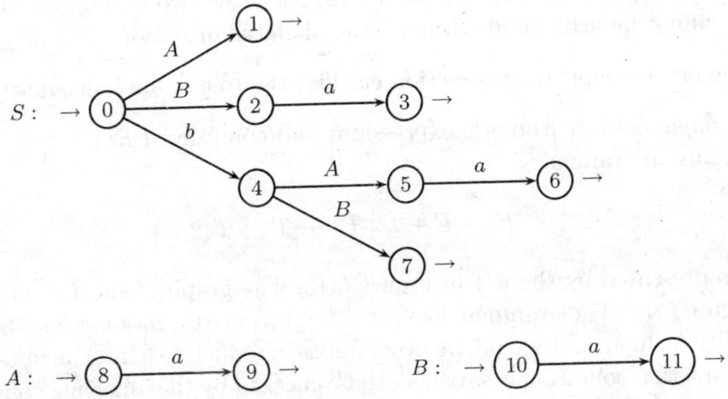


**Fig. 5.11** Machine net of example 5.15.

picted in Figure 5.12, where we list marked rules for reduction macro-states only. Only macro-states $I_4$ and $I_8$ have to be checked because all the oth-

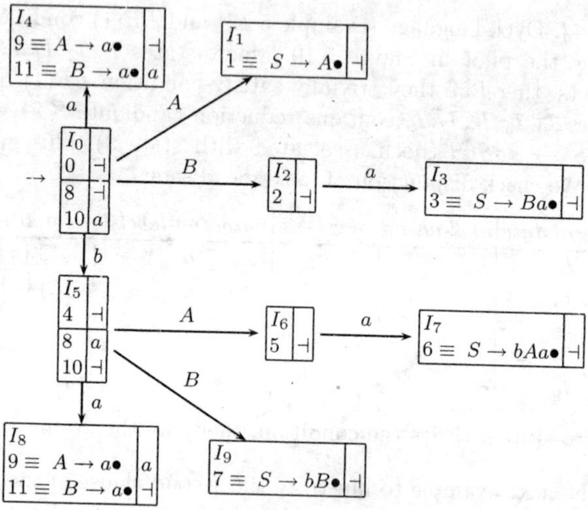

**Fig. 5.12** $LR(1)$ pilot of example 5.15, Figure 5.11.

ers already satisfy the stronger $LR(0)$ condition. Both macro-states contain two reduction candidates and their look-ahead sets are disjoint, so that no reduction-reduction conflicts arise. On the other hand, no arc originates from either macro-state and reduction-shift conflicts are thus excluded.
The grammar is $LR(1)$ but not $LR(0)$ since the two reductions in $I_4$ and in $I_8$ cannot be arbitrated without look-ahead information.

The last example of this section clarifies the role of look-ahead sets.

*Example 5.16.* Arithmetic expressions and condition $LR(1)$
The usual grammar

$$E \to E + T \mid T \qquad T \to T \times a \mid a$$

is represented by the net in Figure 5.13. The graph of the $LR(1)$ pilot is in Figure 5.14. The grammar has the $LR(1)$ property: no macro-state contains multiple final states and in every mixed (reduction/shift) macro-state the disjunction condition is satisfied, to be checked by the following computation:

$$I_3 : \times \notin \{\dashv, +\}, \text{ look-ahead of reduction } E \to E + T$$
$$I_5 : \quad \times \notin \{\dashv, +\}, \text{ look-ahead of reduction } E \to T$$

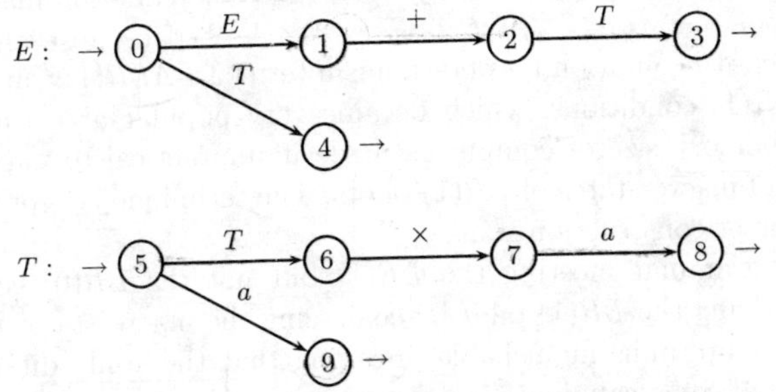


**Fig. 5.13** Machine net for arithmetic expressions (example 5.16).

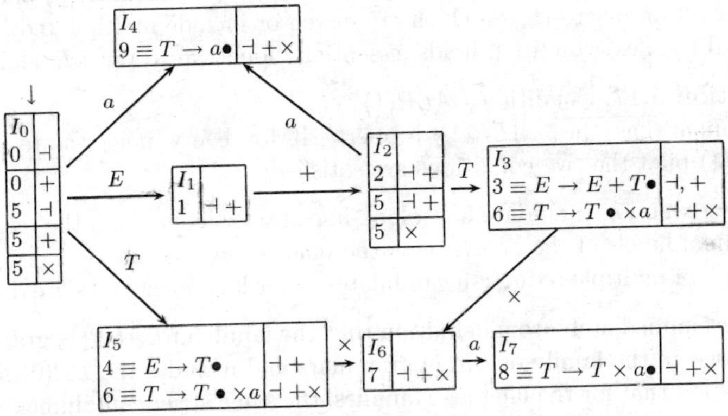


**Fig. 5.14** Pilot of arithmetic expressions (example 5.16, Figure 5.13).

Observe that in macro-state $I_3$ the look-ahead sets of shift candidate $6 \equiv T \rightarrow T \bullet \times a$ and of reduction candidate $3 \equiv E \rightarrow E + T\bullet$ are not disjoint: $\{\dashv, +, \times\} \cap \{\dashv, +\} \neq \emptyset$; yet this is not an infringement of condition $LR(1)$! In fact, the look-ahead set of a shift candidate is not an argument of the $LR(1)$ predicates (definition 5.13 on p. 220), but it is just instrumental for computing the look-ahead sets of the next macro-states.

It follows that after pilot construction the look-ahead sets of any candidate of type shift can be deleted because they are unnecessary for parsing (except maybe for error treatment).

### Lighter Use of Look-Ahead Information: $LALR(1)$

We briefly discuss a condition for determinism termed $LALR(1)$,[2] in between $LR(0)$ and $LR(1)$ conditions, which became very popular at a time when the reduced memory size of computers made it unpractical to manage the large number of macro-states of $LR(1)$ pilots. The technique is supported by widespread parser construction tools.

Consider a grammar meeting the $LR(1)$ but not the $LR(0)$ condition. Imagine simplifying the $LR(1)$ pilot by coalescing the macro-states which in the $LR(0)$ pilot are indistinguishable, meaning that they only differ in the look-ahead set of some candidate. At the same time look-ahead information has to be preserved since the $LR(0)$ condition does not suffice. More precisely, when two macro-states are coalesced, the look-ahead sets of the candidates that coincide in the first component (the state) are united. The $LALR(1)$ pilot graph[3] thus obtained is isomorphic to the graph of the $LR(0)$ pilot. Yet it may contain macro-states which are mixed or include multiple reductions, provided the next condition holds, essentially identical to the $LR(1)$ case.

**Definition 5.17.** Condition $LALR(1)$.
A grammar has the $LALR(1)$ property if for every macro-state of the $LALR(1)$ pilot the two conditions are satisfied:

1. every reduction candidate has a look-ahead set disjoint from the set of the terminal labels of the arcs leaving the macro-state;
2. in case of multiple reduction candidates, their look-ahead sets are disjoint.

It follows immediately from definition that the family of $LALR(1)$ grammars is included in the family of $LR(1)$ grammars and includes the $LR(0)$ family. We mention that for the language families, the same strict containments hold as for grammar families: there exist $LR(1)$ languages that are not $LALR(1)$, as well as $LALR(1)$ languages that are not $LR(0)$.
Some cases are presented next.

*Example 5.18.* Dyck language (example 5.12 continued) and $LALR(1)$ condition
The known machine net is reproduced in Figure 5.15. We coalesce the macro-states of the $LR(1)$ pilot (Figure 5.10 on p. 220), which are not distinguishable for the $LR(0)$ pilot (Figure 5.8 on p. 216) and thus we obtain the $LALR(1)$ pilot in Figure 5.16. This graph is isomorphic to the graph of the $LR(0)$ pilot. As no macro-state contains multiple reductions the related conditions need not be checked. On the other hand, some macro-states are mixed, namely, $I_0$, $[I_3, I_7]$, $[I_5, I_9]$, which falsify condition $LR(0)$. In such mixed macro-states the look-ahead set of reduction $S \to \varepsilon$ is disjoint from the set of terminal labels of outgoing arcs, thus proving that the grammar has property $LALR(1)$.

---

[2] Short for *Look Ahead* $LR(1)$.

[3] We do not describe other direct constructions of the $LALR(1)$ pilot, which do without an $LR(1)$ pilot, see e.g.,[17].

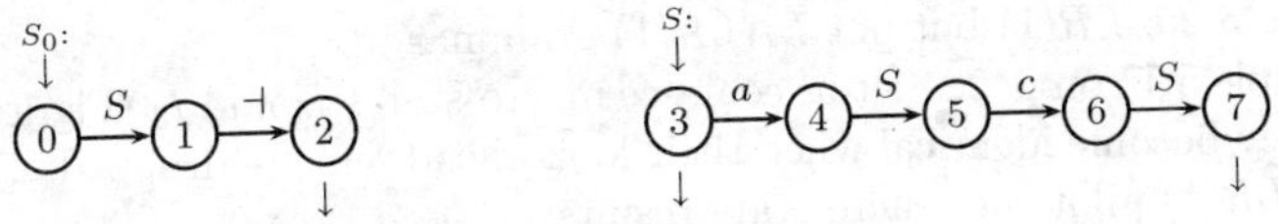


**Fig. 5.15** Machine net of Dyck language (example 5.18).

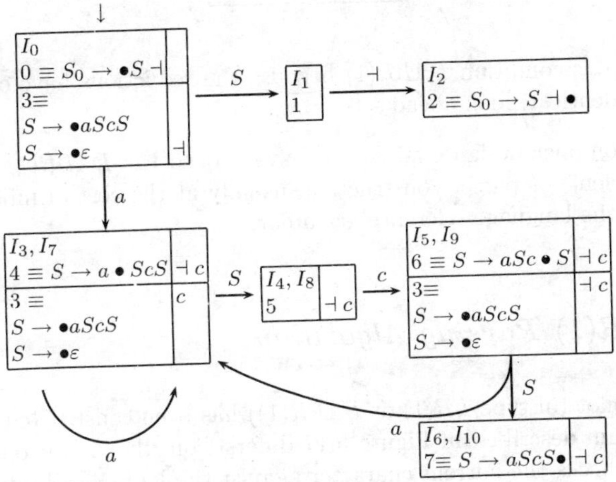


**Fig. 5.16** $LALR(1)$ pilot of Dyck language (Figure 5.15).

The gain is that this pilot does the same service as an $LR(1)$ pilot but uses fewer macro-states.

In the coming example the $LR(1)$, $LALR(1)$ and $LR(0)$ pilot graphs are isomorphic.

*Example 5.19.* Arithmetic expressions (from example 5.16) and condition $LALR(1)$
The $LR(1)$ pilot graph of Figure 5.14 on p. 223 is isomorphic to the $LR(0)$ pilot, so that no coalescing of macro-states is required. This means that grammar

$$E \to E + T \mid T \qquad T \to T \times a \mid a$$

satisfies the $LALR(1)$ condition.

We finish with an example showing the greater generality of $LR(1)$.

*Example 5.20.* $LR(1)$ but not $LALR(1)$ grammar
In example 5.15 on p. 221 let us coalesce macro-states $I_4$ and $I_8$ (Figure 5.12), since they become identical when their look-ahead sets are dropped. Thus for the $LALR(1)$ pilot the macro-state results:

| $I_4, I_8$ | |
|---|---|
| $9 \equiv A \rightarrow a\bullet$ | $\dashv, a$ |
| $11 \equiv B \rightarrow a\bullet$ | $\dashv, a$ |

which violates condition $LALR(1)$ because the reductions have overlapping (actually identical) look-ahead sets.

Many compiler design experiences have proved the $LALR(1)$ method is often sufficient for parser construction, usually at the cost of minor modifications to the language reference grammar.

### 5.2.5 $LR(1)$ Parsing Algorithm

After the pilot (of type $LR(1)$ or $LALR(1)$) has been constructed, the parsing algorithm described in Figure 5.17 differs from the $LR(0)$ one (p. 212) in that it checks the current character against the look-ahead sets, in order to choose the move if the current macro-state is mixed or has multiple reductions. Thanks to the $LR(1)$ (or $LALR(1)$) hypothesis, the macro-state on stack top and the current character uniquely determine the move to be done: shift, reduction with a precise rule, or rejection. Therefore the automaton is deterministic.
We illustrate with a step-by-step trace.

*Example 5.21.* Parsing trace for example 5.16
For the language of arithmetic expressions, we refer to the $LR(1)$ and $LALR(1)$ pilot (Figure 5.14 on p. 223). The trace for string $a + a$ is in Table 5.3. Notice that having omitted the initial rule $S_0 \rightarrow E \dashv$, the final stack configuration contains $E$.

### 5.2.6 Properties of $LR(k)$ Language and Grammar Families

We have studied several classes of grammars from $LL(k)$ to $LR(k)$ generating deterministic languages. It would be too long and out of scope for this book to examine in detail the formal properties and relations for the corresponding

*Algorithm.* Let $G$ be an $LR(1)$ (or $LALR(1)$) grammar and $N = (R, \Sigma \cup V, \vartheta, I_0, R)$ its pilot.

*Stack alphabet*: $R \cup \Sigma \cup V$;
*Set of states* of $A$: irrelevant as it contains just one state;
*Initial configuration*: the stack contains the initial macro-state $I_0$;
Moves: let $I$ be the macro-state on stack top and $a$ the current character:

*Shift* move: if for macro-state $I$ the transition $\vartheta(I, a) = I'$ is defined, the automaton reads terminal $a$, moves ahead the reading head, and pushes string $aI'$ on stack;

*Reduction* move: if macro-state $I$, here denoted $I_n$, contains a reduction candidate

$$\langle q, \pi \rangle \equiv \langle B \to X_1 X_2 \ldots X_n \bullet, \pi \rangle$$

(i.e., $B \to X_1 X_2 \ldots X_n \in reductions(q)$) where $n \geqslant 0$ is the length of the right part, and
if $a$ is in look-ahead set $\pi$, perform the following action.
On stack top there is necessarily string $\beta'$

$$I' \overbrace{X_1 I_1 X_2 I_2 \ldots X_n I_n}^{\beta'}$$

containing $n$ macro-states pushed by preceding moves.
The reduction first pops from stack string $\beta'$ (i.e., $2n$ symbols from top), then pushes string $BI''$, where $I'' = \vartheta(I', B)$ is the macro-state entered by the pilot transition "reading" nonterminal $B$.

*Final configuration*: stack $= I_0$, input entirely scanned.

**Fig. 5.17** Shift-reduce parser with look-ahead, as pushdown automaton $A$.

**Table 5.3** Parsing trace of string $a + a$ (example 5.21).

| *Stack* | $x$ | *Comment* |
|---|---|---|
| $I_0$ | $a + a \dashv$ | shift |
| $I_0 \quad aI_4$ | $+ a \dashv$ | reduce with $T \to a$ |
| $I_0 \quad TI_5$ | $+ a \dashv$ | $+ \in$ look-ahead of 4: reduce with $E \to T$ |
| $I_0 \quad EI_1$ | $+ a \dashv$ | shift |
| $I_0 \quad EI_1 + I_2$ | $a \dashv$ | shift |
| $I_0 \quad EI_1 + I_2 \, aI_4$ | $\dashv$ | reduce with $T \to a$ |
| $I_0 \quad EI_1 + I_2 \, TI_3$ | $\dashv$ | reduce with $E \to E + T$ |
| $I_0$ | $\dashv$ | accept |

families of languages. Therefore we just state the main properties, here for the $LR(k)$ case, and in a later section also in comparison with case $LL(k)$.[4]

*Property 5.22.* The family $DET$ of context-free deterministic languages coincides with the family of languages generated by $LR(1)$ grammars.

---

[4] For a more complete discussion we refer to [25, 50, 51].

This important statement essentially says that the shift-reduce parsing approach with look-ahead 1 perfectly captures the idea of deterministic recognition, using as automaton a machine with a finite memory and an unbounded stack. Obviously this does not say that any grammar generating a deterministic language enjoys the $LR(1)$ property. For instance, the grammar could be ambiguous, or require a look-ahead longer than one. But for sure there exists an equivalent grammar that is $LR(1)$. On the other hand, any context-free language which is not deterministic, as the cases on p. 164, cannot be generated by an $LR(1)$ grammar.

Consider now extending the look-ahead length, much as we did for $LL(k)$ grammars. Trusting the reader's intuition, we are going to talk about an $LR(k)$ grammar and parser without formally defining them. Such a parser is driven by a pilot whose look-ahead sets contain strings of length $k > 1$. Clearly the pilot may have more macro-states than a $k = 1$ pilot because some of the latter macro-states are split due to $k = 2$ look-ahead sets becoming different. However, since, no matter how large is $k$, an $LR(k)$ parser is nothing but a deterministic pushdown automaton having more internal states than an $LR(1)$ parser, from the preceding property we have:

*Property 5.23.* For every $k > 1$, the family of languages generated by $LR(k)$ grammars coincides with the family of languages generated by $LR(1)$ grammars hence also with the $DET$ family.

Now a question arises: since any deterministic language can be defined by means of an $LR(1)$ grammar, what is the use of taking higher values of parameter $k$? The answer comes from consideration of the families of grammars instead of languages. There exist grammars having the $LR(2)$ but not the $LR(1)$ property, and more generally there is an infinite hierarchy of inclusions.

*Property 5.24.* For every $k \geqslant 1$ there exist grammars satisfying condition $LR(k)$ but not condition $LR(k-1)$.

Although property 5.23 ensures that any grammar $LR(k)$, $k > 1$, can be replaced by an equivalent $LR(1)$ grammar, the latter is sometimes less natural (shortly we shall see examples).

We finish with a negative statement.

*Property 5.25.* For a given context-free grammar it is undecidable if there exists an integer $k > 0$ such that the grammar has the $LR(k)$ property; therefore it is undecidable whether the language generated by a grammar is deterministic.

However, if the value $k$ is fixed, it is possible to check whether the grammar is $LR(k)$ by constructing the pilot and verifying that all macro-states are adequate. This is what we have done for $k = 1$ in a number of cases.

### 5.2.7 How to Obtain $LR(1)$ Grammars

More often than not, technical grammars meet the $LR(1)$ condition, but occasionally one finds a grammar that needs adjustment. Imagine we have an unambiguous grammar that is not $LR(1)$. The case of primary interest is when the grammar is $LR(k)$ for some $k > 1$ because then we know from property 5.23 that an equivalent $LR(1)$ grammar exists. We first introduce some useful transformations for lowering the value of $k$ and then we consider a transformation for non-$LR(k)$ grammars.[5]

#### Grammar with Reduce-Reduce Conflict

Suppose the grammar is $LR(2)$ but not $LR(1)$. We consider a violation caused by a reduction-reduction conflict: some macro-state $I$ of the pilot contains two reduction candidates

$$A \to \alpha\bullet, \{a\} \qquad B \to \beta\bullet, \{a\}$$

with the same look-ahead character $a$. Since the grammar is $LR(2)$, the candidates are discriminated by the character following $a$.

To obtain an equivalent $LR(1)$ grammar, we apply a transformation called *early scanning*; the idea is to lengthen the right part of certain rules by appending to them the conflict causing character $a$. In this way the new rules will have in their look-ahead sets the characters following $a$, which from the $LR(2)$ hypothesis do not overlap. More precisely, the transformation introduces two new nonterminals and the rules

$$\langle Aa \rangle \to \alpha a \qquad \langle Ba \rangle \to \beta a$$

For preserving grammar equivalence, we must then adjust the rules containing $A$ or $B$. The transformation must ensure that the derivation

$$\langle Aa \rangle \stackrel{+}{\Rightarrow} \gamma a$$

exists if, and only if, the original grammar has the derivation

$$A \stackrel{+}{\Longrightarrow} \gamma$$

and character $a$ can follow $A$.

*Example 5.26.* Early scanning
Grammar $G_1$

$$S \to Abb \qquad A \to aA \qquad B \to aB$$
$$S \to Bbc \qquad A \to a \qquad B \to a$$

[5] For a broader discussion of such grammar transformations we refer to [12].

has a conflict between $A \to a \bullet \{b\}$ and $B \to a \bullet \{b\}$. Increasing the parameter to $k = 2$, the former reduction has look-ahead $\{bb\}$ while the latter has disjoint look-ahead $\{bc\}$. Applying early scanning, we obtain the $LR(1)$ grammar:

$$S \to \langle Ab \rangle b \qquad \langle Ab \rangle \to a \langle Ab \rangle \qquad \langle Bb \rangle \to a \langle Bb \rangle$$
$$S \to \langle Bb \rangle c \qquad \langle Ab \rangle \to ab \qquad \langle Bb \rangle \to ab$$

### Grammar with Shift-Reduce Conflict

Another common source of conflict occurs when a macro-state $I$ contains two candidates

$$A \to \alpha \bullet a\beta, \pi \qquad\qquad B \to \gamma \bullet, \{a\}$$

causing a violation, because an arc labelled $a$ leaves the macro-state and $a$ is a look-ahead character of the reduction candidate.

How to fix it: create a new nonterminal $\langle Ba \rangle$ to do the same service as $B$ followed by $a$. Replace the second rule with rule $\langle Ba \rangle \to \gamma a$. For consistency, adjust all the rules having $B$ in their right part so as to preserve grammar equivalence. Since we assume the grammar is $LR(2)$, the look-ahead set associated with $\langle Ba \rangle \to \gamma a$ certainly does not include $a$ and the conflict disappears.

The transformation is more involved if the character $a \in \pi$, causing the conflict between candidates $A \to \alpha \bullet a\beta, \pi$ and $B \to \gamma \bullet, \{a\}$, is produced as initial character by a derivation from nonterminal $C$, which immediately follows $B$ in a sentential form:

$$S \overset{+}{\Rightarrow} \ldots BC \ldots \overset{+}{\Rightarrow} \ldots Ba \ldots \ldots$$

Transformation: create a new nonterminal named $\langle a/_L C \rangle$ to generate the strings obtained from those derived from $C$ by cutting prefix $a$. Formally we have

$$\langle a/_L C \rangle \overset{+}{\Rightarrow} \gamma \text{ if, and only if, } C \overset{+}{\Rightarrow} a\gamma \text{ in the original grammar.}$$

Then the affected grammar rules are adjusted to preserve equivalence. Now the grammar thus obtained is amenable to early scanning, which will remove the conflict.

This transformation is called *left quotient*, since it is based on the homonomous operation $/_L$ defined on p. 17.

*Example 5.27.* Left quotient preparation for early scanning
Grammar $G_2$

$$S \to AC \qquad A \to a \qquad C \to c \qquad D \to d$$
$$S \to BD \qquad B \to ab \qquad C \to bC$$

is $LR(2)$ but not $LR(1)$ as evidenced by the reduction-shift conflict

$$A \to a \bullet \{b, c\} \qquad B \to a \bullet b\{d\}$$

After left quotient transformation we obtain grammar

$$\begin{array}{lll} S \to Ab\langle b/_L C\rangle & A \to a & \langle b/_L C\rangle \to b\langle b/_L C\rangle \\ S \to Ac\langle c/_L C\rangle & B \to ab & \langle b/_L C\rangle \to c \\ S \to BD & D \to d & \langle c/_L C\rangle \to \varepsilon \end{array}$$

Now the conflict can be removed applying early scanning transformation.

Finally, we observe that grammar transformations based on left quotient and early scanning can also be used when the grammar meets the $LR$ condition for a value of $k$ larger than two.

### Transformation of Non-$LR(k)$ Grammars

If the given grammar is not $LR(k)$, we do not have systematic transformations, but we may attempt to study the languages generated by the critical nonterminals, to identify the sources of conflict, and finally to adjust the subgrammars to make them $LR(1)$.

Quite often, an effective transformation is to turn left-recursive rules or derivations intc right-recursive ones. The reason stems from the fact that $LR$ parsers carry on multiple computations until the moment when one of them reaches a reduction, which is deterministically decided and applied. A right-recursive rule (more generally a derivation) has the effect of delaying the decision moment, whereas a left-recursive rule does the opposite. In other words, with right-recursive rules the automaton accumulates more information on stack before the time comes to make a reduction. Truly, the stack grows larger with right-recursive grammars, but such increase in memory occupation is negligible for modern computers.

*Example 5.28.* Inverting recursion
The language $a^+b^+ \cup \{a^n b^n b^* c \mid n \geqslant 1\}$ is generated by grammar $G_s$:

$$\begin{array}{llll} S \to X & S \to Yc & & \\ X \to aX & X \to aB & Y \to Yb & Y \to Z \\ B \to bB & B \to b & Z \to aZb & Z \to ab \end{array}$$

The $LR(1)$ pilot exhibits conflicts between a reduction and two shifts:

$$Z \to ab\bullet, \{b, c\} \qquad B \to \bullet bB, \{\dashv\} \qquad B \to \bullet b, \{\dashv\}$$

Notice that it would not help to increase $k$: the conflict persists with $k = 2$ as look-ahead string $bb$ is compatible with the reduction and with the shifts.

Converting the rules of $X$ and $B$ to left-linear form, the languages generated by the two nonterminals are unaffected, yet the automaton can perform shifts earlier and the reduction at the very end. In this way the stack content can keep open all possibilities until the current character is $c$ or the terminator and the correct choice is made accordingly. After this transformation, the $LR(1)$ property is satisfied by the equivalent grammar $G_d$:

$$\begin{array}{llll} S \to X & S \to Yc & & \\ X \to Xb & X \to Ab & Y \to Yb & Y \to Z \\ A \to Aa & A \to a & Z \to aZb & Z \to ab \end{array}$$

### *5.2.8 LR(1) Parsing with Extended Context-Free Grammars*

An advantage of top-down parsers is that they naturally work with grammars extended with regular expressions. On the other hand, to adapt shift-reduce parsers to EBNF grammars, we have to enrich the stack with information needed to correctly perform reductions. The problem with EBNF grammars is that when the pilot enters a reduction macro-state and decides to apply a reduction with a certain rule, the string to be reduced is not immediately available because the right part of the rule may contain star and union operators. The situation is evidenced by the next example.

*Example 5.29.* Shift-reduce for EBNF grammar (Sassa and Nakata)
The grammar

$$\begin{array}{l} R_1 : \; S \to a^*b \mid aAc \\ R_2 : \; A \to a^* \end{array}$$

has the machine network of Figure 5.18. The graph of the $LR(1)$ pilot is in Figure 5.19. As usual a macro-state contains a set of candidates: each one has a machine state (commented with a marked rule) and an $LR(1)$ (but $LALR(1)$ would be enough) look-ahead set. For brevity the sets are omitted in shift candidates.

Take as input string $x_1 = aaac \dashv$. After scanning prefix $aa$ the automaton configuration is

$$\overbrace{I_0\, a\, I_1\, a\, I_2}^{\text{stack}} \mid \overbrace{ac \dashv}^{\text{suffix}}$$

and with $I_2$ as current macro-state and $a$ as look-ahead, the parser decides to shift:

$$\overbrace{I_0\, a\, I_1\, a\, I_2\, a\, I_2}^{\text{stack}} \mid \overbrace{c \dashv}^{\text{suffix}}$$

then, in macro-state $I_2$, the parser performs the reduction $A \to a^*$ in agreement with look-ahead $c$.

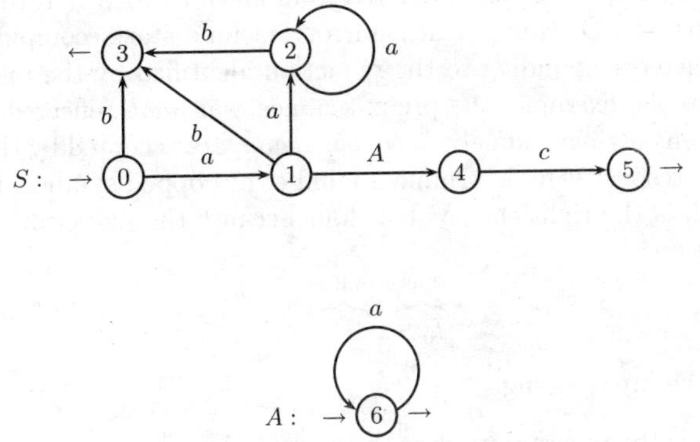


**Fig. 5.18** Machine net of example 5.29.

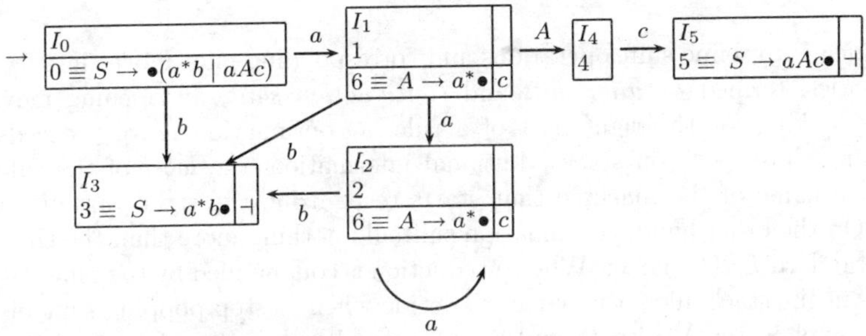


**Fig. 5.19** $LR(0)$ pilot of example 5.29.

Now a new problem arises that did not occur with basic context-free grammars. How many symbol pairs should be popped by the reduction move? At first glance several possibilities exist: zero (case $A \Rightarrow \varepsilon$), one (case $A \Rightarrow a$), or two (case $A \Rightarrow a^2$). On the other hand, the case $A \Rightarrow a^3$ is excluded, because the first $a$ belongs to $S$. But having several choices open, would make the algorithm not deterministic.

Similarly, analyzing string $x_2 = aaab \dashv$, the automaton reaches the configuration

$$\overbrace{I_0\, a\, I_1\, a\, I_2\, a\, I_2\, b\, I_3}^{\text{stack}} \mid \overbrace{\dashv}^{\text{suffix}}$$

Now macro-state $I_3$ prescribes a reduction with rule $S \to a^*b$, which does not specify how many symbols to pop because of the star. To find it, the parser can inspect the stack from the top checking that the terminal and nonterminal symbols orderly belong to the language defined by the reflected regular expression $(a^*b)^R$. In other words, the string of such symbols has to be recognized by a new machine, derived from machine $M_A$ by reversing the direction of arrows. Of course, such mirror machine starts computation in state 3, the one corresponding to the reduction identified by the pilot.

Carrying on the example, the prefix scanned was *aaab* reflected as *baaa*, and several prefix strings, namely, *b*, *ba*, *baa*, *baaa*, are accepted by the mirror machine; they respectively determine a number of popped symbols from one to four. Which is the right choice? It is four because the reduction produces the configuration

$$\overbrace{I_0\, S}^{\text{stack}} \mid \overbrace{\dashv}^{\text{suffix}}$$

that accepts the input string.

In order to solve the uncertainty over the popping length, we present a rather simple method, out of several that have been conceived.[6]

## Reduction Control with Morimoto and Sassa Method

The idea is to refine shift operations and corresponding pilot moves into two categories, termed *opening shift* and *continuation shift*: an opening move starts looking for the right part of a rule, a continuation move proceeds. Opening shifts push on stack additional information: the *label* of the rule, i.e., the name of the machine that starts recognizing the right part of the rule. On the other hand, continuation shifts do nothing more than the shifts of a standard $LR(1)$ parser. When a reduction is commanded by the pilot, the labels in the stack allow the parser to decide when to stop popping symbols.

We explain the Morimoto and Sassa method for constructing the $LR(1)$ pilot. First, the component states in a macro-state are partitioned in two sets, both of which may not be empty: the *kernel* and the *rest*, to be defined next.

1. For the initial macro-state $I_0$ all states are in the rest and the kernel is empty.
2. If the pilot has an arc $I \xrightarrow{X} I'$, the kernel of $I'$ includes all states $q'$ such that there exists a state $q \in I$ with the condition that, in some machine, there exists an arc $\delta(q, X) = q'$:
$$kernel(I') = \{q' \mid \exists I \text{ such that } q \in I \wedge q' = \delta(q, X)\}$$
3. The rest of a not initial macro-state $I$ includes the states $r$ returned by the closure function, applied to some state $q$ in the kernel of $I$:
$$rest(I) = \{r \mid q \in kernel(I) \wedge r \in closure_k(q)\}$$

[6] A survey is in [37].

The closure should be computed with the desired look-ahead length $k \geqslant 0$ (as explained on pp. 206 and 217).

Next we have to describe the shift actions the pilot performs when it goes from macro-state $I$ to macro-state $I'$ "reading" a symbol (terminal or non-) $X$. For this we define two binary relations between states $q$ of $I$ and $q'$ of $I'$, to be denoted as $(I, q)$ and $(I', q')$, respectively. As already mentioned a shift move $I \xrightarrow{X} I'$ is classified in two cases:

*Continuation shift*: let $q \in kernel(I)$ and $q' \in I'$ be states, such that the transition $\delta(q, X) = q'$ exists; then the pilot has the continuation relation:

$$(I, q) \stackrel{X,\, cont}{\longrightarrow} (I', q')$$

*Opening shift*: let $q \in rest(I)$ and $q' \in I'$ be states such that the transition $\delta(q, X) = q'$ exists; then the pilot has the opening relation:

$$(I, q) \stackrel{X,\, open}{\longrightarrow} (I', q')$$

Notice that, depending on the origin state being in the kernel or in the rest, the class of the move is either a continuation or an opening shift.

We show by means of an example how to construct the pilot with continuation and opening moves.

*Example 5.30.* Pilot with opening/continuation moves (from [37])
The grammar

$$S_0 \to A \dashv \qquad\qquad A \to c(A \mid c)a$$

is represented by the network in Figure 5.20. We construct as usual the pilot in Figure 5.21; here look-ahead is not needed since there are no conflicts within $LR(0)$ macro-states. Notice that macro-state frames are divided by a horizontal line: the kernel is above and the rest below the line. Figure 5.22 depicts the opening/continuation relations between individual states belonging to macro-states. Thus the arc $(I_3, 3) \longrightarrow (I_4, 4)$ is an opening relation, since 3 is a rest state in $I_3$. Similarly, since $3 \in rest(I_4)$, arc $(I_4, 3) \longrightarrow (I_4, 4)$ is of opening class.

On the other hand, the arcs $(I_3, 4) \longrightarrow (I_4, 5)$ and $(I_4, 4) \longrightarrow (I_4, 5)$ are continuation relations, since the origin states are in the kernels of the corresponding macro-states. Arc $(I_3, 4) \longrightarrow (I_5, 5)$ too is classified as continuation, since state 4 is in the kernel of $I_3$. In general, different relations may exist between two macro-states, as witnessed by $I_3$ and $I_4$.

Actually the pilot contains a move $I \xrightarrow{X} I'$ if, and only if, at least one relation exists $(I, q) \stackrel{X,(cont|open)}{\longrightarrow} (I', q')$ between states respectively included in $I$ and $I'$. When multiple relations exist between two macro-states, they can be of the same or of different classes, as schematized in Figure 5.23. In such cases, when two macro-states are connected by both opening and continuation

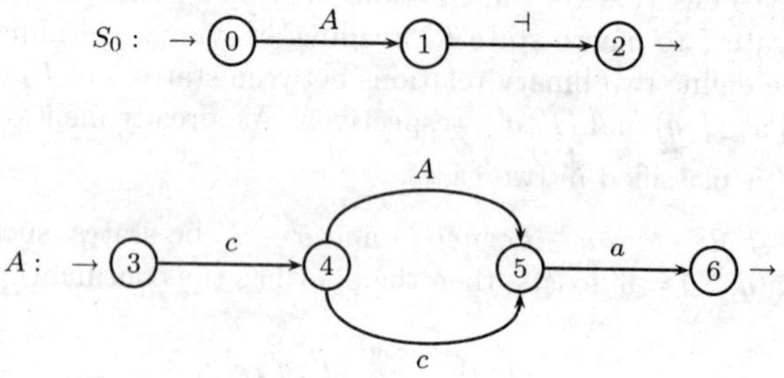


**Fig. 5.20** Machine network of example 5.30.

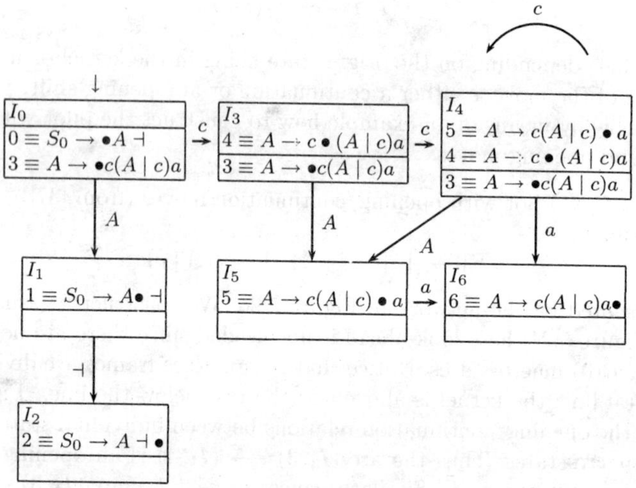


**Fig. 5.21** *LR*(0) pilot of example 5.30.

relations we say there is a *stacking conflict*. Notice this so-called conflict does not hinder the construction of a deterministic parser: in case of conflict the parser will conservatively apply the opening relation in order to push on the stack the additional information consisting of the label of the machine that has possibly been activated. We stress that if several opening relations exist between two macro-states they may involve different machines with the effect that a set of machine labels instead of just one will be pushed on stack.

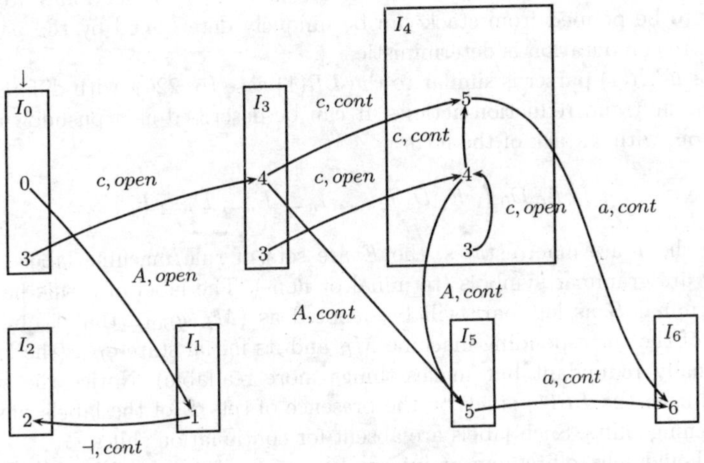


**Fig. 5.22** Pilot with opening/closing relations (example 5.30).

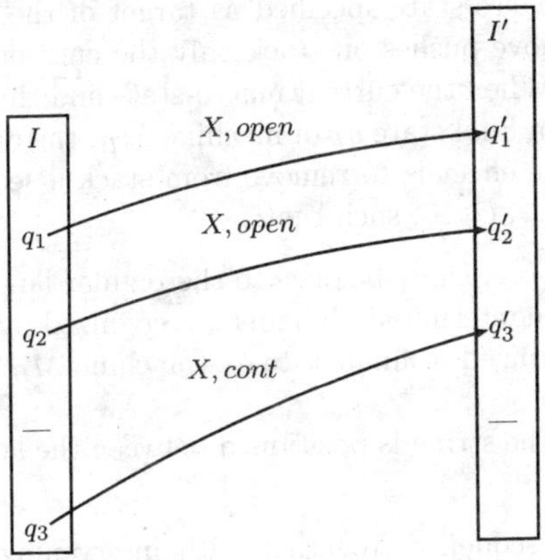


**Fig. 5.23** Multiple relations between states of macro-states.

## *ELR*(1) Parsing Algorithm

We now suppose the pilot is available, with arcs between macro-states qualified as opening or continuation; look-ahead sets are also listed if needed. Furthermore we assume in every macro-state the $LR(1)$ condition (p. 220) is met so that the current character determines the next move, shift or reduction, and in the second case from which final state.

However, in case of reduction, knowing the machine and the final state does not suffice to rule out the existence of multiple machine paths leading from the initial state to the final one. The $ELR(1)$ parsing algorithm to be presented uses the labels stored in the stack: in every reduction state the string to be popped from stack can be uniquely determined by the parser, therefore computation is deterministic.

The $ELR(1)$ parser is similar to the $LR(1)$ case (p. 226), with differences only in shift and reduction actions. It can be described as a pushdown automaton, with a stack of the form

$$I_0\, E_0\, D_0\, I_1\, E_1\, D_1\, I_2\, \ldots\, I_{n-1}\, E_{n-1}\, D_{n-1}\, I_n$$

where the $I$ are macro-states, the $E$ are sets of rule/machine labels, and the $D$ are grammar symbols (terminal or non-). The label of a rule having nonterminal $B$ as left part will be denoted as $(M_B, q_{B,0})$, that is, by the name of the corresponding machine $M_B$ and its initial state $q_{B,0}$ (the latter is actually redundant but makes things more readable). Notice the stack differs from the $LR(1)$ stack by the presence of sets $E$ of the labels pushed by opening shifts. Such labels are absent for continuation shifts.

It should help to first give an informal overview of the algorithm. An opening shift move of the automaton pushes on stack the rule label, the current terminal, and the macro-state specified as target of the pilot transition. A continuation shift move pushes on stack only the current character and the target macro-state. When the current macro-state and character trigger a reduction starting from final state $q_f$ of machine $M_B$, the automaton performs a series of steps. The effect is to remove from stack a sequence of grammar symbols $D_k, D_{k+1}, \ldots, D_{n-1}$, such that:

- the string $D_k D_{k+1} \ldots D_{n-1}$ belongs to the regular language $R(M_B)$, over the terminal and nonterminal alphabets, recognized by machine $M_B$;
- the string is recognized in final state $q_f$ (machine $M_B$ may have multiple final states);
- within the stack, the string is positioned between the label $(M_B, q_{0,B})$ and the top.

After removing the sequence (together with intervening macro-states and labels) the reduction performs a shift (either opening or continuing) of nonterminal $B$, with a transition from the macro-state that has surfaced on stack top.

*Algorithm.* $ELR(1)$ syntax analyzer.
Let $a \in \Sigma$ be the current character. The starting macro-state is $I_0$, the current macro-state is $I$.

*Continuation move*: to be performed if the relation

$$(I, q) \overset{a,cont}{\longrightarrow} (I', q')$$

is defined in $I$. The automaton pushes on stack $a$ and then macro-state $I'$;

*Opening move:* to be performed if one or more opening relations

$$(I, q_1) \xrightarrow{a,open} (I', r_1)$$
$$\dots \xrightarrow{a,open} \dots$$
$$(I, q_m) \xrightarrow{a,open} (I', r_m)$$

are defined in $I$. Let $E$ be the set of labels of the corresponding grammar rules/machines.

The automaton pushes on stack:

1. the label set $E$;
2. the terminal character $a$;
3. macro-state $I'$.

If in the current configuration both a continuation and an opening move are possible, the automaton performs the second one.

*Reduction move:* to be performed if the current macro-state, here named $I_n$, contains a candidate $\langle q_f, \pi\rangle$, where $q_f$ is a final state of machine $M_B$, and the current character $a$ is in look-ahead set $\pi$.

Let the current stack be

$$I_0\, E_0\, D_0\, I_1 \,\dots\, I_{n-k}\, \overbrace{E_{n-k}\, D_{n-k}\, I_{n-k+1} \dots I_{n-1}\, E_{n-1}\, D_{n-1} I_n}^{\beta'}$$

Pop a sequence of one or more stack elements, denoted $\beta'$, until the remaining stack

$$I_0\, E_0\, D_0\, I_1 \,\dots\, I_{n-k}$$

satisfies both of the following conditions:

1. $E_{n-k}$ is the label set (closer to the old stack top) containing the label $(M_B, q_{B,0})$ of the selected reduction.
2. Let $\beta = D_{n-k+1} \dots D_{n-1} \in (V \cup \Sigma)^*$ be the string obtained from $\beta'$, deleting the macro-states and labels. Then $\beta$ is a valid sentence of the regular language accepted by machine $M_B$ with final state $q_f$.

At last the automaton spontaneously executes the transition from macro-state $I_{n-k}$ to macro-state $I'$, "reading" nonterminal $B$. Such move as well is performed according to its class, opening or continuation, as specified in the pilot by the relation between macro-states $I_{n-k}$ and $I'$.

The reduction move substantially differs from the basic parser. It can be implemented using the mirror machine $(M_B)^R$ that accepts the reflected language of machine $M_B$. Then the parser pops grammar symbols and other elements from stack until the following conditions become true: machine $(M_B)^R$

has reached state $q_{B,0}$ (initial state of machine $M_B$); the last popped element is a label set containing the label $(M_B, q_{B,0})$ of the reduction.

We argue that the parser is deterministic. Clearly, if the grammar is $LR(1)$, the choice between reduction and shift is always deterministic. In case of shift, the priority granted to the opening moves arbitrates the conflict, if any, with continuation. It remains to consider reduction moves. Although the label set $E_{n-k}$ may contain several machine labels, condition 2. of reduction moves is satisfied by one, and only one, machine because of the way the stack is filled.

*Example 5.31.* Trace of $ELR(1)$ parser execution (example 5.30 continued) The source string is $cccaa\ \dashv$. The machine net is in Figure 5.20 and the pilot in Figure 5.22.

| *Stack* | $x$ | | *Comment* |
|---|---|---|---|
| $I_0$ | | $c \quad c \quad c \quad a \quad a \dashv$ | opening |
| $I_0$ | $(M_A,3)cI_3$ | $c \quad c \quad a \quad a \dashv$ | opening |
| $I_0$ | $(M_A,3)cI_3\ (M_A,3)cI_4$ | $c \quad a \quad a \dashv$ | opening |
| $I_0$ | $(M_A,3)cI_3\ (M_A,3)cI_4\ cI_4$ | $a \quad a \dashv$ | continuation |
| $I_0$ | $(M_A,3)cI_3\ \underline{(M_A,3)}cI_4\ cI_4\ aI_6$ | $a \dashv$ | reduction: state 6 |

In macro-state $I_6$, the pilot decides for the reduction associated with state 6 of machine $M_A$, corresponding to rule $A \to c(A \mid c)a$. To identify the reducible segment of the stack, the parser uses the mirror machine $(M_A)^R$:

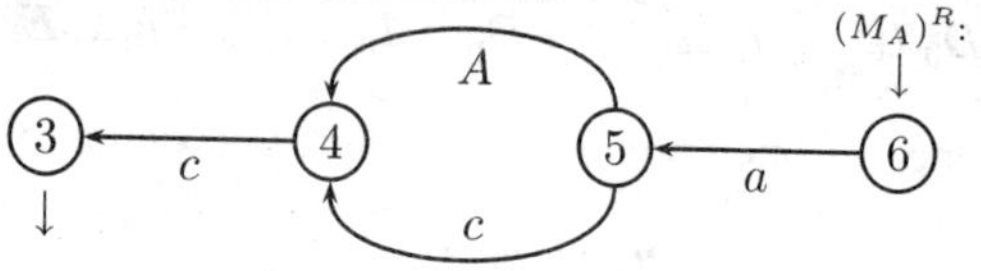


The parser inspects the string $ac$, which is included between stack top and the first (from top) label $(M_A,3)$ corresponding to the reduction started in 6. In so doing it runs a computation on the mirror machine, which reaches state 4. Since 4 is not final for $(M_A)^R$, the string $ac$ is not long enough for the reduction and the parser must go on digging into the stack. Popping continues until the underlined label surfaces from the stack. At this point string $acc$ is accepted by the mirror machine. Then the parser performs reduction $cca \Rightarrow A$ and in the new configuration executes two continuation shifts in a row:

| | | |
|---|---|---|
| $I_0\ (M_A,3)cI_3$ | $a \dashv$ | continuation |
| $I_0\ (M_A,3)cI_3\ AI_5$ | $a \dashv$ | continuation |
| $I_0\ \underline{(M_A,3)}cI_3\ AI_5\ aI_6$ | $\dashv$ | reduction: state 6 |

Reduction $cAa \Rightarrow A$ is consistent with the underlined label set and with acceptance of $aAc$ by the mirror machine. Thereafter the reduction empties the stack and the parser accepts the source string and terminates.

Actually, different implementations have been proposed for controlling reduction moves, instead of the one exploiting the mirror machine. Another technique uses counters or pointers, loaded on stack by opening moves. Others have proposed to modify the grammar in order to simplify the identification of the reducible part of the stack.

### 5.2.9 Comparison of Deterministic Families *REG*, *LL*($k$), and *LR*($k$)

Before we leave the subject of deterministic parsing it is convenient to examine the inclusion relations between the main families of deterministic languages in order to appraise their relative scope. The cases to be discussed are the regular languages $REG$ defined by regular expressions, finite automata, or unilinear grammars; the $LR(k)$ languages with their variants ($LR(0)$ and $LALR(1)$); and the $LL(k)$ languages. Concerning grammars in this section we assume they are basic context-free not extended with regular expressions.

We start comparing regular and $LL(1)$ languages.

*Property 5.32.* Any regular language can be generated by an $LL(1)$ grammar.

The proof is simple. Suppose the language is defined by a deterministic finite machine, hence the machine network contains exactly one machine which only carries terminal labels on its arcs. We show condition $LL(1)$ (p. 183) is satisfied. If two arcs originate from a state, they necessarily carry different labels since the machine is deterministic. If a state is final, the final arrow necessarily has just one element in its guide set (p. 182) the terminator $\dashv$, which does not label any arc of the machine.

The comparison of $LL(k)$ and $LR(k)$ cases is more involved, because we have to consider grammars as well as languages, and also to discuss the role of parameter $k$. Some facts are first recalled.

- Any $LL(k)$ language with $k \geqslant 1$ is deterministic, hence also $LR(1)$ by property 5.22 on p. 227. Of course this is consistent with the fact the top-down parser of an $LL(k)$ language is a deterministic pushdown automaton.
- For every value of $k$ there exist deterministic languages that cannot be defined with an $LL(k)$ grammar.
  It suffices to refer to examples 4.35 and 4.36 (pp. 199, 200).

Next we compare the language generation capacity of $LR$ and $LL$ grammars for the same value of the look-ahead parameter. The following strict inclusion property states the higher capacity of $LR$ grammars.

*Property 5.33.* For every value $k \geqslant 1$, if a grammar satisfies condition $LL(k)$, it also satisfies condition $LR(k)$ (p. 220).[7]

[7] For a formal proof see e.g.,[51].

Justification. Take for simplicity $k = 1$ and examine the grammar (Figure 5.15 on p. 225) of Dyck language, which is clearly $LL(1)$, and the $LR(1)$ pilot in Figure 5.10 on p. 220. A peculiarity of this pilot is that every macro-state contains exactly one state in the area over the horizontal divider. This means that when the pilot is constructed, before the closure operation $closure_1$ is applied, any macro-state contains one state only. The property necessarily descends from condition $LL(1)$. The property, combined with disjointness of guide sets of arcs leaving the same state, has the consequence that $LR(1)$ conflicts in macro-states are impossible.

To complete the comparison we consider different look-ahead lengths, 0 and 1. It is easy to check that the families of $LR(0)$ and $LL(1)$ grammars are distinct and not included in each other. In fact, we recollect:

1. a grammar containing epsilon rules is certainly not $LR(0)$ but it may be $LL(1)$;
2. a grammar with left-recursive rules cannot be $LL(1)$ but it may be $LR(0)$.

To contrast the $LL(1)$ and $LR(0)$ language families, some facts are:

1. a language containing a sentence and also some prefix thereof cannot be $LR(0)$, but it may be $LL(1)$;
2. the language $\{a^* a^n b^n \mid n \geqslant 0\}$ is $LR(0)$ but not $LL(1)$ (p. 199).

Therefore also for languages, the $LL(1)$ and $LR(0)$ families are not comparable by set inclusion.

The comparison of $LL(1)$ and $LALR(1)$ grammars is subtler[8]: it suffices to say that almost all $LL(1)$ grammars excepting some contrived examples are also $LALR(1)$; in substance, the $LALR(1)$ family of grammars is wider than the $LL(1)$ family.

## 5.3 A General Parsing Algorithm

We complete the study of parsing methods with the Earley algorithm that is able to handle any context-free grammar and produces all derivations for ambiguous sentences. The computational complexity is proportional to the cube of the string length and reduces to the square if the grammar is unambiguous and even less if it is deterministic.

This is the last stage of a series that started with deterministic $LL(k)$ algorithms and then introduced a greater capacity of handling nondeterministic situations with the $LR(k)$ approach. We know an $LR(k)$ algorithm carries on multiple parsing attempts but not beyond a reduction operation, when the decision must be unique, i.e., deterministic. This is a connatural limitation of any algorithm simulating a deterministic pushdown automaton since this abstract machine cannot manage multiple stacks.

---

[8] For a careful analysis, see [6].

The Earley algorithm takes inspiration from the $LR(k)$ approach but it soon diverges from the deterministic pushdown model and exploits a richer data structure: a one-dimensional array of sets. This structure efficiently represents multiple partially overlapping stacks and allows polynomial time simulation of a nondeterministic pushdown automaton. In this way it avoids the exponential complexity of the naif nondeterministic recognition algorithm considered on p. 151.

For simplicity we only study basic context-free grammars but the algorithm could be modified to work with EBNF grammars too. It is convenient to represent the grammar by means of syntax rules and also by a network of machines. No hypothesis is needed concerning determinism or the presence of left-recursive derivations. Treatment of empty rules is deferred to a later section.

For source string $x$ of length $n \geqslant 1$ we denote $x_i$ the $i$-th character, and $x_{i..j}$ the substring from character $i$ to $j$, included; thus the source string is $x \equiv x_{1..n}$.

This approach does not rely on a pilot machine (which in general would violate the $LR(k)$ condition). The algorithm records in a vector $E[0..n]$ at position $i$ any state of the network such that a nondeterministic parser could possibly reach it after scanning the $i$-th character. Next to the state the algorithm records an integer (named back pointer), that designates a position in the string: the one from which the current instance of the machine (or grammar rule) has been activated.

More precisely, each vector element or cell $E[i]$, $0 \leqslant i \leqslant n$, contains a set of ordered *pairs*

$$\langle \text{ state, pointer } \rangle = (s, p)$$

where $s$ is a state of the net and $p$ falls in the interval $(0 \ldots i)$. For better readability we often write next to state $s$ the synonymous marked rule (p. 219).

Concerning look-ahead, some versions of the Earley algorithm claim better performances by using it; but using look-ahead does not enlarge the class of grammars or languages that can be handled. For this reason we just consider the basic yet quite practical version that does not inspect any character beyond the current one.

### *5.3.1 Introductory Example*

*Example 5.34.* Introduction to Earley method

The language

$$\{a^n b^n \mid n \geqslant 1\} \cup \{a^{2n} b^n \mid n \geqslant 1\}$$

is not deterministic, therefore the $LR(k)$ condition is violated by the following grammar (as well as by any equivalent one):

$$S \to A \mid B \qquad A \to aAb \mid ab \qquad B \to aaBb \mid aab$$

The machine net is in Figure 5.24. Suppose string $aabb$ of length 4 has to be analyzed. Then the vector $E[0] \ldots E[4]$ is prepared containing the initial cell $E[0]$ and one cell per string position. Each cell will eventually be filled with a set of couples but at start time only cell $E[0]$ is not empty and contains the pair:

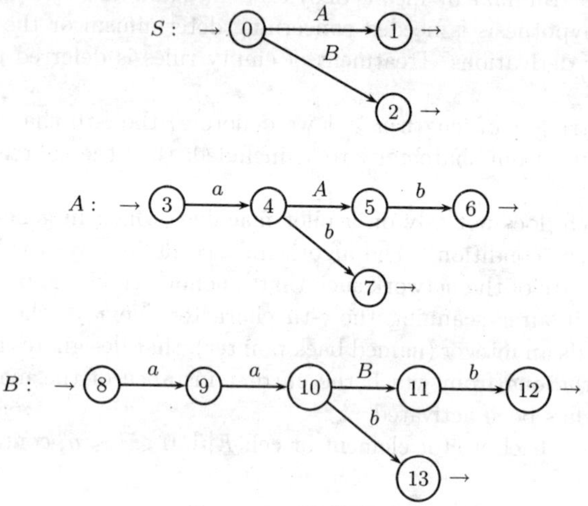


**Fig. 5.24** Machine net of example 5.34.

$$\langle \text{state} = 0, \text{pointer} = 0 \rangle$$

written as $(0, p = 0)$, where the first zero is the initial state (of the net axiom machine) and the pointer is targeted to zero, i.e., to the position preceding the first character of the string. A more verbose notation is

$$E[0] = \{(0 \equiv S \to \bullet(A \mid B), p = 0)\}$$

In broad terms, three types of operations can be done on the cell $E[i]$ indexed by the position of the current character: predicting, scanning, and completing.

*Prediction* is just another name for the $LR(0)$ closure function (p. 206). Prediction applies to a pair, having a state from where an arc originates with a nonterminal label. (In terms of marked rule there is a nonterminal to the right of the bullet.) The operation adds to set $E[i]$ a new pair: its state is the initial state of the machine (equivalently the bullet precedes the right part of the rule). The pointer has $i$ as value, which says the pair has been created at step $i$ starting from a pair already present in $E[i]$.

The purpose of prediction is to add to set $E[i]$ all the initial states of the machines that may possibly be invoked to recognize a substring starting from character $x_{i+1}$.

In our example the prediction adds to $E[0]$ the pairs

$$(3 \equiv A \to \bullet aAb \mid \bullet ab, p = 0), \qquad (8 \equiv B \to \bullet aaBb \mid \bullet aab, p = 0)$$

As no further prediction applies to the new pairs, the second operation comes into play.

*Scan* is applied to a state from which an arc labelled with a terminal originates. It is similar to a terminal shift operation of an $LR$ parser. If the label is equal to $x_{i+1}$, a new pair is written into cell $E[i+1]$. Its state is the destination state of the arc; the pointer is the same as in the pair the scan is applied to. This operation says the terminal has been scanned by the parser.

Here, with $i = 0$ and $x_1 = a$, scanning inserts into $E[1]$ the pairs

$$(4 \equiv A \to a \bullet Ab \mid a \bullet b, p = 0), \qquad (9 \equiv B \to a \bullet aBb \mid a \bullet ab, p = 0)$$

Then a prediction is again applied to the new pairs, with the effect to add to $E[1]$ the pair

$$(3 \equiv A \to \bullet aAb \mid \bullet ab, p = 1)$$

where we notice the value 1 of the pointer.

If $i < n$ and no scan operation can be successfully applied to the couples of $E[i]$, cell $E[i+1]$ remains empty and the source string is rejected.

Next, from $E[1]$, scanning $x_2 = a$, we add to $E[2]$ the pairs

$$(10 \equiv B \to aa \bullet Bb \mid aa \bullet b, p = 0), \qquad (4 \equiv A \to a \bullet Ab \mid a \bullet b, p = 1)$$

and, applying a prediction to them, we add the pairs

$$(8 \equiv B \to \bullet aaBb \mid \bullet aab, p = 2), \qquad (3 \equiv A \to \bullet aAb \mid \bullet ab, p = 2)$$

Scanning $x_3 = b$ produces in $E[3]$ the pairs

$$(13 \equiv B \to aab\bullet, p = 0), \qquad (7 \equiv A \to ab\bullet, p = 1)$$

Now the third operation comes into play.

*Completion* is similar to a reduction move of a shift-reduce parser. It applies to a pair $(s, j) \in E[i]$ such that state $s$ is final for a machine $M_A$, i.e., it is synonymous to a rule $s \equiv A \to \ldots\bullet$ with trailing mark. The operation goes back to the set $E[j]$ pointed to by $j$; we observe relation $j \leqslant i$ holds in general, but here it is $j < i$ because the grammar does not contain empty rules. In set $E[j]$ we find every pair (at least one exists) $(q, k)$, such that from $q$ an arc $q \xrightarrow{A} r$ originates. At last we update the current cell $E[i]$ and we add the pair with state $r$ and pointer $k$. In other words we add to the current cell the marked rule found in $E[j]$ and we shift the bullet to the right of nonterminal $A$.

Now completion applies to both pairs present in $E[3]$ since 13 and 7 are final states of $B$ and $A$, respectively. The pointer of 13 points to $E[0]$, which intuitively is the set of partial derivations at the time when the parser started to recognize this instance of $B$ in the string.

In $E[0]$ we find the pair $(0 \equiv S \rightarrow \bullet A \mid \bullet B, p = 0)$, and from state 0 the arc $0 \xrightarrow{B} 2$; then we insert in $E[3]$ the pair with state 2 and the same pointer:

$$(2 \equiv S \rightarrow B\bullet, p = 0)$$

Similarly, for pair $(7 \equiv A \rightarrow ab\bullet, p = 1)$ we find in cell $E[1]$ pair $(4 \equiv A \rightarrow a \bullet Ab \mid a \bullet b, p = 0)$ and we add to $E[3]$ pair

$$(5 \equiv A \rightarrow aA \bullet b, p = 0)$$

If the string ended at this point, the prefix $aab$ scanned up to now would be accepted; acceptance is shown by the presence in the last set, $E[3]$, of pair $(2 \equiv S \rightarrow B\bullet, p = 0)$, characterized by a final state of the net and by a zero pointer. Actually one more character $b$ remains and a scan produces in $E[4]$ pair $(6 \equiv A \rightarrow aAb\bullet, p = 0)$. Completing the latter, through the pair $(0 \equiv S \rightarrow \bullet A \mid \bullet B, p = 0) \in E[0]$, we add to $E[4]$ pair $(1 \equiv S \rightarrow A\bullet, p = 0)$. The last pair causes string $aabb$ to be accepted.

The whole computation trace is listed in Table 5.4.

**Table 5.4** Earley parsing of string $aabb$ (example 5.34).

| | |
|---|---|
| $E[0]$ | $(0 \equiv S \rightarrow \bullet(A \mid B), p = 0)$<br>$(3 \equiv A \rightarrow \bullet aAb \mid \bullet ab, p = 0)$<br>$(8 \equiv B \rightarrow \bullet aaBb \mid \bullet aab, p = 0)$ |
| $a$ $E[1]$ | $(4 \equiv A \rightarrow a \bullet Ab \mid a \bullet b, p = 0)$<br>$(9 \equiv B \rightarrow a \bullet aBb \mid a \bullet ab, p = 0)$<br>$(3 \equiv A \rightarrow \bullet aAb \mid \bullet ab, p = 1)$ |
| $a$ $E[2]$ | $(10 \equiv B \rightarrow aa \bullet Bb \mid aa \bullet b, p = 0)$<br>$(4 \equiv A \rightarrow a \bullet Ab \mid a \bullet b, p = 1)$<br>$(8 \equiv B \rightarrow \bullet aaBb \mid \bullet aab, p = 2)$<br>$(3 \equiv A \rightarrow \bullet aAb \mid \bullet ab, p = 2)$ |
| $b$ $E[3]$ | $(13 \equiv B \rightarrow aab\bullet, p = 0)$<br>$(7 \equiv A \rightarrow ab\bullet, p = 1)$<br>$(2 \equiv S \rightarrow B\bullet, p = 0)$<br>$(5 \equiv A \rightarrow aA \bullet b, p = 0)$ |
| $b$ $E[4]$ | $(6 \equiv A \rightarrow aAb\bullet, p = 0)$<br>$(1 \equiv S \rightarrow A\bullet, p = 0)$ |

### 5.3.2 Earley Algorithm

The algorithm carries on in parallel all possible leftmost derivations[9] while it scans string $x_{1...n}$ from left to right. Upon examining character $x_i$, it produces a two-field record, i.e., a pair of the form $\langle$state, pointer$\rangle$ shortened in $(s, p = \ldots)$, where pointer $p$ is in the interval from 0 to $i$. The state may alternatively be denoted by a marked grammar rule $A \to \alpha \bullet \beta$.

Intuitively, a pair $(s \equiv A \to \alpha \bullet \beta,\ j)$ states an assertion and an objective:

Assertion: the parser has found a substring $x_{j+1..i}$ $(0 \leqslant j < i)$ that derives from $\alpha$, in formula

$$\alpha \stackrel{*}{\Rightarrow} x_{j+1..i}$$

Objective: to find all the positions $k$ with $i < k \leqslant n$, such that substring $x_{i+1..k}$ derives from $\beta$, in formula

$$\beta \stackrel{*}{\Rightarrow} x_{i+1..k}$$

When the algorithm finds any such position $k$, it is entitled to assert that nonterminal $A$ derives substring $x_{j+1..k}$, i.e.,

$$A \stackrel{*}{\Rightarrow} x_{j+1..k}$$

A pair $(q \equiv A \to \alpha\bullet, j)$ where $q$ is a final state (i.e., the bullet terminates the marked rule), is termed *completed*.

*Algorithm.* Earley parser.
It constructs a vector $E[0..n]$, one cell longer than the source string, containing a set of pairs in each cell $E[i]$ (associated with position $x_i$). $E[0]$ is the initial set. The initial set is initialized as explained next; the other sets are initially empty.

*Step 0: Initialization.* (It sets the objectives, to find every prefix of $x$, which may derive from $S$. The pointer is set to zero.)

$E[0]$ := $(q_{ini},\ 0)$, where $q_{ini}$ is the initial state of the net;
$E[i]$ := $\emptyset$, for $i = 1, \ldots, n$;
$i := 0$.

Then the algorithm applies in the natural order $0, 1, \ldots, n$ the operations of prediction, completion, and scan to compute all the sets $E[i]$. At step $i$ the algorithm may add some pairs only to the current set $E[i]$ and the next one $E[i+1]$. When all possible operations have beenperformed and no pair has

[9] Actually, the algorithm does more than finding the derivations of $x$: it also checks whether every prefix of $x$ derives from the axiom.

been added to cell $E[i]$, the algorithm moves on to compute $E[i+1]$. If $E[i+1]$ remains empty and $i < n$, the string is rejected.

*Prediction.* (Any objective present in cell $E[i]$ can spawn other objectives, which are added to the same cell; the pointer is set to the current index.)

for each pair in $E[i]$ of form $(q \equiv A \to \alpha \bullet B\gamma\ j)$,
where state $q$ is the origin of an arc $q \xrightarrow{B} s$,
add to cell $E[i]$ the pair $(r, i)$,
where $r$ is the initial state of machine $M_B$.

*Completion.* (A completed pair $(q \equiv A \to \alpha\bullet,\ j)$ asserts that a derivation of string $x_{j+1..i}$ from nonterminal $A$ has been discovered. Then cell $E[i]$ is updated with such assertion.)

for each completed pair $(q \equiv A \to \alpha\bullet, j)$ in $E[i]$
for each pair in $E[j]$ of the form $(r \equiv B \to \beta \bullet A\gamma, k)$,
such that state $r$ is the origin of an arc $r \xrightarrow{A} s$,
add to cell $E[i]$ the pair $(s \equiv B \to \beta A \bullet \gamma, k)$.

*Scan.* (Update the objectives in cell $E[i+1]$ in agreement with the current character. The pointer is set equal to the one of the pair under examination.)

for each pair in $E[i]$ of the form $(q \equiv A \to \alpha \bullet a\gamma, j)$, if $a = x_{i+1}$:
add to cell $E[i+1]$ the pair $(r \equiv A \to \alpha a \bullet \gamma, j)$
where state $r$ is the target of the arc $q \xrightarrow{a} r$.

The algorithm terminates when the construction of set $E[n]$ is finished; it may terminate prematurely with failure, if a scan does not find a pair to add to cell $E[i+1], i < n$.
If the final set $E[n]$ contains (at least) one completed pair $(q_{term} \equiv S \to \alpha\bullet, 0)$, where $q_{term}$ is the final state of the axiom machine, the source string is accepted.

For understanding the algorithm it helps to imagine the three operations as progressively constructing several syntax trees. From this standpoint, each cell or set represents a set of trees. In particular, in $E[i]$ we find a pair $(A \to \alpha \bullet \beta, p = j)$ if, and only if, the grammar generates a syntax tree of the following form:

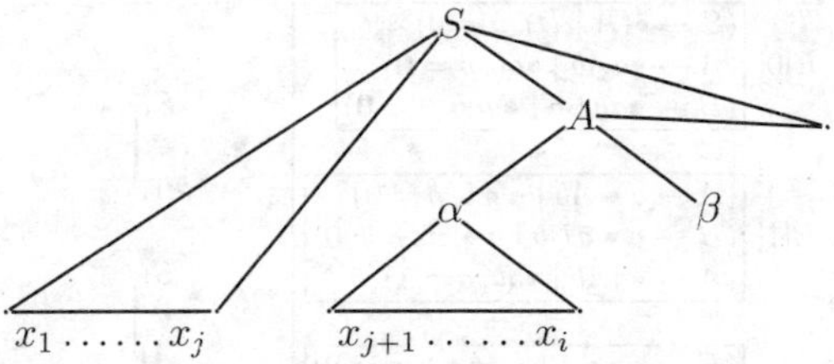


Upon termination the string is accepted if, and only if, among the trees associated with the last set, there is a complete syntax tree rooted at the axiom.

Notes:

Each character of the string is examined by a scan only one time.

A prediction repeatedly examines the pairs in the current cell and possibly adds new pairs to it. If the cell contents is organized as a FIFO list, it is easy to avoid multiple examinations of the same pair.

For completion operations: if in a pair $(r \equiv B \rightarrow \beta \bullet A\gamma, k) \in E[j]$ string $\gamma$ is empty, the new pair $(s \equiv B \rightarrow \beta A \bullet, k)$ added to $E[i]$ is completed, which triggers another iteration on the same cell.

It would be rather easy to prove that the algorithm accepts a string if it is a phrase of language $L(G)$: in fact, a pair is only added to a set if the derivation asserted by the pair is possible. On the other hand, the proof that every phrase of the language is recognized by the algorithm is more involved and is omitted.[10]

## Construction of Syntax Tree

In truth we have dealt only with string recognition, but producing the syntax tree(s) turns out to be rather simple, starting from the pairs inserted by the algorithm in the last cell. We explain the construction by means of an example.

*Example 5.35.* Syntax tree construction for example 5.34 (p. 243)
The vector computed by the parser for string *aabb* is reproduced in Figure 5.25, left. To the right we see from top to bottom three stages of tree construction. We start from the last cell, $E[4]$. Since it contains the completed pair $(S \rightarrow A\bullet, p = 0)$, derivation $S \Rightarrow A \overset{*}{\Rightarrow} x_{1\ldots4}$ surely exists, and we represent it in the topmost tree. The last subscript of nonterminal $A$ in the tree is 4, therefore we search in the fourth set $E[4]$ for a completed pair having nonterminal $A$ as left part. We find pair $(A \rightarrow aAb\bullet, p = 0)$ that we graft under $A_{1\ldots4}$ thus obtaining the tree in the middle. The subscript values 2 and 3 come from trivial arithmetics on previous subscripts.

---

[10] The reader may find it in the original paper by Earley [18] or in textbooks such as [20, 43, 24].

| | |
|---|---|
| $E[0]$ | $(S \to \bullet(A \mid B), p = 0)$<br>$(A \to \bullet aAb \mid \bullet ab, p = 0)$<br>$(B \to \bullet aaBb \mid \bullet aab, p = 0)$ |
| $a\ E[1]$ | $(A \to a \bullet Ab \mid a \bullet b, p = 0)$<br>$(B \to a \bullet aBb \mid a \bullet ab, p = 0)$<br>$(A \to \bullet aAb \mid \bullet ab, p = 1)$ |
| $a\ E[2]$ | $(B \to aa \bullet Bb \mid aa \bullet b, p = 0)$<br>$(A \to a \bullet Ab \mid a \bullet b, p = 1)$<br>$(B \to \bullet aaBb \mid \bullet aab, p = 2)$<br>$(A \to \bullet aAb \mid \bullet ab, p = 2)$ |
| $b\ E[3]$ | $(B \to aab\bullet, p = 0)$<br>$(A \to ab\bullet, p = 1)$<br>$(S \to B\bullet, p = 0)$<br>$(A \to aA \bullet b, p = 0)$ |
| $b\ E[4]$ | $(A \to aAb\bullet, p = 0)$<br>$(S \to A\bullet, p = 0)$ |

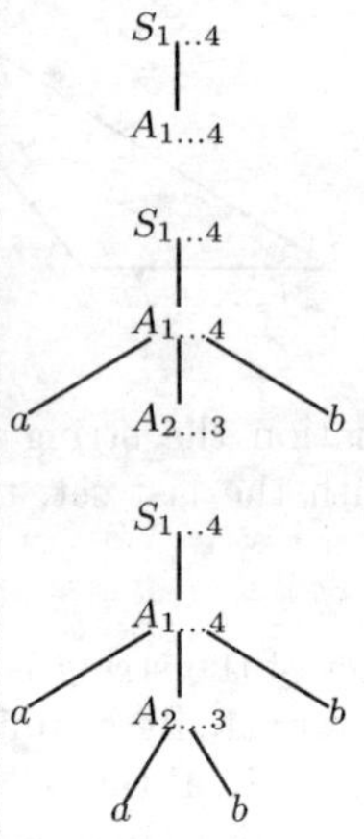


**Fig. 5.25** Left: sets computed by parser (example 5.35) for *aabb*. Right: syntax tree construction from top to bottom.

Now the central subtree $A_{2...3}$ has to be grown. It covers the string between positions 2 and 3; the latter tells us to search set $E[3]$, in order to find the next step of a derivation from $A_{2...3}$. More precisely, we look for a completed pair of $A$ having value 2 as pointer, because the first subscript of $A_{2...3}$ specifies the derivation started at position 2. In $E[3]$ we find pair $(A \to ab\bullet, p = 1)$ and we append derivation $A \Rightarrow ab$ thus obtaining the whole tree at bottom.

## Parsing Ambiguous Sentences

If the grammar is ambiguous, the parser actually produces all the possible leftmost derivations of a sentence. Notice that the derivations are not listed separately but the linked pointer data structure provides a concise representation of common parts of different derivations. This is explained in the coming example.

*Example 5.36.* Parsing an ambiguous language
The next grammar is bilaterally recursive hence ambiguous (p. 49).

$$S \to E \qquad E \to E + E \qquad E \to a$$

The sets computed for source string $a + a + a$ are tabulated in Figure 5.26 where in each set a divider separates the pairs computed by subsequent iterations of completion operations. Notice the repetition of the same pairs in

| | | |
|---|---|---|
| | $E[0]$ | $S \to \bullet E, 0$ |
| | | $E \to \bullet E + E \mid \bullet a, 0$ |
| $a$ | $E[1]$ | $E \to a\bullet, 0$ |
| | | $S \to E\bullet, 0$ |
| | | $E \to E \bullet +E, 0$ |
| $+$ | $E[2]$ | $E \to E + \bullet E, 0$ |
| | | $E \to \bullet E + E \mid \bullet a, 2$ |
| $a$ | $E[3]$ | $E \to a\bullet, 2$ |
| | | $E \to E + E\bullet, 0$ |
| | | $E \to E \bullet +E, 2$ |
| | | $S \to E\bullet, 0$ |
| | | $E \to E \bullet +E, 0$ |
| $+$ | $E[4]$ | $E \to E + \bullet E, 0$ |
| | | $E \to E + \bullet E, 2$ |
| | | $E \to \bullet E + E \mid \bullet a, 4$ |
| $a$ | $E[5]$ | $E \to a\bullet, 4$ |
| | | $E \to E + E\bullet, 2$ |
| | | $E \to E \bullet +E, 4$ |
| | | $E \to E + E\bullet, 0$ |
| | | $E \to E \bullet +E, 2$ |
| | | $S \to E\bullet, 0$ |
| | | $E \to E \bullet +E, 0$ |

**Fig. 5.26** Sets computed for ambiguous sentence $a + a + a$ (example 5.36).

several sets. In the last set $E[5]$ the completed pair $(S \to E\bullet, 0)$ evidences that the string is valid. We show how to recognize and construct multiple syntax trees, actually two for this sentence. For the first tree, Figure 5.27 lists on the left the relevant pairs and on the right the corresponding stages of construction. Notice the question mark at some stages of construction says that the corresponding subscript value is not known at that moment.

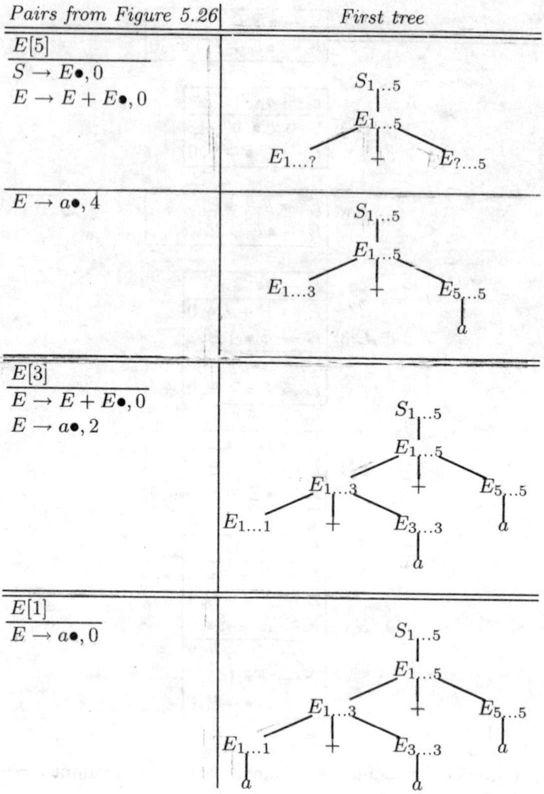


**Fig. 5.27** Constructing a syntax tree for example 5.36. Sets of pairs (left) used to grow the trees (right), from top to bottom.

For the second tree, the same information is given in Figure 5.28.

### 5.3.3 Computational Complexity

We have seen this parser does much more work than the deterministic top-down and bottom-up algorithms which we know to have linear time complexity with respect to the input string length. How much more work does it do? It is not difficult to compute the asymptotic time complexity in the worst case.

For a string of length $n$, we compute the number of pairs produced and of operations performed on them.

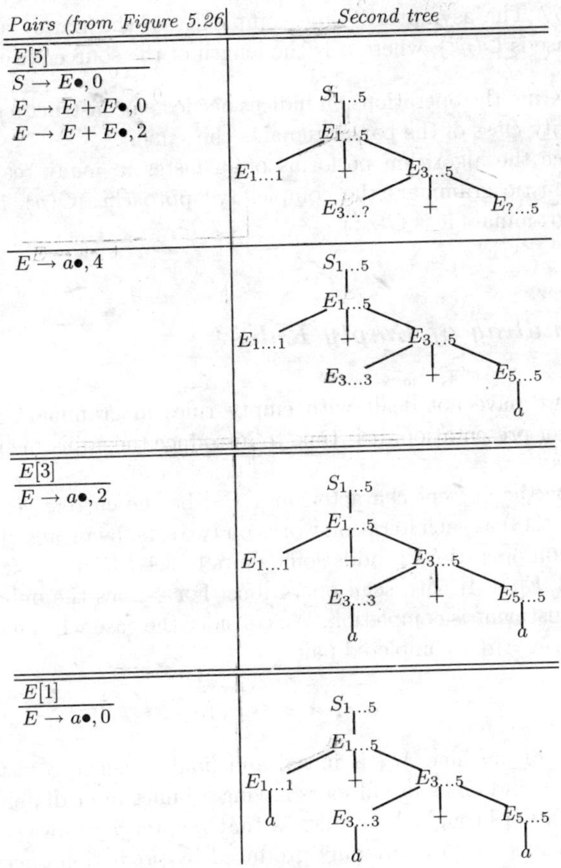


**Fig. 5.28** Constructing a second syntax tree for example 5.36. Sets of pairs at left are used to grow the trees (right), from top to bottom.

1. Each set $E[i], i \leqslant n$, may contain a number of pairs which is linear in $i$. We conservatively assume such number is bounded by a linear function of $n$.
2. On each pair present in set $E[i]$, scan and prediction operations may execute a number of steps that is independent of $n$.
3. A completion operation may execute $\mathcal{O}(i)$ steps on each pair it applies to. The reason is that a completion may add to set $E[i]$ a number of pairs of the order of $\mathcal{O}(j)$, where $E[j]$, $0 \leqslant j < i$, is a preceding set. Taking $n$ as upper bound of both $i$ and $j$, completion altogether needs no more than $\mathcal{O}(n^2)$ steps.
4. Summing up the numbers of steps performed for every index $i$ from 0 to $n$, we obtain the upper bound $\mathcal{O}(n^3)$.

*Property 5.37.* The asymptotic time complexity of the Earley algorithm in the worst case is $\mathcal{O}(n^3)$, where $n$ is the length of the source string.

Even considering the operations on indices needed to construct a syntax tree, the complexity class of the parser remains the same.

In practice the algorithm performs often faster in many realistic cases. For deterministic grammars the complexity approaches $\mathcal{O}(n)$, and for not ambiguous grammars it is $\mathcal{O}(n^2)$.

### 5.3.4 Handling of Empty Rules

Up to now we have not dealt with empty rules in grammars in order to simplify parser presentation. It is time to introduce the adjustments required for such rules.

Let $x(i)$ be the current character, and $E[i]$ be the current set. We recall the parser (p. 248) at each iteration works on two sets: by means of prediction and completion operations it adds some pairs to set $E[i]$ and it inserts some pairs into set $E[i+1]$ with scan operations. For $\varepsilon$-rules the only operation requiring adjustment is completion. We consider the case when a completion step finds in set $E[i]$ a completed pair

$$(q \equiv A \to \varepsilon\bullet,\ j) \tag{5.1}$$

where state $q$ of machine $M_A$ is initial and final. Then it goes to set $E[j]$ pointed to by $j$ and looks for all pairs having a bullet immediately left of $A$. The new situation brought by $\varepsilon$-rules is that pointer $j$ is always equal to $i$ because pairs such as (5.1) are only produced by prediction operations and a prediction always assigns the current index to the pointers of the pairs it creates.

We first describe a naif approach for handling such cases. A completion operation looks into the partially computed set $E[i]$ and invokes a prediction operation, which then invokes a completion, and so on, while either operation succeeds in adding a pair to the set.

A more efficient technique due to *Aycock and Horspool*[11] is next described. We list the algorithm with changes, restricted to prediction operation, shown in bold. We recall the nullability predicate from p. 60: a nonterminal $A$ is nullable if it can generate the empty string in one or more steps.

[11] See [5].

*Prediction,* with $\epsilon$-rules:

for each pair in $E[i]$ of the form $(q \equiv A \rightarrow \alpha \bullet B\gamma, j)$
where state $q$ is the origin of arc $q \xrightarrow{B} s$,
add to set $E[i]$ the pair $(r \equiv B \rightarrow \bullet\delta, i)$
where $r$ is the initial state of machine $M_B$.
**If $B$ is nullable, add to $E[i]$ the pairs**
$(s \equiv A \rightarrow \alpha B \bullet \gamma, j)$

Differently stated, a prediction operation moves the bullet from the left to the right of the nonterminal if the empty string can derive from it: this action simulates the fact that a derivation would cause the nonterminal symbol to disappear.

*Example 5.38.* Grammar with empty rules
In grammar

$$S' \rightarrow S \quad S \rightarrow AAAA \quad A \rightarrow a \quad A \rightarrow E \quad E \rightarrow \varepsilon$$

all nonterminals are nullable. We show in Figure 5.29 the sets computed while parsing string $a$ and two out of the possible derivations.

$E[0]$:

$S' \rightarrow \bullet S, 0$
$S \rightarrow \bullet AAAA, 0$
$S' \rightarrow S\bullet, 0$
$A \rightarrow \bullet a, 0$
$A \rightarrow \bullet E, 0$
$S \rightarrow A \bullet AAA, 0$
$E \rightarrow \bullet, 0$
$A \rightarrow E\bullet, 0$
$S \rightarrow AA \bullet AA, 0$
$S \rightarrow AAA \bullet A, 0$
$S \rightarrow AAAA\bullet, 0$

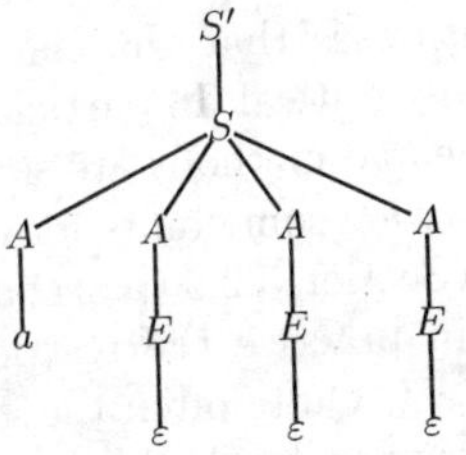


$a$ $E[1]$:

$A \rightarrow a\bullet, 0$
$S \rightarrow A \bullet AAA, 0$
$S \rightarrow AA \bullet AA, 0$
$S \rightarrow AAA \bullet A, 0$
$S \rightarrow AAAA\bullet, 0$
$A \rightarrow \bullet a, 1$
$A \rightarrow \bullet E, 1$
$S' \rightarrow S\bullet, 0$
$E \rightarrow \bullet, 1$
$A \rightarrow E\bullet, 1$

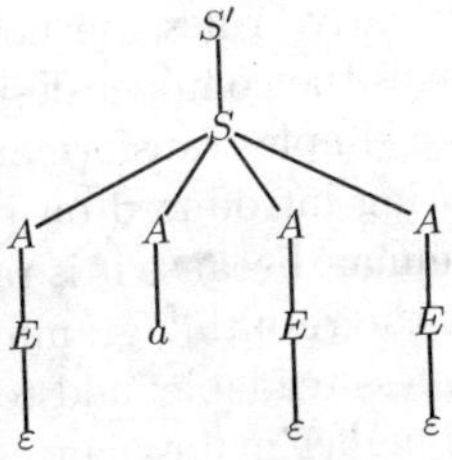


**Fig. 5.29** Sets computed by parser (left) and two syntax trees, for example 5.38.

### 5.3.5 Further Developments

The possibility was already mentioned to enrich the pairs (*state, pointer*) with look-ahead information, which may be computed as in the $LR(1)$ method. If a state is accompanied by a set of look-ahead terminals, the parser can decide not to add to the current sets $E[i]$ and $E[i+1]$ certain pairs that are destined to failure because they are inconsistent with the lookahead terminals. At first glance this provision looks like an improvement that should speed up recognition, especially when the grammar (or a part of it) meets the $LR(1)$ condition. However, in practice the number of pairs to be created and examined by the parser may actually increase with look-ahead sets, because of a splitting effect: a pair of the basic algorithm typically spawns multiple pairs differing in their look-ahead sets. This increase has a computational cost that makes the benefit of using look-ahead with Earley parsers controversial.

Finally we consider extended grammars: it is not difficult to modify the parser in order to work with EBNF rules.[12]

## 5.4 How to Choose a Parser

We complete the presentation of parsers with a discussion of choice criteria.

For the primary technical languages compilers exist that use both deterministic methods $LL(1)$ and $LR(1)$, the latter often in the simpler $LALR(1)$ variant. This witnesses that the choice between top-down and bottom-up parsers is not really critical. In particular, computational performance differences between the two methods are small and often negligible. The following considerations provide some hints for choosing one or the other technique.

We know from Section 5.2.9 (p. 241 and following) that the family of $LR(1)$ languages (also in practice the restricted $LALR(1)$ family) is larger than family $LL(k)$, $k \geqslant 1$. Quite often the grammar listed in the official language reference manual is not $LL(1)$, because it contains left-recursive rules or the guide sets of alternative rules are not disjoint. In that case choosing top-down parsing obliges the compiler designer to transform the grammar. More often than not, the simple transformations (such as moving recursion to the right or left factoring introduced on p. 193) suffice to obtain an equivalent $LL(k), k \geqslant 1$, grammar, because it is rarely the case that the source language is not $LL(k)$. But the resulting grammar is typically very different from the original and often less readable; add to it that having two grammar versions to manage carries higher maintenance costs when the language evolves over time.

Another relevant difference is that a software tool (such as *yacc* or *bison*) is needed to construct a shift-reduce parser, whereas recursive descent parsers

[12] A sketch of how to do it is in [18].

can be easily hand coded since the layout of a syntax procedure essentially mirrors the graph of the corresponding machine. For this reason the code of such compilers is easier to understand and may be preferred by the non-specialist. Actually, some tools also exist for helping in designing $LL$ parsers: they compute guide sets and generate the stubs of recursive procedures.

An advantage of the top-down approach is its direct handling of EBNF grammars, in contrast to the popular $LR$ or $LALR$ parser generation tools that do not accept such grammars. The annoying but not serious consequence is that the regular expressions present in the rules must be eliminated by means of standard transformations.

A parser is not an isolated application, but it is always interfaced with a translation algorithm (or semantic analyzer) to be described in the next chapter. Anticipating some discussion, top-down and bottom-up parsers differ with respect to the type of translation they can support. A formal property of syntax-directed translation, to be presented later, makes top-down parsers more convenient for designing simple translation procedures, obtained by inserting output actions into the body of parsing procedures. Such one-pass translators are less convenient to implement on top of bottom-up parsers.

If the reference grammar of the source language does not meet the $LL(.)$ or $LR(.)$ conditions, the compiler designer may choose to adopt a general parser, like Earley, instead of modifying the grammar. But he should be aware that the parser will be slower and more memory demanding than a deterministic one. Actually this situation is more common for natural language processing (computational linguistic) than for programming languages, because natural languages are much more ambiguous than artificial ones.

We should mention that other parsing algorithms exist that fall in between deterministic parsers and general parsers with respect to generality and computational performance. Derived from $LL(k)$ top-down algorithms, parsers exist, like ANTLR mentioned on p. 197, that may perform unbounded look-ahead in order to decide the next move. For bottom-up parsing, a practical almost deterministic algorithm existing in several variants is due to Tomita.[13] The idea is to carry on in parallel a bounded number of alternative parsing attempts.

Sometimes an entirely different strategy for curtailing the combinatorial explosion of nondeterministic attempts is followed, especially when the syntax is highly ambiguous but only one semantic interpretation is possible. In that case it would be wasteful to construct a number of syntax trees, just to delete at a later time all but one of them using semantic criteria. It is preferable to anticipate semantic checks during parsing thus preventing meaningless syntactic derivations to be carried on. Such strategy, called *semantics-directed parsing*, is presented in the next chapter.

In some situations another capability is requested from a parser (more generally from a compiler): to be able to incrementally process the grammar or

---

[13] See [54].

the input string. As a matter of fact, the concept of incremental compilation takes two different meanings.

*Incrementality with respect to the grammar.* This situation occurs when the source language is subjected to change, implying the grammar is not fixed. When changes are maybe minor but frequent it is rather annoying or even impossible to create a new parser after each change. Such is the case of so-called extensible languages, where the language user may modify the syntax of some constructs or introduce new instructions. It is then mandatory to be able to automatically construct the parser, or better to incrementally modify the existing parser after each syntax change.[14]

*Incrementality with respect to the source string.* A more common requirement is to quickly reconstruct the syntax tree after some change or correction of the input string has taken place, following perhaps some error indication provided by a previous run of the parser.

A good program construction environment should interact with the user and allow him to edit the source text and to quickly recompile it, minimizing time and effort. In order to reduce recompilation time after a change, incremental compilation methods have been developed that are based on special algorithms for syntax and semantic analysis. Focussing on the former, suppose the parser has analyzed a text, identified some error, and produced an error message. Then the author has done some corrections typically in a few points.

A parser qualifies as incremental if the time it takes to analyze the corrected text is much shorter than the time for parsing the first time. To this end, the algorithm has to save the result of the previous analysis in such form that updates can be just made in the few spots affected by changes. In practice, the algorithm saves the configurations traversed by the pushdown automaton recognizing the previous text and rolls back to the last configuration that has not been affected by the changes to the text. From there the algorithm resumes parsing.[15]

---

[14] For this problem see [26].

[15] The main ideas on incremental parsing can be found in [22, 33].

# Chapter 6
# Translation Semantics and Static Analysis

## 6.1 Introduction

In addition to recognition and parsing, most language processing tasks perform some transformation of the original sentence. For instance, a compiler translates a program from a high-level programming language, e.g., *Java*, to the machine code of some microprocessor. This chapter presents a progression of translation models and methods.

A translation is a function or more generally a mapping from the strings of the source language to the strings of the target language. As for string recognition, two approaches are possible. The generative point of view relies on two coupled grammars, termed a syntactic translation schema, to generate a pair of strings which correspond to each other in the translation. The other approach uses a transducer, which differs from an automaton by its capability to emit a target string.

Such methods may be termed (purely) syntactic translations. They extend and complete the language definition and parsing methods of previous chapters, but we hasten to say they are not adequate for implementing the rather involved translations required for typical compilers. What is lacking in purely syntactic methods is the concern for the meaning or semantics of the language. For that we shall present the attribute grammar model, which is a valuable software engineering method for designing well-structured translators by taking advantage of the syntactic modularity of grammar rules.

We are going to clarify the distinction between *syntax* and *semantics* of a language. The etymology of the two terms says rather vaguely that the former has to do with the structure and the latter with the meaning or the message to be communicated. In linguistics the two terms have often been taken as emblems representing forms and contents but this reference to human studies does not make the distinction any more precise or formal.

In the case of computer languages there is a sort of consensus on a demarcation line between syntactic and semantic methods. The first difference comes from the domains of the entities and operations used by syntax versus semantics. Syntax uses the concepts and operations of formal language theory and represents the algorithms as automata. The entities are alphabets, strings, and syntax trees; the operations are concatenation, morphisms on characters and strings, and tree construction primitives. On the negative side, the concepts of number and arithmetic operation (sum, product, etc.) are extraneous to syntax. On the other hand, in semantics the entities are not a priori limited: numbers and any type of data structures available to programmers (such as tables or linked lists) may be defined and used as needed by semantic algorithms. These can take advantage of the syntactic structure as a skeleton for orderly processing of language components.

The second difference is the higher computational complexity of semantic algorithms with respect to syntactic ones. We recall that the formal languages of concern to compilers belong almost exclusively to the regular and deterministic context-free families. String recognition, parsing, and syntactic translation are typical syntactic tasks and can be performed in linear time, i.e., in a time proportional to the length of the source text. But such very efficient algorithms fall short of all controls required to check program correctness with respect to the language reference manual. For instance, it is not possible to check with a parser that an object used in a *Java* expression has been consistently defined in a declaration. As a matter of fact, such control cannot be done in linear time. This and similar operations are performed by a compiler subsystem usually referred to as a semantic analyzer.

Going deeper into the comparison, the distinction between syntax and semantic models is imposed by pragmatic considerations. In fact, it is well-known from computational theory that any computable function, such as the one deciding whether a source string is a valid *Java* program, can in principle be realized by a Turing machine. This is for sure a syntactic formalism since it operates just on strings and uses the basic operations of formal language theory. But in practice a Turing machine is too complicated to program for any realistic problem, least for compilation.

Years of attempts at inventing grammars or automata that would allow some of the usual semantic controls to be performed by the parser, have shown that the legibility and convenience of syntactic methods rapidly decay, as soon as the model goes beyond context-free languages and enters the context-dependent (p. 87) range of languages. In other words, practical syntactic methods are limited to the context-free range.

### 6.1.1 Chapter Outline

The word *translation* signifies a correspondence between two texts in different languages, having the same meaning. Many cases of translation occur with artificial languages: compilation of a programming language to machine code, transformation of an HTML document to the PDF format used for portable documents, etc.. The given text and language are termed the *source* and the other text and language are the *target*.

In our presentation, the first grade of translation to be considered will be an abstract mapping between two formal languages. The second grade are the translations obtained by applying local transformations to the source text, such as replacing a character with a string in accordance with a transliteration table. The third grade consists of the translations defined by regular expressions and finite transducers that are finite automata enriched with an output function. The fourth grade presents the syntactic translation schemata or translation grammars that differ from the previous grade by the use of a context-free grammar instead of a regular expression for defining the source and target languages. Such translations are also characterized by the abstract machine computing them, the pushdown transducer, that can be implemented using the parsing algorithms of previous chapters.

All previous classes of translations are purely syntactic and fall short of the requirements of compilation, as various typical transformations to be performed cannot be expressed with such methods. Nevertheless, syntactic translation models are important as a conceptual foundation of the actual methods used in compilation. Moreover, they have another use as a method for abstracting from the concrete syntax in order to manifest similarities between languages.

It is enlightening to show a structural analogy between the theories of previous chapters and of the present one. At the level of set theoretical definition: the set of sentences of the source language becomes the set of matching pairs (source string, target string) of the translation relation. At the level of generative definition: the language grammar becomes a translation grammar generating pairs of source/target strings. Finally, at the level of operational definitions: the finite or pushdown automaton or parser recognizing a language becomes a translator computing the transformation. Such conceptual correspondences will clearly surface in this chapter.

The fifth and last conceptual model is the syntax-directed semantic translation, a semiformal approach based on the previous models. This makes a convenient engineering method for designing well-structured modular translators. Its presentation relies on attribute grammars consisting of a combination of syntax rules and semantic functions.

Several typical examples will be presented. A lexical analyzer or scanner is specified by the addition of simple semantic attributes and functions to a finite transducer. Other important examples are: type control in expressions, translation of conditional instructions into jumps, and semantic-directed parsing.

The last part of the chapter presents another central method of language compilers, namely, static program analysis. This analysis applies to executable programs rather than to generic technical languages. The flowchart or control flow graph of the program to be analyzed is viewed as a finite automaton. Static analysis detects on this automaton various properties of the program related to correctness or needed to perform program optimizations. This final topic completes the well-balanced exposition of elementary compilation methods.

## 6.2 Translation Relation and Function

We introduce some notions from the mathematical theory of translations[1] that suffice for the scope of the book.

Let the *source* and *target* alphabets be respectively denoted by $\Sigma$ and $\Delta$. A translation is a correspondence between source and target strings, to be formalized as a binary relation between the universal languages $\Sigma^*$ and $\Delta^*$, that is, as a subset of the cartesian product $\Sigma^* \times \Delta^*$.

A *translation relation* $\rho$ is a set of pairs of strings $(x, y)$, with $x \in \Sigma^*$ and $y \in \Delta^*$:

$$\rho = \{(x, y), \ldots\} \subseteq \Sigma^* \times \Delta^*$$

We say that the target string $y$ is the *image* or *translation* of the source string $x$ and that the two strings correspond to each other in the translation. Given a translation relation $\rho$, the *source language* $L_1$ and *target language* $L_2$ are respectively defined as the projection of the relation on the first and second component:

$$L_1 = \{x \in \Sigma^* \mid \text{ for some } y : (x, y) \in \rho\}$$
$$L_2 = \{y \in \Delta^* \mid \text{ for some } x : (x, y) \in \rho\}$$

Alternatively a translation can be formalized by taking the set of all the images of each source string. Then a translation is a *function* $\tau$:

$$\tau : \Sigma^* \rightarrow \text{ powerset of } \Delta^*; \qquad \tau(x) = \{y \in \Delta^* \mid (x, y) \in \rho\}$$

where $\rho$ is a translation relation. This function maps a source string on the set of its images, that is, on a language.

Notice that the repeated application of the function to each string of the source language produces a set of languages; their union gives the target language:

$$L_2 = \tau(L_1) = \bigcup_{x \in \Sigma^*} \tau(x)$$

In general a translation is not a total function, i.e., for some strings over the source alphabet the translation function is undefined. A simple expedient to make the function total is to posit that where $\tau(x)$ is undefined, it is assigned the value *error*.

[1] A rigorous presentation can be found in Berstel [8] and in Sakarovitch [46].

A particular but practically most important case occurs when the image of each string is unique.

The *inverse translation* $\tau^{-1} : \Delta^* \to \Sigma^*$ maps the target strings on the source ones:

$$\tau^{-1}(y) = \{x \in \Sigma^* \mid y \in \tau(x)\}$$

Depending on the mathematical properties of the function, the following cases arise for a translation:

- total: any source string has an image;
- single-valued: no string has two distinct images;
- multi-valued : some source string has two images;
- injective: distinct source strings have distinct images or, differently stated, any target string corresponds to at most one source string; in this case the inverse translation is single-valued;
- surjective: a function is surjective when the image coincides with the range, that is, when any string over the target alphabet is the image of at least one source string;
- bijective: the correspondence between source and target strings is one to one.

To illustrate, consider a high-level, say *Java*, source program and its image in the code of a certain machine. Clearly the translation is total because any valid program can be compiled to machine code and any incorrect program has the value *error* (i.e., a diagnostic) for image.
Such translation is multi-valued because usually the same *Java* statement admits several different machine code realizations.
The translation is not injective because two source programs may have the same machine code image: just think of two `while` and `for` loops translated to the same code that uses conditional and unconditional jumps.
The translation is not surjective since some machine programs operating on special hardware registers cannot be expressed by *Java* programs.

On the other hand, if we consider a particular compiler from *Java* to machine code, the translation is totally defined as before and in addition is single valued, because the compiler chooses exactly one out of the many possible machine implementations of the source program.
The translation is not necessarily injective (for the same reasons as above) and certainly is not surjective, because a typical compiler does not use all the instructions of a machine.

A decompiler reconstructs a source program from a given machine program. Notice that this translation is not the reverse translation of the compilation, because compiler and decompiler are independently designed algorithms and are unlikely to make the same design decisions for their mappings. A trivial example: the decompiler $\delta$, given a machine program $\tau(x)$ produced by the compiler $\tau$, will output a *Java* program $\delta(\tau(x))$ that almost certainly differs from $x$ with respect to the presence of blank spaces!

Since compilation is a mapping between two languages which are not finite, it cannot be specified by the exhaustive enumeration of the corresponding pairs of source/target strings. The chapter continues with a gradual presentation of methods to specify and implement such infinite translations.

## 6.3 Transliteration

A naif way to specify text transformations is to apply in each position of the source string a local mapping. The simplest transformation is the transliteration or alphabetic homomorphism, introduced in Chapter 2, p. 80. Each source character is transliterated to a target character (or more generally to a string).

Let us read example 2.83 on p. 81 anew. The translation defined by an alphabetic homomorphism is clearly single-valued whereas the inverse translation may or may not be single-valued: in the example the little square $\square$ is the image of any Greek letter, hence the inverse translation is multi-valued:

$$h^{-1}(\square) = \{\alpha, \ldots, \omega\}$$

If the homomorphism erases a letter, i.e., it maps it to the empty string, as happens with characters start-text, end-text, the inverse translation is multi-valued because any string made with erasable characters can be inserted in any text position.

If the inverse function too is single-valued, the source/target mapping is a one-to-one or bijective function and it is possible to reconstruct the source string from a given target string. This situation occurs when encryption is applied to a text. A historical example defined by transliteration is Julius Caesar's encryption method that replaces a letter at position $i$, with $i = 1, \ldots, 26$, in the Latin alphabet, by the letter at position $(i+k)$ mod 26, where $k$ is the secret key, a constant.

To finish we stress that transliteration transforms a letter to another one, totally ignoring the context of occurrence. It goes without saying that such process falls short of the needs of compilation.

## 6.4 Regular Translations

Regular expressions can be modified in order to specify a translation relation, by a simple change: the arguments of the expression, instead of being characters as customary, are pairs of source/target strings. Then a sentence generated by such regular expression is a sequence of pairs; by separating the source component of each pair from the target one we obtain two strings, which can be interpreted as a pair belonging to the translation relation. In this manner such regular expression defines a translation relation to be called *regular* or *rational*.

*Example 6.1.* Consistent transliteration of an operator
The source text is a list of numbers separated by a division sign "/" . The translation may replace the sign by either one of the signs ":" or "÷", but it must consistently choose the same sign throughout. For simplicity we assume the numbers to be unary. The alphabets are

$$\Sigma = \{1, /\} \qquad \Delta = \{1, \div, :\}$$

The source strings have the form $c(/c)*$, where $c$ stands for a unary number, $1^+$. Two valid translations are

$$(3/5/2,\ 3:5:2), \qquad (3/5/2,\ 3 \div 5 \div 2)$$

On the contrary, $(3/5/2,\ 3 : 5 \div 2)$ is wrong, because division signs are differently transliterated.

Notice this translation cannot be expressed by a homomorphism, since the image of the division sign is not single-valued. Incidentally the inverse translation is an alphabetic homomorphism. The regular expression of the translation is

$$(1,1)^+ \left((/,:)(1,1)^+\right)^* \cup (1,1)^+ \left((/,\div)(1,1)^+\right)^*$$

For readability, it is convenient to write the matching pairs as fractions, with the source string over the target string:

$$\left(\frac{1}{1}\right)^+ \left(\frac{/}{:}\left(\frac{1}{1}\right)^+\right)^* \cup \left(\frac{1}{1}\right)^+ \left(\frac{/}{\div}\left(\frac{1}{1}\right)^+\right)^*$$

The terms produced by applying a derivation are strings of fractions, i.e., string pairs, e.g., $\frac{/}{\div}$. Consider the derived string

$$\frac{1}{1}\frac{/}{\div}\frac{1}{1}\frac{1}{1}$$

and project it on the top and bottom components thus obtaining the pair of source/target strings $(1/11,\ 1 \div 11)$.

**Definition 6.2.** A *regular* or *rational translation expression* (r.t.e.) $r$ is a regular expression with union, concatenation, star (and cross) operators, having as arguments some pairs $(u, v)$, also written as $\frac{u}{v}$, where $u$ and $v$ are possibly empty strings respectively on the source and on the target alphabet.

Let $C \subset \Sigma^* \times \Delta^*$ be the set of pairs $(u, v)$ occurring in the expression. The regular or rational translation relation defined by the r.t.e. consists of the pairs $(x, y)$ of source/target strings such that:

- there exists a string $z \in C^*$ in the regular set defined by $r$;
- $x$ and $y$ are respectively the projection of $z$ on the first and second component.

It is straightforward to see that the set of source strings defined by an r.t.e. (as well as the set of target strings) is a regular language. But notice that not every translation relation, having as source and target languages two regular sets, can be defined with an r.t.e.: an example, to be discussed later, is the relation mapping each string to its mirror string.

### 6.4.1 Two-Input Automaton

Since the set $C$ of pairs occurring in an r.t.e. can be viewed as a new terminal alphabet, the regular language over $C$ can be recognized by a finite automaton, as illustrated in the coming example.

*Example 6.3.* Example 6.1 continued
The recognizer of the regular translation relation is shown in Figure 6.1.

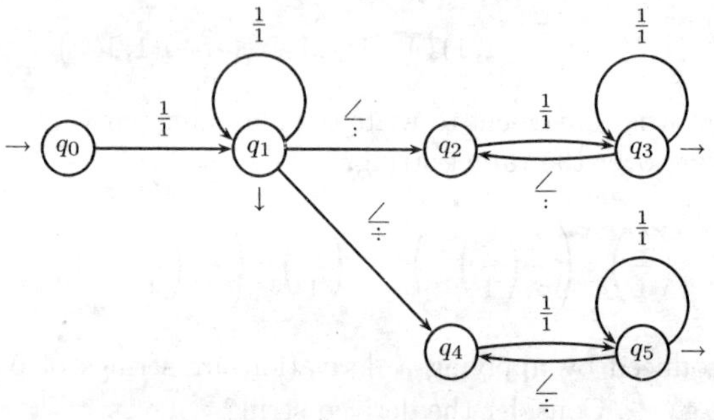


**Fig. 6.1** 2$I$-automaton of the r.t.e. of examples 6.1 and 6.3.

This automaton can be viewed as a machine with two read-only input tapes, in short a 2$I$-machine, each one with an independent reading head, respectively containing the source string $x$ and the target string $y$. Initially the heads are positioned on the first characters and the machine is in the starting state. The machine performs as specified by the state-transition graph; e.g.,in $q_1$, reading a slash "/" from the source tape and a sign "÷" from the target tape, the automaton moves to state $q_4$ and shifts both heads by one position. If the machine reaches a final state and both tapes have been entirely scanned, the pair $(x, y)$ belongs to the translation relation.[2]

This automaton can check that two strings such as

$$(11/1,\ 1 \div 1) \equiv \frac{11/1}{1 \div 1}$$

do not correspond in the translation, because the computation

$$q_0 \xrightarrow{\frac{1}{1}} q_1$$

admits no continuation with the next pair, $\frac{1}{\div}$.

It is sometimes convenient to assume each tape is delimited to the right by a reserved character marking the end.

At first glance, regular translation expressions and two-input machines may seem to be the wrong idealizations for modelling a compiler, because in compilation the target string is not given but must be computed by the translator. Yet this conceptualization is valuable for specifying some simple translations, and also as a rigorous method for studying translation functions. Moreover, it offers a unified viewpoint towards the translations computed by lexical and syntactic analyzers.

### Forms of Two-Input Automata

When designing a two-input recognizer we can assume without loss of generality that each move reads exactly one source character while it may read zero or more characters from the target tape.

**Definition 6.4.** $2I$-automaton.
A finite automaton with two inputs or $2I$-*automaton* is defined as a usual finite automaton (p. 110) by a set of states $Q$, an initial state $q_0$ and a set $F \subseteq Q$ of final states. The transition function is

$$\delta : (Q \times \Sigma \times \Delta^*) \rightarrow \text{ powerset of } Q$$

If $q' \in \delta(q, a, u)$, the automaton has a move that reads $a$ from the first tape and $u \in \Delta^*$ from the second one, and enters the next state $q'$. The condition for recognition is that a computation reaches a final state.

Imagine now to project the arc labels of a $2I$-automaton on the first component. The resulting automaton has just one input tape with symbols from the source alphabet $\Sigma$ and is termed the input automaton *subjacent* to the original machine; it recognizes the source language.

---

[2] This model is known as a Rabin and Scott machine. For greater generality such machine may be equipped with more than two tapes in order to define a relation between more than two languages.

Sometimes another *normal* form of a $2I$-automaton is used characterized by the fact that each move reads exactly one character either from the source or from the target tape, but not from both. More precisely the arc labels are of the following types:

$$\frac{a}{\varepsilon},\ a \in \Sigma, \quad \text{read from source}$$
$$\frac{\varepsilon}{b},\ b \in \Delta, \quad \text{read from target}$$

This means that a normal form machine shifts only one head per move. It is to be expected that such normalization may often increase the number of states because a nonnormalized move

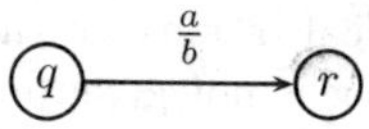


is replaced by a cascade of normalized moves

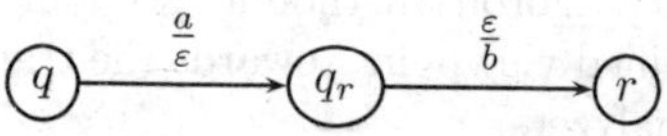


where $q_r$ is a new state.

On the other hand, in order to make the model more expressive and concise, it is convenient to allow regular translation expressions as arc labels. As for finite automata, this generalization does not change the computational power but helps in hiding the details of complicated examples.
Finally a short notation: in an arc label we usually drop a component when it is the empty string. Thus we may write

$$\frac{a^*b}{d} \mid \frac{a^*c}{e}$$

in place of

$$\frac{a^*}{\varepsilon}\frac{b}{d} \mid \frac{a^*}{\varepsilon}\frac{c}{e}$$

This expression says that a sequence of $a$'s, if followed by $b$, is translated to $d$; if it is followed by $c$, it is translated to $e$.

## Equivalence of Models

In agreement with the well-known equivalence of regular expressions and finite automata, we state a corresponding property for translations.

*Property 6.5.* The families of translations defined by regular translation expressions and by finite (nondeterministic) $2I$-automata coincide.

We recall that an r.t.e. defines a regular language $R$ over an alphabet consisting of a finite set of pairs of strings $(u, v) \equiv \frac{u}{v}$, where $u \in \Sigma^*, v \in \Delta^*$. By separately extracting from each string in $R$ the source and target elements, we obtain a crisp formulation of the relation between source and target languages.

*Property 6.6.* Nivat theorem.
The following conditions are equivalent:

1. The translation relation $\rho \subseteq \Sigma^* \times \Delta^*$ is regular.
2. There exists an alphabet $\Omega$, a regular language $R$ over $\Omega$ and two alphabetic homomorphisms $h_1 : \Omega \to \Sigma \cup \{\varepsilon\}$ and $h_2 : \Omega \to \Delta \cup \{\varepsilon\}$ such that
$$\rho = \{(h_1(z), h_2(z)) \mid z \in R\}$$
3. If the source and target alphabets are disjoint, there exists a regular language $R'$ over the alphabet $\Sigma \cup \Delta$ such that
$$\rho = \{(h_\Sigma(z), h_\Delta(z)) \mid z \in R'\}$$
where $h_\Sigma$ and $h_\Delta$ are respectively the projections from the alphabet $\Sigma \cup \Delta$ to the source and target alphabets.

*Example 6.7.* Division by two
The image string is the halved source string. The translation relation $\{(a^{2n}, a^n) \mid n \geqslant 1\}$ is defined by r.t.e.
$$\left(\frac{aa}{a}\right)^+$$
An equivalent $2I$-automaton $A$ is shown below:

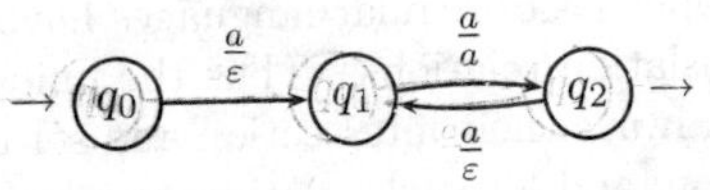


To apply the Nivat theorem (statement 2), we derive from automaton $A$ the following r.t.e.:
$$\left(\frac{a}{\varepsilon}\frac{a}{a}\right)^+$$
and we rename for clarity the pairs:
$$\frac{a}{\varepsilon} = c \qquad \frac{a}{a} = d$$
Next consider the alphabet $\Omega = \{c, d\}$. The r.t.e. defines the regular language $R = (cd)^+$, obtained replacing each fraction with a character of the new alphabet. The alphabetic homomorphisms

| | $h_1$ | $h_2$ |
|---|---|---|
| $c$ | $a$ | $\varepsilon$ |
| $d$ | $a$ | $a$ |

produce the intended translation relation. Thus, for $z = cdcd \in R$, we have $h_1(z) = aaaa$ and $h_2(z) = aa$.

To apply case 3. of the theorem, change first the target alphabet to $\Delta = \{b\}$, to make the two alphabets disjoint, and redefine the translation as $\{(a^{2n}, b^n) \mid n \geqslant 1\}$. Propagating the change to the r.t.e.

$$\left(\frac{a}{\varepsilon}\frac{a}{b}\right)^+$$

we obtain the regular language $R' \subseteq (\Sigma \cup \Delta)^*$ to be used in the statement. Concatenating the strings occurring at the numerator and denominator, then erasing the fraction lines, we have

$$R' = (aa\varepsilon b)^+ = (aab)^+$$

The projections of this language on the source and target alphabets define the source/target string mapping.

Applying the well-known equivalence of finite automata and right-linear grammars (p. 106), we can represent a $2I$-automaton by a so-called *translation grammar*. We illustrate with the previous example:

$$S \to \tfrac{a}{\varepsilon}Q_1 \qquad Q_1 \to \tfrac{a}{a}Q_2 \qquad Q_2 \to \tfrac{a}{\varepsilon}Q_1 \mid \varepsilon$$

Each grammar rule corresponds to a move of the $2I$-automaton. Rule $Q_2 \to \varepsilon$ is a short notation for $Q_2 \to \frac{\varepsilon}{\varepsilon}$.

The notation using a translation grammar instead of a $2I$-automaton or a r.t.e. will be preferred for the syntactic translations, which have a context-free grammar as their support.

Several but not all properties of regular languages have an analogous formulation for regular translation relations.[3] Thus the union of regular translation relations, but not always their intersection and set difference, yields a regular translation relation; and for such relations it is possible to formulate a pumping lemma similar to the one for regular languages on p. 73.

### 6.4.2 Translation Functions and Finite Transducers

It is time to abandon the overly static perspective of a translation as a relation between two strings and to focus instead on the process of translation viewing an automaton as an algorithmic implementation of a translation function. The model offering this perspective is the *finite transducer* or *IO-automaton*. This machine reads the source string from the input tape and writes the image on the output tape. We shall mostly study single-valued translation and

---

[3] See the books [8, 46].

especially those that are computed by deterministic machines. We introduce the model by an example.

*Example 6.8.* Nondeterministic translation
It is required to translate a string $a^n$ to the image $b^n$, if $n$ is even, or to $c^n$, if $n$ is odd. The relation

$$\rho = \{(a^{2n}, b^{2n}) \mid n \geqslant 0\} \cup \{(a^{2n+1}, c^{2n+1}) \mid n \geqslant 0\}$$

defines the translation function

$$\tau(a^n) = \begin{cases} b^n, n \text{ even} \\ c^n, n \text{ odd} \end{cases}$$

The r.t.e. is

$$\left(\frac{a^2}{b^2}\right)^* \cup \frac{a}{c}\left(\frac{a^2}{c^2}\right)^*$$

A simple deterministic two-input automaton recognizes this relation:

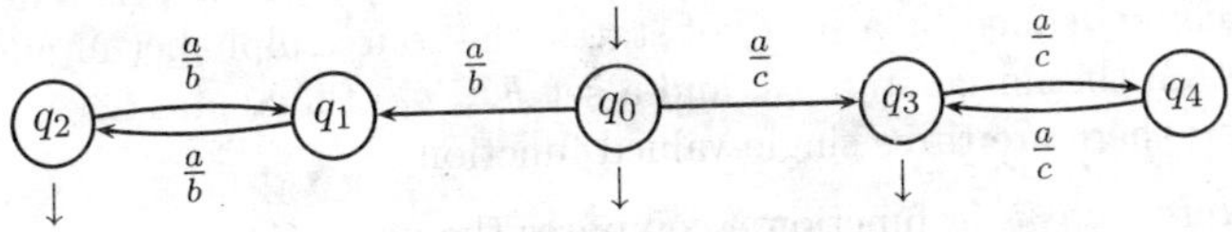


To check for determinism, observe that only state $q_0$ has two outgoing arcs but their labels are different.[4] Therefore the 2I-machine can deterministically decide if a pair of strings memorized on the two tapes, such as $\frac{aaaa}{bbbb}$, are one the image of the other in the translation relation.

Although the transducer or *IO*-automaton has the same graph as the 2*I*-automaton, the meaning of an arc $q_0 \xrightarrow{\frac{a}{b}} q_1$ is entirely different: in state $q_0$ it reads $a$ from the input, writes $b$ to the output, and enters state $q_1$. We observe that arc $q_0 \xrightarrow{\frac{a}{c}} q_3$ instructs the machine to perform a different action, while reading the same character $a$ in the same state $q_0$. In other words the choice between the two moves is not deterministic. As a consequence, two computations are possible for the input string $aa$:

$$q_0 \to q_1 \to q_2; \qquad q_0 \to q_3 \to q_4$$

but only the former succeeds in reaching a final state and only its output is considered: $\tau(aa) = bb$. Notice that the nondeterminism of the transducer shows up in the input automaton subjacent to the transducer, which is non-deterministic.

Moreover, it should be intuitively clear that the requested translation cannot be done by a deterministic finite transducer because the choice of the

[4] If the 2*I*-automaton has some moves that do not read from either tape, the determinism condition has to be formulated more carefully, see e.g.,[46].

character to emit may only be done when the input has been entirely scanned, but then it is too late to decide how many characters have to be output.

To sum up the findings of this example, there are single-valued regular translations which cannot be computed by a deterministic finite *IO*-automaton. This is a striking difference with respect to the well-known equivalence of deterministic and nondeterministic models of finite automata.

## Sequential Transducers

In some applications it is necessary to efficiently compute the translation in real time, implying that the translator must produce the output while scanning the input. At last, when the input is finished, the automaton may append to the output a finite piece of text that depends on the final state reached. This is the behavior of a sort of deterministic machine 3 called a sequential transducer. [5]

**Definition 6.9.** A *sequential transducer* or *IO-automaton* $T$ is a deterministic machine defined by a set $Q$ of states, the source alphabet $\Sigma$ and target alphabet $\Delta$, the initial state $q_0$, and a set $F \subseteq Q$ of final states. Moreover, there are three single-valued functions:

1. the *state transition* function $\delta$ computes the next state;
2. the *output function* $\eta$ computes the string to be emitted in a move;
3. the *final function* $\varphi$ computes the last suffix to be appended to the target string at termination.

The function domains are

$$\delta : Q \times \Sigma \to Q, \qquad \eta : Q \times \Sigma \to \Delta^*, \qquad \varphi : F \times \{\dashv\} \to \Delta^*$$

In the graphical presentation the two functions $\delta(q, a) = r$ and $\eta(q, a) = u$ are represented by arc $\textcircled{q} \xrightarrow[u]{a} \textcircled{r}$, which means: in state $q$, reading character $a$, emit string $u$ and move to state $r$.
The final function $\varphi(r, \dashv) = v$ means: when the source string has been entirely scanned, if the final state is $r$, then write string $v$.
For a source string $x$, the translation $\tau(x)$ computed by $T$ is the concatenation of two strings, produced by the output function and by the final one:

$$\tau(x) = \{yz \in \Delta^* \mid \exists \text{ a labelled computation } \frac{x}{y} \text{ ending in state } r \in F$$
$$\wedge\ z = \varphi(r, \dashv)\}$$

The machine is deterministic because the input automaton $\langle Q, \Sigma, \delta, q_0, F\rangle$ subjacent to $T$ is deterministic and the output and final functions are single-valued.

[5] This is the terminology of [46]; others [8] call subsequential the same model.

However, the condition that the subjacent input automaton be deterministic does not ensure by itself that the translation is single-valued, because between two states of $T$ there may be an arc labelled $\frac{a}{\{b\} \cup \{c\}}$, causing the output to be nonunique.

We call *sequential* a translation function computable by a sequential transducer.

*Example 6.10.* Meaningless zeros
The source text is a list of binary integers separated by a blank ($b$). The single-valued translation deletes all meaningless zeros. The translation is defined by the r.t.e.:

$$\left(\left(\frac{0^+}{0} \mid \left(\frac{0}{\varepsilon}\right)^* \frac{1}{1} \left(\frac{0}{0} \mid \frac{1}{1}\right)^*\right) \frac{b}{b}\right)^* \left(\frac{0^+}{0} \mid \left(\frac{0}{\varepsilon}\right)^* \frac{1}{1} \left(\frac{0}{0} \mid \frac{1}{1}\right)^*\right) \frac{\dashv}{\varepsilon}$$

The equivalent sequential transducer is in Figure 6.2. The final function $\varphi$ writes nothing in final state $q_1$, whereas it writes 0 in state $q_2$.

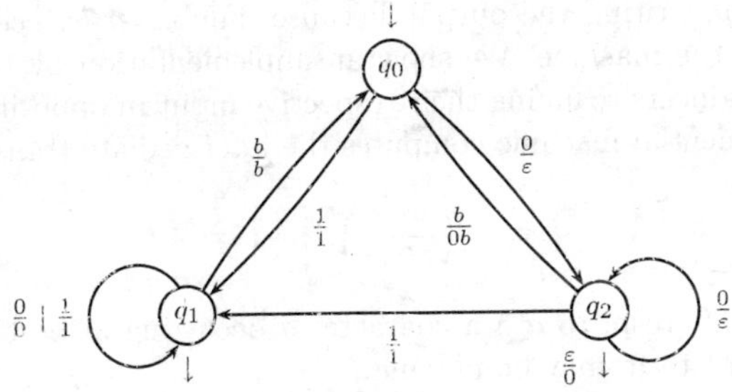


**Fig. 6.2** Sequential transducer (*IO*-machine) of example 6.10.

Examples of computation. When translating $00b01$, the machine traverses the states $q_0q_2q_2q_0q_2q_1q_1$ and writes $\varepsilon.\varepsilon.0b.\varepsilon.1.\varepsilon = 0b1$. For source string 00 the machine traverses the states $q_0q_2q_2$, writes $\varepsilon.\varepsilon$, and at last writes 0.

We show a second example of sequential transducer that makes an essential use of the final function to compute the translation specified by:

$$\tau(a^n) = \begin{cases} e, & n \text{ even} \\ o, & n \text{ odd} \end{cases}$$

The sequential transducer has two states, both final, corresponding to the classes of parity of the source strings. The machine writes nothing while it commutes from one state to the other; at the end, depending on the final state, it writes $e$ or $o$.

To conclude, we mention a practically relevant property: the composition of two sequential functions is a sequential function. This means that the cascade composition of two sequential transducers can be replaced by just one (typically larger) transducer of the same kind.

### Two Opposite Passes

Given a single-valued translation, specified by a regular translation expression or by a $2I$-automaton, we have seen that it is not always possible to implement the translation by means of a sequential transducer, i.e., a deterministic $IO$-automaton. On the other hand, even in such cases, the translation can always be implemented by two cascaded (deterministic) sequential passes, scanning the string in opposite directions. In the first pass a sequential transducer converts the source string to an intermediate string. Then in the second pass another sequential transducer scans the intermediate string from right to left and produces the specified target string.

*Example 6.11.* Regular translation by two opposite passes (example 6.8 on p. 271 continued)
We recall the translation of string $a^n$ to $b^n$, if $n$ is even, to $c^n$, if $n$ is odd, cannot be deterministically computed by an $IO$-automaton. The reason is that just at the end the parity class of the string becomes known, but then it is too late for writing the output because number $n$ exceeds the memory capacity of the machine. We show an implementation by two cascaded sequential transducers scanning their respective input in opposite directions.

The first sequential machine computes the intermediate translation:

$$\tau_1 = \left(\frac{a}{a'}\frac{a}{a''}\right)^* \left[\frac{a}{a'}\right]$$

which maps to $a'$ (resp. to $a''$) a character $a$ occurring at odd (resp. even) position. The last term may be missing.

The second transducer scans the intermediate text from right to left and computes the translation:

$$\tau_2 = \left(\frac{a''}{b}\frac{a'}{b}\right)^* \cup \left(\frac{a'}{c}\frac{a''}{c}\right)^* \frac{a'}{c}$$

where the choice between the two alternatives is controlled by the first character being $a'$ or $a''$ in the reversed intermediate string. Thus for the source string $aa$ we have

$$\tau_2\left((\tau_1(aa))^R\right) = \tau_2\left((a'a'')^R\right) = \tau_2(a''a') = bb$$

We anticipate that a cascade of reversely operating sequential transducers is equivalent to a transducer equipped with a pushdown stack, a more powerful model to be studied soon.

In several applications the computing capacity of the sequential translator model is adequate to the intended job. In practice, the sequential transducer is often enriched with the capability to look-ahead on the input string, in order to anticipate the choice of the output to be emitted. This enhancement is similar to what has been extensively discussed for parsing. The model of sequential translator with look-ahead is implemented by widespread compiler construction tools such as *lex* and *flex*.[6]

## 6.5 Purely Syntactic Translation

The sequential translations of the previous section are within the reach of a deterministic algorithm with a finite memory, scanning the source text from left to right. But surely the finite memory hypothesis is too constraining for a majority of practically relevant text transformations. Possibly the simplest example is string reflection. The relation $\{(x, x^R) \mid x \in (a \mid b)^*\}$ is not regular, by two reasonings. First, the source string must be stored in an unbounded memory before producing the translation. Second, in view of the Nivat theorem (more precisely statement 3 on p. 269), if we concatenate the source string $x$ and the target string $y = (x')^R$, recoded in the alphabet $\{a', b'\}$ disjoint from the source alphabet, the set of such strings is context-free but not regular.
This and other relevant transformations can be easily obtained by the next model of syntactic translation schemata or translation grammars.

Since the source language is defined by a grammar, it is natural to consider a translation model where each syntactic component, i.e., a subtree, is individually mapped to a target component. The latter are then assembled into the target syntax tree that represents the translation. Such structural translation is now formalized as a mapping scheme, relating source grammar rules with target grammar rules.

**Definition 6.12.** A *translation grammar* $G = (V, \Sigma, \Delta, P, S)$ is a context-free grammar having as terminal alphabet a set $C \subseteq \Sigma^* \times \Delta^*$ of pairs $(u, v)$ of source/target strings, also written as a fraction $\frac{u}{v}$.
The translation relation $\rho(G)$ defined by grammar $G$ is

$$\rho(G) = \{(x, y) \mid \exists z \in L(G) \wedge x = h_\Sigma(z) \wedge y = h_\Delta(z)\}$$

where $h_\Sigma : C \rightarrow \Sigma$ and $h_\Delta : C \rightarrow \Delta$ are the projections from the terminal alphabet of the grammar to the source and target alphabets.
Such *translation* is termed *context-free* or algebraic.[7]
The *syntactic translation scheme* associated with the translation grammar is a set of pairs of source/target syntax rules, obtained by respectively cancelling from the rules of $G$ the characters of the target alphabet or of the source alphabet. The set of source/target rules respectively comprise the *source grammar* $G_1$ and the *target grammar* $G_2$ of the translation scheme.

---

[6] For a formalization of look-ahead sequential transducers we refer to Yang [58].

[7] Another historical name for such translations is *simple syntax-directed translations*.

A translation grammar and a translation scheme are just notational variations of the same model. Intuitively a pair of corresponding source/target strings are obtained taking a sentence $z$ generated by $G$ and projecting on the two alphabets.

*Example 6.13.* Translation grammar for reflection
Take string $aab$; its translation is the mirror string $baa$. The translation grammar $G$ is

$$S \to \frac{a}{\varepsilon} S \frac{\varepsilon}{a} \mid \frac{b}{\varepsilon} S \frac{\varepsilon}{b} \mid \frac{\varepsilon}{\varepsilon}$$

Equivalently, the translation grammar can be replaced with the translation scheme:

| *Source grammar* $G_1$ | *Target grammar* $G_2$ |
|---|---|
| $S \to aS$ | $S \to Sa$ |
| $S \to bS$ | $S \to Sb$ |
| $S \to \varepsilon$ | $S \to \varepsilon$ |

The two columns list the source and target grammars and each row contains two *corresponding rules.* For instance, the second row is obtained by the projections

$$h_\Sigma\left(S \to \frac{b}{\varepsilon} S \frac{\varepsilon}{b}\right) = S \to bS$$

and

$$h_\Delta\left(S \to \frac{b}{\varepsilon} S \frac{\varepsilon}{b}\right) = S \to Sb$$

To obtain a pair of corresponding strings in the translation relation, we construct a derivation

$$S \Rightarrow \frac{a}{\varepsilon} S \frac{\varepsilon}{a} \Rightarrow \frac{a\,a}{\varepsilon\,\varepsilon} S \frac{\varepsilon\,\varepsilon}{a\,a} \Rightarrow \frac{a\,a\,b}{\varepsilon\,\varepsilon\,\varepsilon} S \frac{\varepsilon\,\varepsilon\,\varepsilon}{b\,a\,a} \Rightarrow \frac{a\,a\,b\,\varepsilon\,\varepsilon\,\varepsilon\,\varepsilon}{\varepsilon\,\varepsilon\,\varepsilon\,\varepsilon\,b\,a\,a} = z$$

and then project the sentence $z$ of $L(G)$ on the two alphabets

$$h_\Sigma(z) = aab, \qquad h_\Delta(z) = baa$$

Otherwise, using the translation scheme, we generate a source string by a derivation of $G_1$ and its image by a derivation of $G_2$, paying attention to use corresponding rules at each step.

The reader may have noticed that the preceding translation grammar is almost identical to the grammar of palindromes. The latter, marking with a prime the characters in the second half of a string, becomes

$$G_p = \{S \to aSa' \mid bSb' \mid \varepsilon\}$$

Recoding $\frac{a}{\varepsilon}$ as $a$, $\frac{b}{\varepsilon}$ as $b$, $\frac{\varepsilon}{a}$ as $a'$, and $\frac{\varepsilon}{b}$ as $b'$, the two grammars $G$ and $G_p$ coincide. This remark leads to the next property, which is a sort of restatement of the Nivat theorem for the case of context-free instead of regular translations.

*Property 6.14.* Context-free language and translation.
The following conditions are equivalent:

1. The translation relation $\rho \subseteq \Sigma^* \times \Delta^*$ is defined by a translation grammar $G$.
2. There exist an alphabet $\Omega$, a context-free language $L$ over $\Omega$, and two alphabetic homomorphisms (transliterations) $h_1 : \Omega \to \Sigma$ and $h_2 : \Omega \to \Delta$ such that
$$\rho = \{(h_1(z), h_2(z)) \mid z \in L\}$$
3. If the alphabets $\Sigma$ and $\Delta$ are disjoint, there exists a context-free language $L$ over the united alphabets $\Sigma \cup \Delta$, such that
$$\rho = \{(h_\Sigma(z), h_\Delta(z)) \mid z \in L\}$$
where $h_\Sigma$ and $h_\Delta$ are the respective projections of alphabet $\Sigma \cup \Delta$ on the source and target alphabets.

*Example 6.15.* Example 6.13 continued
We illustrate with the translation of string $x \in (a \mid b)^*$ to its mirror. From condition 2., the translation can be expressed using the alphabet $\Omega = \{a, b, a', b'\}$, and the following language (quite similar to palindromes):

$$L = \{u(u^R)' \mid u \in (a \mid b)^*\} = \{\varepsilon, aa', \ldots, abbb'b'a', \ldots\}$$

where $(v)'$ is the primed copy of string $v$. The homomorphisms are

| | $h_1$ | $h_2$ |
|---|---|---|
| $a$ | $a$ | $\varepsilon$ |
| $b$ | $b$ | $\varepsilon$ |
| $a'$ | $\varepsilon$ | $a$ |
| $b'$ | $\varepsilon$ | $b$ |

Then the string $abb'a' \in L$ is transliterated to the two strings

$$(h_1(abb'a'),\ h_2(abb'a')) = (ab,\ ba)$$

belonging to the translation relation.

### 6.5.1 Infix and Polish Notations

A relevant application of context-free translation is to convert back and forth between various representations of arithmetic (or logical) expressions, differing by the relative positions of operands and signs and by the use of parentheses or other delimiters.

The *degree of an operator* is the number of arguments or operands it may have. The degree can be fixed or variable and in the latter case the operator is called *variadic.* Degree two or *binary* operators are the most common; for instance, comparison operators, such as equal or nonequal, are binary. Arithmetic addition has a degree $\geqslant 1$; but in a typical machine language the *add* operation is binary, since it adds two registers. Moreover, since addition is usually assumed to satisfy the associative property, a many operand addition can be decomposed in a series of binary additions, to be performed, say, from left to right.

Arithmetic subtraction provides an example of noncommutative binary operation, whereas a change of sign (as in $-x$) is a *unary* operation. If the same sign "−" is used to denote both operations, the operator becomes variadic, with degree one or two.

Examining now the relative positions of signs and operands, we have the following cases. An *operator* is *prefix* if it precedes its arguments, it is *postfix* if it follows them.

A binary operator is *infix* if it is placed between its arguments. One may also generalize the notion of being infix to higher degree operators. An operator of degree $n \geqslant 2$ is *mixfix* if its representation can be segmented into $n+1$ parts

$$o_0 \, arg_1 \, o_1 \, arg_2 \, \ldots \, o_{n-1} \, arg_n \, o_n$$

that is, if the arguments list starts with an opening mark $o_0$, is followed by $(n-1)$ (possibly different) separators $o_i$, and terminates with a closing mark $o_n$. The opening and closing marks are sometimes missing.

For instance, the conditional operator of programming languages is mixfix with degree two, or three if the "else" clause is present:

$$\text{if } arg_1 \text{ then } arg_2 \text{ [ else } arg_3]$$

Because of the varying degree, this representation is ambiguous, if the second argument can be in turn a conditional operator (as seen on p. 55). In certain languages, e.g., ADA, to remove ambiguity, the conditional construct is terminated by a closing mark "end_if".
In machine language the binary conditional operator is usually represented in prefix form by an instruction such as

$$\text{jump\_if\_false } arg_1 \, arg_2$$

More generally every machine instruction is of the prefix type since it begins with an operation code, and it is of fixed degree because a fixed number of instruction fields is set for the operands.

A representation is called *polish*[8] if it does not use parentheses and if the operators are all prefix or all postfix. The elementary grammar of polish expression is printed on p. 50.

The next example shows a frequent transformation performed by compilers to eliminate parentheses, by converting an arithmetic expression from infix to polish notation. For simplicity, we prefer to use disjoint source/target alphabets, thus avoiding the need of fractions in the rules.

*Example 6.16.* From infix to prefix operators
The source language comprises arithmetic expressions with (infix) addition and multiplication, parentheses, and the terminal $i$ denoting a variable identifier. The translation is to polish prefix: operators are moved to the prefix position, parentheses disappear, and identifiers are transcribed to $i'$.

Alphabets:

$$\Sigma = \{+, \times, (, ), i\} \qquad \Delta = \{\text{add}, \text{mult}, i'\}$$

Translation grammar:

$$E \to \text{add}\, T + E \mid T \qquad T \to \text{mult}\, F \times T \mid F \qquad F \to (E) \mid ii'$$

Notice that $E \to \text{add}\, T + E$ abridges $E \to \frac{\varepsilon}{\text{add}} T \frac{+}{\varepsilon} E$, with no confusion because the alphabets are disjoint.

The equivalent translation scheme is

| *Source grammar* $G_1$ | *Target grammar* $G_2$ |
|---|---|
| $E \to T + E$ | $E \to \text{add}\, TE$ |
| $E \to T$ | $E \to T$ |
| $T \to F \times T$ | $T \to \text{mult}\, FT$ |
| $T \to F$ | $T \to F$ |
| $F \to (E)$ | $F \to E$ |
| $F \to i$ | $F \to i'$ |

An example of translation is the source-target syntax tree in Figure 6.3. Imagine to erase the dashed part of the tree, then the source syntax tree of $(i+i) \times i$, as the parser would construct using the source grammar $G_1$, shows up. Conversely, erasing from the tree the leaves of the source alphabet and their edges, we would see a tree generated by the target grammar for the image string: mult add $i'i'i'$.

[8] From the nationality of the logician Jan Lukasiewicz, who proposed its use for compacting and normalizing logical formulas.

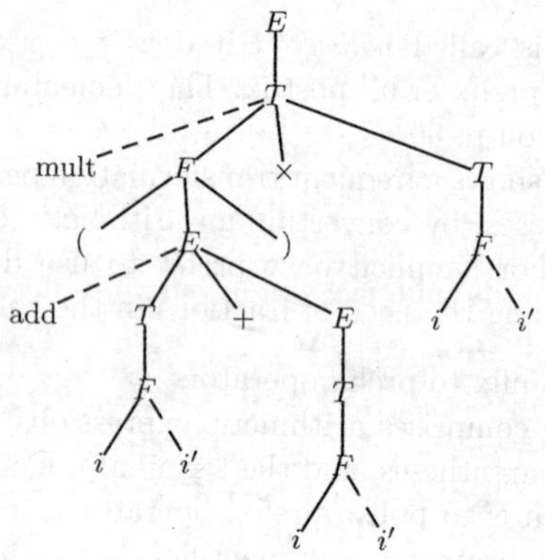


**Fig. 6.3** Source-target tree generated by the translation grammar of example 6.16.

## Construction of Target Syntax Tree

In a translation scheme the rules of the two grammars are in one-to-one correspondence. We observe that corresponding rules have identical left parts and, in their right parts, the nonterminal symbols occur in identical order.

Given a translation grammar, in order to compute the image of a source sentence $x$, we do the following. First we parse the string, using grammar $G_1$, constructing the source syntax tree $t_x$ of $x$ (which is unique if the sentence is unambiguous). Then we traverse tree $t_x$, in some suitable order such as pre-order. At each step, if the current node of the tree has a certain grammar rule of $G_1$, we apply the corresponding rule of grammar $G_2$, thus appending some sibling nodes to the target syntax tree. At the end of visit the target tree is complete.

## Abstract Syntax Tree

Syntactic translations are a convenient method for trimming and transforming source syntax trees, to remove elements that are irrelevant for later stages of compilation, and to reformat the tree as needed. This transformation is an instance of a language abstraction (p. 25). A case has already been considered: elimination of parentheses from arithmetic expressions. One can easily imagine other cases, such as elimination or recoding of separators between elements of a list; or of the mixfix keywords of conditional instructions if ... then... else... end_if. The result of such transformation is called an *abstract syntax tree*.

### 6.5.2 Ambiguity of Source Grammar and Translation

We have already observed that a majority of applications are concerned with single-valued translations. However, if the source grammar is ambiguous, a sentence admits two different syntax trees, each one corresponding to a target syntax tree. Therefore the sentence will have two, generally different, images.

*Example 6.17.* Redundant parentheses
A case of multi-valued translation is exhibited by the conversion from prefix polish to infix notation, the latter using parentheses. It is straightforward to write the translation scheme, as it is the inverse translation of example 6.16 on p. 279; therefore it suffices to interchange source and target grammars, obtaining

| *Source grammar* $G_1$ | *Target grammar* $G_2$ |
|---|---|
| $E \to \text{add}\ TE$ | $E \to T + E$ |
| $E \to T$ | $E \to T$ |
| $T \to \text{mult}\ FT$ | $T \to F \times T$ |
| $T \to F$ | $T \to F$ |
| $F \to E$ | $F \to (E)$ |
| $F \to i'$ | $F \to i$ |

Here the source grammar $G_1$ has an unbounded degree ambiguity, coming from the circular derivation

$$E \Rightarrow T \Rightarrow F \Rightarrow E$$

For instance, consider the multiple derivations of the source string $i'$:

$$E \Rightarrow T \Rightarrow F \Rightarrow i', \qquad E \Rightarrow T \Rightarrow F \Rightarrow E \Rightarrow T \Rightarrow F \Rightarrow i', \qquad \ldots$$

each one produces a distinct image:

$$E \Rightarrow T \Rightarrow F \Rightarrow i, \qquad E \Rightarrow T \Rightarrow F \Rightarrow (E) \Rightarrow (T) \Rightarrow (F) \Rightarrow (i), \qquad \ldots$$

The fact is hardly surprising since in the conversion from prefix to infix one can insert as many pairs of parentheses as he wishes, but the translation scheme does not prescribe their number and allows insertion of redundant parentheses.

On the other hand, suppose the source grammar is unambiguous, so that any sentence has a unique syntax tree. Yet it may happen that the translation is multi-valued, if in the translation schema different target rules correspond to the same source rule. An example is the next translation grammar:

$$S \to \frac{a}{b}S \mid \frac{a}{c}S \mid \frac{a}{d}$$

where $G_1 = \{S \to aS \mid a\}$ is nonambiguous, yet the translation $\tau(aa) = \{bd, cd\}$ is not single-valued, because the first two rules of the translation grammar correspond to the same source rule. The next statement gives sufficient conditions for avoiding ambiguity.

*Property 6.18.* Let $G = (G_1, G_2)$ be a translation grammar such that

1. the source grammar $G_1$ is unambiguous, and
2. two rules of the target grammar $G_2$ do not correspond to the same rule of $G_1$.

Then the translation specified by $G$ is single-valued, i.e., it defines a function.

In the previous discussion of ambiguity we did not consider the ambiguity of the translation grammar $G$ because it is not relevant to ensure the single-value translation property. The next example shows a nonambiguous translation grammar may have an ambiguous source grammar, thus causing the translation to be ambiguous.

*Example 6.19.* End mark in conditionals
The translation places the end mark "end_if" after an instruction if ... then ... [ else]. The translation grammar $G$

$$S \to \frac{\text{if } c \text{ then}}{\text{if } c \text{ then}} S \frac{\varepsilon}{\text{end\_if}} \mid \frac{\text{if } c \text{ then}}{\text{if } c \text{ then}} S \frac{\text{else}}{\text{else}} S \frac{\varepsilon}{\text{end\_if}} \mid a$$

is unambiguous, yet the underlying source grammar, which defines the conditional instructions without end marks, is a classical case of ambiguity (p. 55). The translation produces two images of the source string

$$\text{if } c \text{ then} \;\; \text{if } c \text{ then } a \overset{\text{end\_if}}{\downarrow} \text{ else } a \overset{\text{end\_if}}{\downarrow} \quad \underset{\text{end\_if end\_if}}{\uparrow}$$

obtained by inserting the end marks in the positions indicated by arrows over or under the line.

Compiler designers should pay attention to avoid translation grammars causing the translation to become multi-valued. Parser construction tools help, because they routinely check the source grammar for determinism which excludes ambiguity.

### 6.5.3 Translation Grammars and Pushdown Transducers

The finite-state *IO*-machine model, which recognizes a source string and emits its image, can be naturally applied to context-free translations. Much as the recognizer of a context-free language, context-free transducers too need a pushdown or LIFO store.

A *pushdown transducer* or *IO-automaton* is like a pushdown automaton, enriched with the capability to output zero or more characters at each move. More precisely, to define such a machine eight items have to be specified:

$Q$, set of states;

$\Sigma$, source alphabet;

$\Gamma$, pushdown stack alphabet;

$\Delta$, target alphabet;

$\delta$, state transition and output function;

$q_0 \in Q$, initial state;

$Z_0 \in \Gamma$, initial symbol on the stack;

$F \subseteq Q$, set of final states.

The function $\delta$ is defined in the domain $Q \times (\Sigma \cup \{\varepsilon\}) \times \Gamma$ and has as range[9] the set $Q \times \Gamma^* \times \Delta^*$. The function meaning, schematized in Figure 6.4, is the following: if $(q'', \gamma, y) = \delta(q', a, Z)$ and the present state is $q'$, the machine reads $a$ from the input and $Z$ from the stack top, enters state $q''$, and writes $\gamma$ on top of the stack and $y$ on the output. The final states coincide with $Q$, if the automaton recognizes the source string by empty stack.

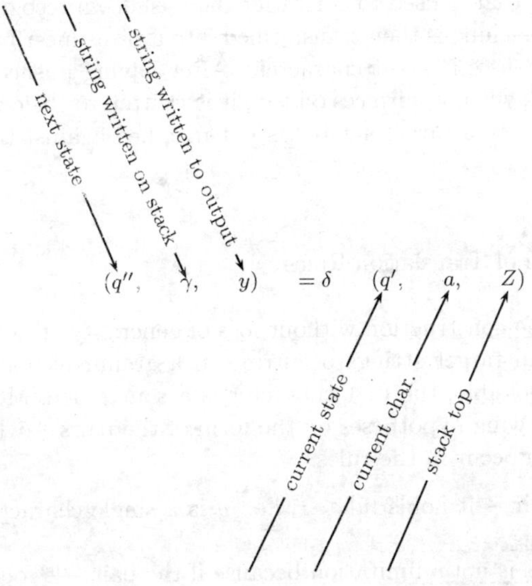


**Fig. 6.4** Scheme of a move of a pushdown transducer.

---

[9] As in the case of sequential finite transducers (p. 272), it would be possible to specify the output by a separate output function. We skip the formalization of the case of nondeterministic transducer: the range of function $\delta$ would become the powerset of the preceding cartesian product.

As in the finite case, the *subjacent automaton* of the translator is obtained by erasing from the definitions the target alphabet symbols and the output string actions.

We pass over the formalization of the translation computed by a pushdown translator, as it is entirely similar to the case of finite transduction on p. 272.

## From Translation Grammar to Pushdown Transducer

Translation schemes and pushdown transducers are two ways of representing language transformations: the former is a generative model suitable for specification, the latter is procedural. Their equivalence is stated next.

*Property 6.20.* A translation relation is defined by a translation grammar or scheme if, and only if, it is computed by a (nondeterministic) pushdown transducer.

For brevity we only describe the conversion from a grammar to a transducer, because the other direction is less pertinent to compilation.

Consider a translation grammar $G_t$. A first way to derive the equivalent pushdown translator $T$ is by applying essentially the same algorithm (Table 4.1 on p. 149) that is used to construct the pushdown recognizer of language $L(G_t)$. This machine is then transformed into a transducer by a small change of the operations on target characters. After having pushed on the stack a target symbol, when it surfaces on top, it is written to the output; but unlike source characters, a target symbol is not matched against the current input character.

### Normalization of Translation Rules

To simplify the construction without loss of generality, it helps to reorganize the source and target strings occurring in a grammar rule, in such a way that, where possible, the first character is a source one. More precisely, we make the following hypotheses on the form of the pairs $\frac{u}{v}$ where $u \in \Sigma^*$ and $v \in \Delta^*$, which occur in the rules:

1. For any pair $\frac{u}{v}$ it holds $|u| \leqslant 1$, i.e., $u$ is a single character $a \in \Sigma$ or the empty string.
   Clearly this is not a limitation because if the pair $\frac{a_1 a_2}{v}$ occurs in a rule, it can be replaced by the pair $\frac{a_1}{v}\frac{a_2}{\varepsilon}$, without affecting the translation.
2. No rule may contain the substrings

$$\frac{\varepsilon}{v_1}\frac{a}{v_2} \qquad \frac{\varepsilon}{v_1}\frac{\varepsilon}{v_2} \qquad \text{where } v_1, v_2 \in \Delta^*$$

   Should such combinations be present in a rule, they can be respectively replaced by the equivalent pair $\frac{a}{v_1 v_2}$ or by $\frac{\varepsilon}{v_1 v_2}$.

We are ready to describe the correspondence between grammar rules of $G_t = (V, \Sigma, \Delta, P, S)$ and the moves of so-called *predictive* transducers.

*Algorithm.* Construction of (nondeterministic) predictive pushdown transducer.
Let $C$ be the set of pairs of type $\frac{\varepsilon}{v}$ with $v \in \Delta^+$ and of type $\frac{b}{w}$ with $b \in \Sigma, w \in \Delta^*$, occurring in some grammar rule. The transducer moves are constructed as described in Table 6.1. Rows 1, 2, 3, 4, and 5 apply when the stack top is a nonterminal symbol. In case 2 the right part begins with a source terminal and the move is conditioned by its presence in the input. Rows 1, 3, 4, and 5 give rise to spontaneous moves, which do not shift the reading head. Rows 6 and 7 apply when a pair surfaces on top of stack. If the pair contains a source character (7), it must coincide with the current input character; if it contains a target string (6,7), the latter is output.

**Table 6.1** Correspondence between translation grammar rules and pushdown translator moves.

| | *Rule* | *Move* | *Comment* |
|---|---|---|---|
| 1 | $A \to \frac{\varepsilon}{v} B A_1 \ldots A_n$<br>$n \geqslant 0$,<br>$v \in \Delta^+$, $B \in V$,<br>$A_i \in (C \cup V)$ | if *top* = $A$ then write($v$); pop; push($A_n \ldots A_1 B$); | Emit the target string $v$ and push on stack the string ("prediction") $B A_1 \ldots A_n$ |
| 2 | $A \to \frac{b}{w} A_1 \ldots A_n$<br>$n \geqslant 0$,<br>$b \in \Sigma, w \in \Delta^*$,<br>$A_i \in (C \cup V)$ | if *cc* = $b$ ∧ *top* = $A$ then write($w$); pop; push($A_n \ldots A_1$); advance the reading head; | $b$ was the next expected char. and has been read; emit the target string $w$; push the prediction $A_1 \ldots A_n$ |
| 3 | $A \to B A_1 \ldots A_n$<br>$n \geqslant 0, B \in V$,<br>$A_i \in (C \cup V)$ | if *top* = $A$ then pop; push($A_n \ldots A_1 B$); | push the prediction $B A_1 \ldots A_n$ |
| 4 | $A \to \frac{\varepsilon}{v}$<br>$v \in \Delta^+$ | if *top* = $A$ then write($v$); pop; | emit the target string $v$ |
| 5 | $A \to \varepsilon$ | if *top* = $A$ then pop; | |
| 6 | for every pair $\frac{\varepsilon}{v} \in C$ | if *top* = $\frac{\varepsilon}{v}$ then write($v$); pop; | the past prediction $\frac{\varepsilon}{v}$ is now completed by writing $v$ |
| 7 | for every pair $\frac{b}{w} \in C$ | if *cc* = $b$ ∧ *top* = $\frac{b}{w}$ then write($w$); pop; advance the reading head; | the past prediction $\frac{b}{w}$ is now completed by reading $b$ and writing $w$ |
| 8 | – – – | if *cc* =⊣ ∧ stack is empty then accept; halt; | the source string has been entirely scanned and no goal is present in the stack |

Initially the stack contains the axiom $S$, and the reading head is positioned on the first character of the source string. At each step the automaton (nondeterministically) chooses an applicable rule and executes the corresponding move. Finally row 8 accepts the string if the stack is empty and the current character marks the end of text.

Notice the automaton does not make use of states, i.e., the stack is the only memory used; as we did for recognizers, we will later enrich the machine with states in order to obtain a more efficient deterministic algorithm.

*Example 6.21.* Nondeterministic pushdown transducer
Consider language

$$L = \{a^* a^m b^m \mid m > 0\}$$

and define translation

$$\tau(a^k a^m b^m) = d^m c^k$$

The transformation first changes $b$ to $d$ and then transcribes to $c$ any letter $a$ which exceeds the number of letters $b$.
Transducer moves are listed next to the corresponding rules of the translation grammar:

| | *Rule* | *Move* |
|---|---|---|
| 1 | $S \to \frac{a}{\varepsilon} S \frac{\varepsilon}{c}$ | if $cc = a \quad \wedge \quad top = S$ then pop; push($\frac{\varepsilon}{c}S$); advance the reading head; |
| 2 | $S \to A$ | if $top = S$ then pop; push($A$); |
| 3 | $A \to \frac{a}{d} A \frac{b}{\varepsilon}$ | if $cc = a \quad \wedge \quad top = A$ then pop; write($d$); push($\frac{b}{\varepsilon}A$); advance the reading head; |
| 4 | $A \to \frac{a}{d}\frac{b}{\varepsilon}$ | if $cc = a$ and $top = A$ then pop; write($d$); push($\frac{b}{\varepsilon}$); advance the reading head; |
| 5 | — | if $top = \frac{\varepsilon}{c}$ then pop; write($c$); |
| 6 | — | if $cc = b \quad \wedge \quad top = \frac{b}{\varepsilon}$ then pop; advance the reading head; |
| 7 | — | if $cc = \dashv \quad \wedge$ stack is empty then accept; halt; |

The choice of moves 1 or 2 is not deterministic, and so is the choice of 3 or 4. Move 5 outputs a target character that had been pushed by move 1. The subjacent pushdown automaton is not deterministic.

The following example reasserts for context-free translations a fact already known for regular translations and finite transducers: that not all such translations can be computed by a pushdown transducer of the deterministic kind.

*Example 6.22.* Context-free nondeterministic translation
The translation function

$$\tau(u) = u^R u, \qquad \text{where } u \in \{a, b\}^*$$

that maps any string into a reflected copy followed by the same string, is easily specified by the scheme:

| Source grammar $G_1$ | Target grammar $G_2$ |
|---|---|
| $S \to Sa$ | $S \to aSa$ |
| $S \to Sb$ | $S \to bSb$ |
| $S \to \varepsilon$ | $S \to \varepsilon$ |

This translation cannot be deterministically computed by a pushdown machine. The reason[10] is that the machine should output the mirror copy of the input before the copy of the input. The only way to reverse a string, using a pushdown device, is to store it in the stack and to output it in the popping order; but popping destroys the string and makes it unavailable for copying to the output at a later moment.

Nondeterministic algorithms are rarely used in compilation. In the next section we develop translator construction methods suitable for use with the widespread deterministic parsers.

### 6.5.4 Syntax Analysis with Online Translation

Given a context-free translation scheme, the previous construction produces a pushdown transducer, which is often nondeterministic and unpractical to use in a compiler. To construct an efficient well-engineered translator, it is convenient to resume from the point reached in Chapter 4 with the construction of deterministic parsers and to enrich them with output actions.

Given a context-free translation grammar or scheme, we make the assumption that the source grammar is suitable for deterministic parsing. To compute the image of a string, as the parser completes a syntactic subtree, it emits the corresponding translation.

We know that bottom-up and top-down parsers differ in the construction order of syntax trees. A question to be investigated is how the order interferes with the possibility of correctly producing the target image. The main result will be that the top-down parsing order is fully compatible, whereas the bottom-up order places some restriction on the translation.

### 6.5.5 Top-Down Deterministic Translation

We assume the source grammar satisfies condition $LL(1)$ on p. 183, or more generally condition $LL(k)$. For constructing an efficient translator, we only have to explain how to add output actions to the parser.

---

10 For a proof see [2, 3].

We recall there are two approaches for building such parsers: as pushdown automata or as recursive descent procedures. Both will be simply extended toward translator construction. The construction producing an automaton is discussed first. For simplicity we assume translation grammar rules to be normalized (p. 284).

*Algorithm.* Constructs a deterministic pushdown transducer from a given translation grammar $G_t = (\Sigma, \Delta, V, P, S)$, such that the source grammar is $LL(1)$.
The stack alphabet comprises the nonterminal symbols and the set $C$ of pairs $\frac{b}{v}$ occurring in the rules: remember $b$ is a source character or is empty, and $v$ is a target string (excluding that both components are empty). The projection of string $z$ on the source alphabet is denoted by $h_\Sigma(z)$. The current input character is in variable $cc$.

1. The automaton starts with axiom $S$ on stack.
2. Let $A$ be the stack top. For any rule $A \to \frac{b}{w}\beta$, where $b \in \Sigma, w \in \Delta^*, \beta \in \{V \cup C\}^*$, the machine, if $b$ is the $cc$, emits string $w$, replaces in the stack the symbol $A$ with the string $\beta^R$, and steps forward the reading head.
3. Let $A$ be the stack top. For any rule $A \to \frac{\varepsilon}{v}\beta$, where $v \in \Delta^*$ and $\beta \in \{V \cup C\}^*$, the guide[11] set is the one computed for the corresponding source grammar rule, i.e., the set $Gui\left(A \to h_\Sigma\left(\frac{\varepsilon}{v}\beta\right)\right)$.
The automaton, if $cc$ is in the guide set of the rule, emits the string $v$ and replaces in the stack symbol $A$ with string $\beta^R$, without shifting the reading head.
4. With $\frac{b}{w}, b \in \Sigma$ as stack top and $b$ as $cc$, the machine writes $w$ and reads the next input character.
5. The machine has successfully completed the translation when the current character is the text terminator and the stack is empty.

Notice that case 3. takes care of empty rules such as $A \to \varepsilon$. In 3. the guide set test is used to select the move and condition $LL(1)$ guarantees the choice is deterministic.

*Example 6.23.* Example 6.13 on p. 276 continued
A string is mapped to its mirror by the translation grammar:

$$S \to \frac{a}{\varepsilon}S\frac{\varepsilon}{a} \mid \frac{b}{\varepsilon}S\frac{\varepsilon}{b} \mid \varepsilon$$

[11] Also known as look-ahead set.

The source grammar is $LL(1)$, with respective guide sets $\{a\}$, $\{b\}$ , and $\{\dashv\}$. The automaton is described by the table:

| *stack* | $cc = a$ | $cc = b$ | $cc = \dashv$ | $\varepsilon$ |
|---|---|---|---|---|
| $S$ | pop; push($\frac{\varepsilon}{a}S$) | pop; push($\frac{\varepsilon}{b}S$) | pop | |
| $\frac{\varepsilon}{a}$ | | | | write($a$) |
| $\frac{\varepsilon}{b}$ | | | | write($b$) |

## Implementation by Recursive Procedures

In order to streamline the design of syntactic translation algorithms for grammars extended with regular expressions, it is convenient to represent the translation grammar $G_t$ by means of a recursive network of finite machines, as we did in Chapter 4.

We show how to realize the pushdown translator using recursive procedures. Assuming the source grammar is $LL(k)$, we recall the organization of the recursive descent parser (p. 190). For each nonterminal symbol, a procedure has the task of recognizing the substrings derived from it. The procedure body blueprint is identical to the state-transition graph of the corresponding machine, in the network representing the grammar.

For computing the translation, we simply insert a writing instruction in the procedure body, in all the places where the machine graph has an arc labelled by a target element. An example should be enough to explain such straightforward modification of a recursive descent parser.

*Example 6.24.* Recursive descent translator from infix to postfix
The source language consists of arithmetic expressions with two levels of operators and parentheses. The translation from infix expressions to postfix polish notation, exemplified by

$$v \times (v + v) \qquad \Rightarrow \qquad vvv\ add\ mult$$

is defined by the extended BNF translation grammar:

$$E \rightarrow T\left(\frac{+}{\varepsilon} T \frac{\varepsilon}{add} \mid \frac{-}{\varepsilon} T \frac{\varepsilon}{sub}\right)^*$$

$$T \rightarrow F\left(\frac{\times}{\varepsilon} F \frac{\varepsilon}{mult} \mid \frac{\div}{\varepsilon} F \frac{\varepsilon}{div}\right)^*$$

$$F \rightarrow \frac{v}{v} \mid \frac{'('}{\varepsilon} E \frac{')'}{\varepsilon}$$

where

$$\Sigma = \{+, \times, -, \div, (, ), v\} \qquad \text{and} \qquad \Delta = \{add, sub, mult, div, v\}$$

Figure 6.5 represents the first machine of the network, with guide sets enclosed by braces. From the graph of machine $M_E$ it is straightforward to code the corresponding translator procedure. The programming style is terser if `while` loops are used to implement the star operations of the grammar. We recall that function *Next* returns the current input character.

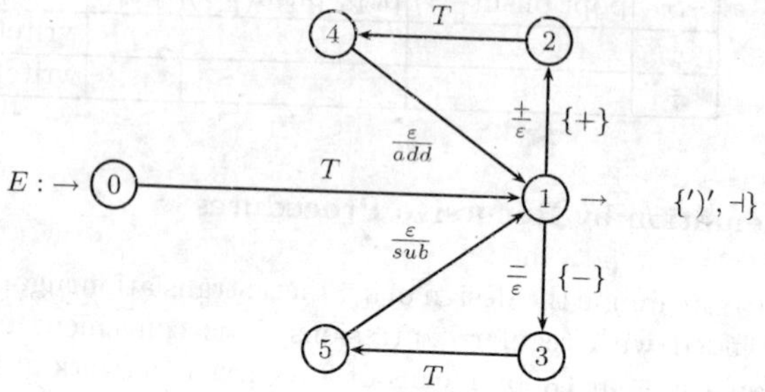


**Fig. 6.5** Machine $M_E$ representing the first rule of the translation grammar of example 6.24.

*procedure* $E$
*call* $T$;
*while* $cc \in \{+, -\}$
*do*
  *case*
    $cc =' +'$: *begin* $cc :=$ Next; *call* $T$; *write*('add'); *end*
    $cc =' -'$: *begin* $cc :=$ Next; *call* $T$; *write*('sub'); *end*
  *end case*
*end do*
*end*

The procedure can be refined so that at loop exit it checks whether the current character is in the set $\{')', \dashv\}$, thus anticipating error detection. Similar procedures for the other nonterminals are omitted.

### 6.5.6 Bottom-Up Deterministic Translation

Consider again a context-free translation scheme, this time assuming the source grammar (or machine network) is suitable for bottom-up deterministic parsing, no matter whether by the $LR(k)$ or $LALR(k)$ condition. We also assume the grammar is in the basic context-free form. Unlike the top-down case, it is not always possible to extend the parser with the writing actions that compute the translation, without jeopardizing determinism. Intuitively the impediment is simple to understand. We know (from p. 212 and following) the parser works by shifts and reductions; a shift pushes on stack a macro-state of the pilot finite automaton, i.e., a set of states of some machines (tantamount to a set of marked grammar rules). Of course, when a shift is performed, the parser does not know which rule will be used in the future for a reduction, and conservatively keeps all the candidates open. Imagine two distinct marked rules occur as candidates in the current macro-state, and make the likely hypothesis that different output actions are associated with them. Then, when the parser shifts, the translator should perform two different and contradictory writing actions, which is impossible for a deterministic transducer. This reasoning explains the impediment to emit the output during a shift move of the translator.

On the other hand, when a reduction applies, exactly one source grammar rule has been recognized (i.e., the final state of the corresponding machine has been entered). Since the mapping between source and target rules in the scheme is surjective, a reduction identifies exactly one target rule and can safely output the associated target string.

Next we illustrate the shift-reduce translation algorithm.

*Example 6.25.* Translation of expressions to postfix notation
The grammar of example 5.16 on p. 222 specifies certain formulas that use two infix signs, to be translated to postfix operators. The translation grammar below is represented in Figure 6.6 as a machine network. Notice that care has been taken to position all target characters as suffixes, at the end of rules:

$$E \to E\frac{+}{\varepsilon}T\frac{\varepsilon}{add} \mid T \qquad T \to T\frac{\times a}{\varepsilon}\frac{\varepsilon}{a\ mult} \mid \frac{a}{\varepsilon}\frac{\varepsilon}{a}$$

The $LR(1)$ pilot machine has been previously constructed, and can be easily upgraded for translation by inserting the output actions in the reductions, as shown in Figure 6.7. The parser will of course execute a writing instruction when it performs the associated reduction.

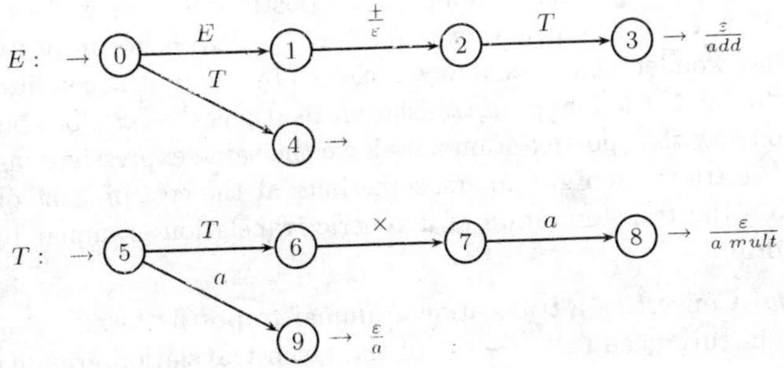


**Fig. 6.6** Machine net of translation grammar of example 6.25.

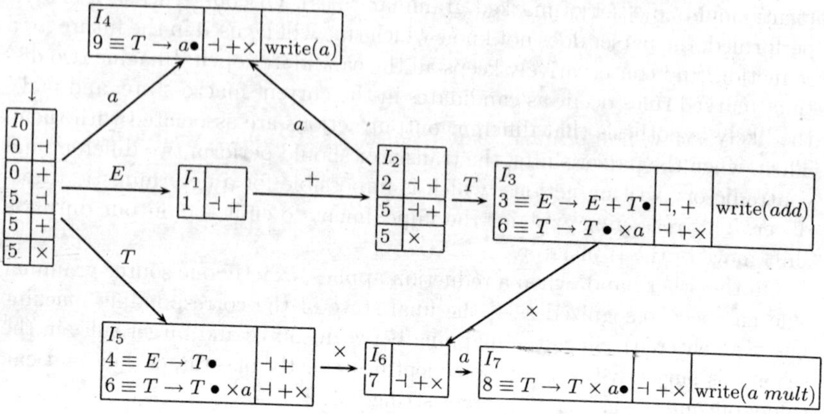

**Fig. 6.7** Pilot of translator of example 6.25 with output actions in reduction states.

## Postfix Normal Form

In practice, when specifying a context-free translation intended for bottom-up parsing, it is necessary to put the translation grammar in a form that confines writing actions within reduction moves.

**Definition 6.26.** *Postfix* translation grammar.
A translation grammar or scheme is in postfix normal form if every target grammar rule has the form $A \to \gamma w$, where $\gamma \in V^*$ and $w \in \Delta^*$.

Differently stated, no target string may occur as inner substring of a rule, but only as suffix. The previous example is in postfix form, as well as example 6.13 (p. 276). On the contrary, example 6.22 (p. 286) is not in postfix form.

One may wonder what loss, if any, is caused by the postfix condition. From the standpoint of the family of translation relations that can be specified, it is easy to show that postfix grammars have the same expressivity as general context-free translation grammars, sometimes at the cost of some obscurity. We explain the transformation of a generic translation grammar to postfix normal form.

*Algorithm.* Converting a translation grammar to postfix form.
Consider in turn each rule $A \to \alpha$ of the given translation grammar $G_t$. If the rule violates the postfix condition, find the longest target string $v \in \Delta^+$ that occurs in the rightmost position in $\alpha$, and transcribe the rule as

$$A \to \gamma \frac{\varepsilon}{v} \eta$$

where $\gamma$ is any string, and $\eta$ is a nonempty string devoid of target characters. Replace this rule with the next ones:

$$A \to \gamma Y \eta \qquad Y \to \frac{\varepsilon}{v}$$

where $Y$ is a new nonterminal. The second rule complies with the postfix condition; if the first rule does not, find anew the rightmost target string within $\gamma$, and repeat the transformation. Eventually all target elements occurring in the middle of a rule will have been moved to suffix positions, and the resulting grammar is in postfix normal form.

The coming example illustrates the transformation and should convince the reader that the original and transformed grammar define the same translation.

*Example 6.27.* Grammar transformation to postfix normal form
The translation of an infix expression to prefix form is specified by grammar $G_t$, where we ascertain that the first rule is not in postfix form, by looking at the target grammar $G_2$.

| $G_t$ *original* | $G_1$ | $G_2$ |
|---|---|---|
| $E \to \frac{\varepsilon}{add} E \frac{+a}{a}$ | $E \to E + a$ | $E \to add\ Ea$ |
| $E \to \frac{a}{a}$ | $E \to a$ | $E \to a$ |

The postfix version of the translation grammar is $G'_t$, whose target grammar $G'_1$ complies with the postfix condition.

| $G'_t$ *postfix* | $G'_1$ | $G'_2$ |
|---|---|---|
| $E \to YE \frac{+a}{\varepsilon} \frac{\varepsilon}{a}$ | $E \to YE + a$ | $E \to YEa$ |
| $E \to \frac{a}{\varepsilon} \frac{\varepsilon}{a}$ | $E \to a$ | $E \to a$ |
| $Y \to \frac{\varepsilon}{add}$ | $Y \to \varepsilon$ | $Y \to add$ |

It is easy to check that this grammar defines the same translation as the original one.

We proceed to the application of the previous discussion to bottom-up translators.

*Property 6.28.* A translation defined by a translation grammar in postfix normal form, such that the source grammar satisfies condition $LR(k)$, can be computed by a bottom-up parser, which only writes on output at reduction moves.

Obviously the same holds true if $LALR(.)$ are considered instead. In essence the postfix form allows the parser to defer writing actions until the parser reaches a state where the action is uniquely identified.

This method has some inconveniences. The introduction of new nonterminal symbols, such as $Y$ in example 6.27, makes the new grammar less readable. Another nuisance may come from rule normalization, when empty rules, such as $Y \to \varepsilon$, are added to the source grammar. We know empty rules cause the grammar to lose the $LR(0)$ property and tend to increase the length $k$ of look-ahead needed for parsing; in some cases the $LR(k)$ property may be lost.

*Example 6.29.* Loss of $LR(1)$ property caused by normalization
This negative effect occurs when the grammar of example 6.27 is converted to the normal form $G_t'$ reproduced in Figure 6.8. The original source grammar $G_1$ satisfies the $LR(0)$ condition, but the new rule $Y \to \varepsilon$ of the postfix grammar introduces an $LR(1)$ shift-reduce conflict in the macro-states $I_0$ and $I_1$ of the pilot machine shown in Figure 6.9.

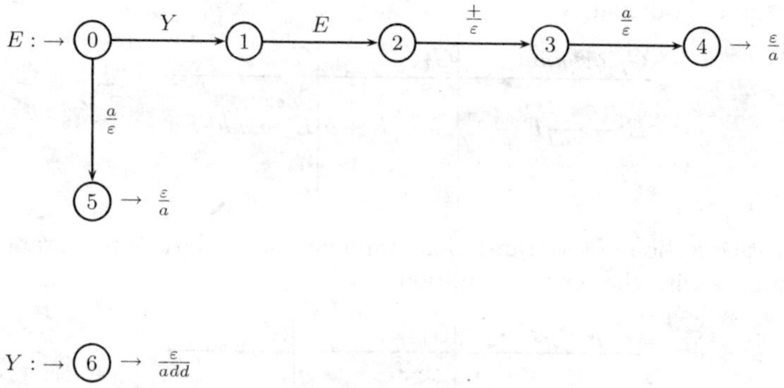


**Fig. 6.8** Machine net of normalized translation grammar (example 6.29.

Fortunately, in many practical situations grammar normalization to postfix form does not hinder deterministic parsing.

## Syntax Tree as Translation

A common utilization of syntactic translation (both bottom-up and top-down) is to construct the syntax tree of the source text. Programs usually represent a tree as a linked data structure. To construct such representation, we need semantic actions, to be discussed in later sections. Here, instead of producing a linked list, which would be impossible to do with purely syntactic translations, we are content with outputting the sequence of labels of source

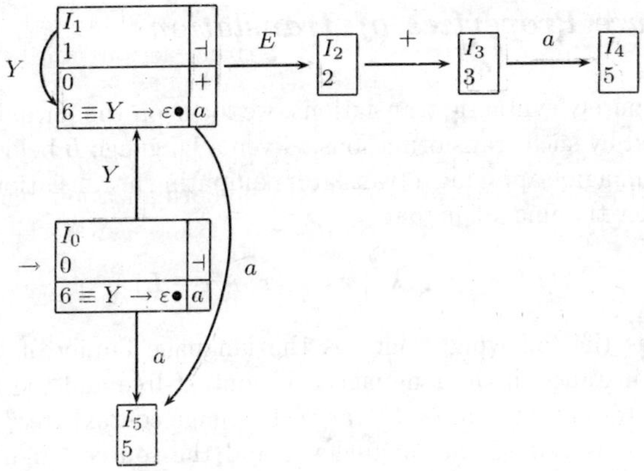


**Fig. 6.9** $LR(1)$ pilot of the grammar of Figure 6.8, with conflicts in macro-states $I_0$ and $I_1$.

rules, in the order they occur in the derivation of the tree.
Given a source grammar, with rules labelled for reference, the next syntactic translation scheme produces the label sequence of a derivation:

| *label* | *original translation rule* | *modified rule* |
|---|---|---|
| $r_i$ | $A \to \alpha$ | $A \to \alpha \frac{\varepsilon}{r_i}$ |

The image produced by this translation is exactly the sequence of rule labels used by the rightmost derivation. Since by hypothesis the source grammar is $LR(1)$ and the scheme is postfix, the parser enriched with writing actions easily computes this translation.

### 6.5.7 Comparisons

We recapitulate the main considerations on upgrading parsers to translators. The main argument in favor of top-down methods is that they suffer no limitation, as they allow the implementation of any syntactic translation scheme, provided of course that the source grammar meets the suitable condition for parsing. Moreover, a recursive descent translator can be easily constructed by hand, and the resulting program is easy to understand and to maintain.

On the other hand, for bottom-up methods the limitation imposed by the postfix normal form of the translation grammar may be compensated by the superiority of $LR(k)$ over $LL(k)$ grammars for source language definition. In conclusion, neither method is entirely superior to the other one.

### 6.5.8 Closure Properties of Translations

To finish with purely syntactic translations, we focus on the formal language families induced by such transformations. Given a language $L$ belonging to a certain family, imagine applying a translator computing a translation function $\tau$. Then consider the image language

$$\tau(L) = \{y \in \Delta^* \mid y = \tau(x) \wedge x \in L\}$$

The question is the following: which is the language family of the image language? For instance, if the language $L$ is context-free and the translator is a pushdown $IO$-automaton, is the target language context-free?

One should not confuse the language $L$ and the source language $L_1$ of the transducer, though both have the same alphabet $\Sigma$. The source language includes all and only the strings recognized by the automaton subjacent to the translator (i.e., the sentences of the source grammar of the translation scheme). The transducer converts a string of language $L$ to a target string, if the string is a sentence of the source language of the transducer; otherwise an error occurs and nothing is produced.

The essential closure properties are in the next table:

| $L$ | *Finite transducer* | *Pushdown transducer* |
|---|---|---|
| $L \in REG$ | 1 $\tau(L) \in REG$ | 2 $\tau(L) \in CF$ |
| $L \in CF$ | 3 $\tau(L) \in CF$ | 4 $\tau(L)$ not always $\in CF$ |

Cases 1 and 3 descend from the Nivat theorem (p. 269) and from the fact that both families $REG$ and $CF$ are closed under intersection with regular languages (p. 160). In more detail, the recognizer of language $L$ can be combined with the finite transducer, thus obtaining a new transducer having as source language the intersection $L \cap L_1$. The new transducer model is the same as the model of the recognizer of $L$: a pushdown machine if $L$ is context-free, a finite machine if $L$ is regular. To complete the proof of cases 1 and 3, it suffices to convert the new transducer into a recognizer of target language $\tau(L)$, by deleting from the moves all source characters while preserving all target characters. Clearly the machine thus obtained is of the same model as the recognizer of $L$.

For case 2 essentially the same reasoning applies and produces a pushdown automaton as recognizer of the target language. An example of case 2 is the translation of a string $u \in L = \{a, b\}^*$ to the palindromic image $uu^R$, clearly belonging to a context-free language.

Case 4 is different because, as we know from p. 79, the intersection of two context-free languages $L$ and $L_1$ is not always in family $CF$. Therefore there is no guarantee that a pushdown automaton will be able to recognize the image of $L$ computed by a pushdown translator.

*Example 6.30.* Pushdown translation of a context-free language
To illustrate case 4, consider the translation of the context-free language

$$L = \{a^n b^n c^* \mid n \geqslant 0\}$$

to the three exponents language (example 2.80 on p. 76)

$$\tau(L) = \{a^n b^n c^n \mid n \geqslant 0\}$$

which is not context-free as we know.
The image is defined by the translation grammar

$$S \to (\frac{a}{a})^* X \qquad X \to \frac{b}{b} X \frac{c}{c} \mid \varepsilon$$

which constrains the numbers of $b$ and $c$ in a target string to be equal, whereas equality of the numbers of $a$ and $b$ is externally imposed by the fact that any source string must be in $L$.

## 6.6 Semantic Translations

None of the previous purely syntactic translation models is able to compute but the simplest transformations, because they rely on too elementary devices: finite and pushdown $IO$-automata. On the other hand, most compilation tasks need more involved translation functions.

A first elementary example is the conversion of a binary number to decimal. Another typical case is the compilation of data structures to addresses: for example, a `record` declaration as

```
BOOK :
record
AUT: char(8); TIT: char(20); PRICE: real; QUANT: int;
end
```

is converted to a table describing each symbol: type, dimensions in bytes, offset of each field relative to a base address; assuming the base address of the record is fixed say at 3401, the translation is

| symbol | type | dimension | address |
|---|---|---|---|
| BOOK | record | 34 | 3401 |
| AUT | string | 8 | 3401 |
| TIT | string | 20 | 3409 |
| PRICE | real | 4 | 3429 |
| QUANT | int | 2 | 3433 |

In both examples, to compute the translation we need some arithmetic functions which are beyond the capacity of pushdown transducers. Certainly it would not be a viable remedy to adopt more powerful automata, such as Turing machines or context-sensitive translation grammars, as we have argued (Chapter 2, p. 87) that such models are already too intricate for language definition, not to mention for specifying translation functions.

A pragmatic solution is to encode the translation function in some programming language or in a more relaxed pseudo-code, as used in software engineering. To avoid confusion, such language is called *compiler language* or *semantic metalanguage.*

The translator is then a program implementing the desired translation function. The implementation of a complex translation function would produce an intricate program, unless care is taken to modularize it, in accordance with the syntax structure of the language to be translated. This approach to compiler design has been used for years with varying degrees of formalization under the title of *syntax-directed translation*. Notice the term "directed" marks the difference from the purely syntactic methods of previous sections.

The leap from syntactic to semantic methods occurs when the compiler includes tree-walking procedures, which move along the syntax tree and compute some variables, called *semantic attributes*. The attribute values, computed for a given source text, compose the translation or, as it is customary to say, the *meaning* or *semantics*.

A syntax-directed translator is not a formal model, because attribute computing procedures are not formalized. It is better classified as a software design method, based on syntactic concepts and specialized for designing input-output functions, such as the translation function of a compiler.

We mention that formalized semantic methods exist, which can accurately represent the meaning of programming languages, using logical and mathematical functions. Their study is beyond the scope of this book.[12]

A syntax-directed compiler performs two cascaded phases:

1. parsing or syntax analysis;
2. semantic evaluation or analysis.

Phase 1. is well known: it computes a syntax tree, usually condensed into a so-called abstract syntax tree, containing just the essential information for the next phase. In particular, most source language delimiters are deleted from the tree.

The semantic phase consists of the application of certain semantic functions, on each node of the syntax tree until all attributes have been evaluated. The set of evaluated attribute values is the meaning or translation.

A benefit of decoupling syntax and semantic phases is that the designer has greater freedom in writing the concrete and abstract syntaxes. The former must comply with the official language reference manual. On the other hand, the abstract syntax should be as simple as possible, provided it preserves the

[12] Formal semantic methods are needed if one has to prove that a compiler is correct, i.e., that for any source text the corresponding image expresses the intended meaning. For an introduction to formal semantics, see for instance [57, 16].

essential information for computing meaning. It may even be ambiguous: ambiguity does not jeopardize the single value property of translation, because in any case the parser passes just one abstract syntax tree per sentence to the semantic evaluator.

The above organization, termed *two-pass compilation*, is most common, but simpler compilers may unite the two phases. In that case there is just one syntax, the one defining the official language.

## 6.6.1 Attribute Grammars

We need to explain more precisely how the meaning is superimposed on a context-free language. The meaning of a sentence is a set of attribute values, computed by so-called semantic functions, and assigned to the nodes of the syntax tree. The syntax-directed translator contains the definition of the semantic functions, which are associated with the grammar rules. The set of grammar rules and associated semantic functions is called an *attribute grammar*.

To avoid confusion, in this part of the book a context-free grammar will be called *syntax*, reserving the term *grammar* to attribute grammars. For the same reason syntactic rules will be called *productions*.

### Introductory Example

Attribute grammar concepts are now introduced on a running example.

*Example 6.31.* Converting a fractionary binary number to base 10 (Knuth[13]) The source language, defined by the regular expression

$$L = \{0, 1\}^+ \bullet \{0, 1\}^+$$

is interpreted as the set of fractional base 2 numbers, with the point separating the integer and fractional parts. Thus the meaning of string $1101 \bullet 01$ is the number 13.25 in base ten. The attribute grammar is in Table 6.2. The syntax is listed in column one. The axiom is $N$, nonterminal $D$ stands for a binary string (integer or fractional part), and $B$ stands for a bit. In the second column we see the semantic functions or rules, which compute the following attributes:

---

[13] This historical example by D. Knuth introduced [30] attribute grammars as a systematization of compiler design techniques used by practitioners.

| *attribute* | *domain* | *nonterminals possessing the attribute* |
|---|---|---|
| $v$, value | decimal number | $N, D, B$ |
| $l$, length | integer | $D$ |

A semantic function needs the *support* of a production, but several functions may be supported by the same production. Productions 1, 4, and 5 support one function while productions 2 and 3 support two functions.

**Table 6.2** Attribute grammar of example 6.31.

| *syntax* | *semantic functions* | | *comment* |
|---|---|---|---|
| $N \to D \bullet D$ | $v_0 := v_1 + v_2 \times 2^{-l_2}$ | | add integer to fractional value divide by weight $2^{l_2}$ |
| $D \to DB$ | $v_0 := 2 \times v_1 + v_2$ | $l_0 := l_1 + 1$ | compute value and length |
| $D \to B$ | $v_0 := v_1$ | $l_0 := 1$ | |
| $B \to 0$ | $v_0 := 0$ | | value initialization |
| $B \to 1$ | $v_0 := 1$ | | |

Notice the subscript of attribute instances, such as $v_0, v_1, v_2, l_2$, on the first row of the grammar. A subscript cross-references the grammar symbol possessing that attribute, in accordance with the following stipulation:[14]

$$\underbrace{N}_{0} \to \underbrace{D}_{1} \bullet \underbrace{D}_{2}$$

stating that $v_0$ is associated with the left part $N$, $v_1$ with the first nonterminal of the right part, etc. However, if in a production a nonterminal symbol occurs exactly once, as $N$ in the first production, the more expressive notation $v_N$ can be used instead of $v_0$, without confusion.

The first semantic rule assigns to attribute $v_0$ a value computed by the expressions containing the attributes $v_1, v_2, l_2$, the function arguments. We can write in functional form:

$$v_0 := f(v_1, v_2, l_2)$$

We explain how to compute the meaning of a given source string. First we construct its syntax tree, then for each node we apply a function supported by the corresponding production. Functions are first applied to the nodes such that the arguments of their functions are available. The computation terminates when all the attributes have been evaluated.

[14] Alternatively, a more verbose style is used in other texts, e.g.,for the first function: $v$ *of* $N$ instead of $v_0$.

The tree is then said to be *decorated* with attribute values. The decorated tree, representing the translation or semantics of source text $10 \bullet 01$, is shown in Figure 6.10.

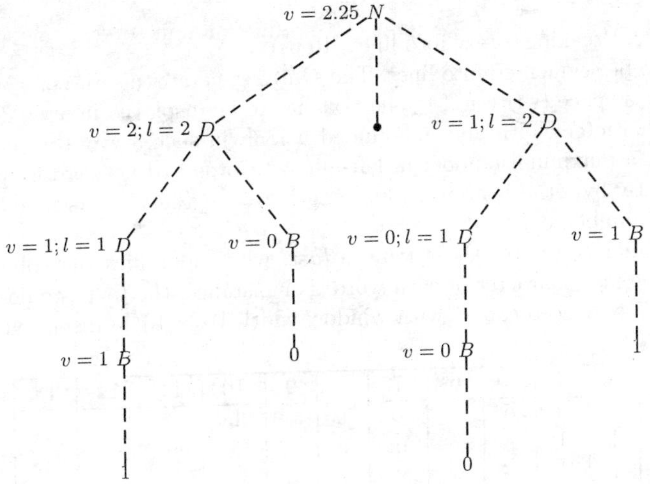


**Fig. 6.10** Decorated syntax tree of example 6.31.

There are several possible orders or schedules for attribute evaluation: for a schedule to be valid, it must satisfy the condition that no function $f$ is applied before the functions returning the arguments of $f$.

In this example the final result of semantic analysis is an attribute of the root, $v = 2.25$. The other attributes act as intermediate results. The root attribute is then the *meaning* of the source text $10 \bullet 01$.

## 6.6.2 Left and Right Attributes

In the grammar of example 6.31, attribute computation essentially flows from bottom to top because an attribute of the left part (father) of a production is defined by a function having as arguments some attributes of the right part (siblings). But in general, considering the relative positions of symbols in the supporting production, the result and arguments of a semantic function may occur in various positions, to be discussed.

Consider a function supported by a production and assigning a value to an attribute (result). We name *left* (or *synthesized*) the attribute if it is associated with the left part of the production. Otherwise, if the result is associated with a symbol of the right part of the production, we say it is a *right* (or *inherited*[15]) attribute. By the previous definition, also the arguments of a function can be classified as left or right, with respect to the supporting production.

To illustrate the classification we show a grammar featuring both left and right attributes.

*Example 6.32.* Breaking a text into lines (Reps)
A text has to be segmented into lines. The syntax generates a series of words separated by a space (written $\perp$). The text has to be displayed in a window having $W$ character width and unbounded height, in such a way that each line contains a maximum number of left-aligned words and no word is split across lines. By hypothesis no word has length greater than $W$. Assume the columns are numbered 1 to $W$.

The grammar computes the attribute *last*, which identifies the column number of the last character of each word. For instance, the text "no doubt he calls me an outlaw to catch" with window width $W = 13$, is displayed as follows:

| 1 | 2 | 3 | 4 | 5 | 6 | 7 | 8 | 9 | 10 | 11 | 12 | 13 |
|---|---|---|---|---|---|---|---|---|---|---|---|---|
| n | o | | d | o | u | b | t | | h | e | | |
| c | a | l | l | s | | m | e | | a | n | | |
| o | u | t | l | a | w | | t | o | | | | |
| c | a | t | c | h | | | | | | | | |

Variable *last* takes value 2 for word no, 8 for doubt, 11 for he, ..., and 5 for catch.
The syntax generates lists of words separated by a blank space. The terminal symbol $c$ represents any character. To compute the text layout, we use the following attributes:

*length*, the length of a word (left attribute);
*prec*, the column of the last character of the preceding word (right attribute);
*last*, the column of the last character of the current word (left attribute).

To compute attribute *last* for a word, we must first know the column of the last character of the preceding word, denoted by attribute *prec*. For the first word of the text, the value of *prec* is set to -1.

Attribute computation is expressed by the rules of the attribute grammar in Table 6.3. Two remarks on the syntax: first, the subscripts of nonterminal symbols are added as reference for the semantic functions, but they do not differentiate the syntactic classes; i.e., the productions with and without subscripts are equivalent. Second, the syntax has an ambiguity caused by production $T \rightarrow T \perp T$, which is bilaterally recursive. But the drawbacks an ambiguous syntax has for parsing do not concern us here, because the semantic evaluator receives exactly one parse tree to work on. The ambiguous syntax is more concise, and this reduces also the number of semantic rules.

---

[15] The word *inherited* is used by object-oriented languages in a totally unrelated sense.

**Table 6.3** Attribute grammar of example 6.32.

| *syntax* | *right attributes* | *left attributes* |
|---|---|---|
| 1 $S_0 \to T_1$ | $prec_1 := -1;$ | |
| 2 $T_0 \to T_1 \bot T_2$ | $prec_1 := prec_0$ | |
| | $prec_2 := last_1$ | $last_0 := last_2$ |
| 3 $T_0 \to V_1$ | | $last_0 :=$ if $(prec_0 + 1 + length_1) \leqslant W$ then $(prec_0 + 1 + length_1)$ else $length_1$ |
| 4 $V_0 \to cV_1$ | | $length_0 := length_1 + 1$ |
| 5 $V_0 \to c$ | | $length_0 := 1$ |

The length of a word $V$ is assigned to left attribute *length* in the rules associated with the last two productions. Attribute *prec* is a right one, because the value is assigned to a symbol of the right part of the first two productions. Attribute *last* is a left one; its value decorates the nodes with label $T$ of a syntax tree and provides the final result in the root of the tree.

In order to choose a feasible attribute evaluation schedule, let us examine the dependencies between the assignment statements for a specific syntax tree. In Figure 6.11 the left and right attributes are respectively placed to the left and the right of a node; the nodes are numbered for reference. To simplify drawing, the subtrees of $V$ are omitted, but attribute *length*, which is the relevant information, is present with its value.

The attributes of a decorated tree can be viewed as nodes of another directed graph, the (data) *dependence graph*. For instance, observe arc $last(2) \to prec(4)$: it represents a dependence of the latter attribute from the former, induced by function $prec_2 := last_1$, which is supported by production 2. A function result has as many dependence arcs as it has arguments. Notice the arcs interconnect only attributes pertaining to the same production.

To compute the attributes, the assignments must be executed in any order satisfying the precedences expressed by the dependence graph. At the end, the tree is completely decorated with all the attribute values.

An important quality of the attribute evaluation process is that the result is independent of the application order of functions. This property holds for grammars complying with certain conditions, to be considered soon.

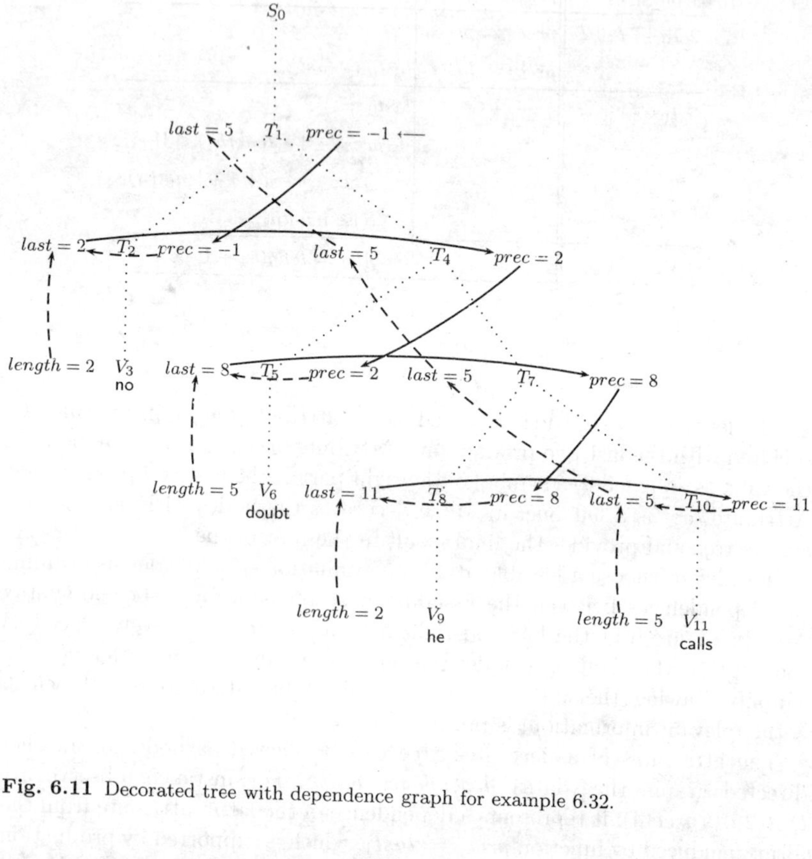


**Fig. 6.11** Decorated tree with dependence graph for example 6.32.

## Usefulness of Right Attributes

This grammar uses both left and right attributes, so the questions arise: can we define the same semantics without using right attributes (as we did in the first example of attribute grammar)? And then, is it convenient to do so?

The first answer is yes, since we show the position of the last letter of a word can be computed by a different approach. Initially compute the left attribute *length*, then construct a new left attribute *list*, having as domain a list of integers representing word lengthes. In Figure 6.11, node $T_7$, which covers the text he calls, would have the attribute $list =< 2, 5 >$. After processing all the nodes, the value *list* in the subroot $T_1$ of the tree is available, $list =< 2, 5, 2, 5 >$. It is then straightforward, knowing the page width $W$, to compute the position of the last character of each word.

But this solution is fundamentally bad, because the computation required at the root of the tree has essentially the same organization and complexity as the original text segmentation problem: nothing has been gained by the syntax-directed approach, since the original problem has not been decomposed into simpler subproblems.

Another drawback is that information is now concentrated in the root, rather than distributed on all nodes, as in the previous grammar, by means of the right attribute *last*.

Finally, to counterbalance the suppression of right attributes, it is often necessary to introduce nonscalar attributes, such as lists or sets, or other complex data structures.

In conclusion, when designing an attribute grammar the most elegant and effective design is often obtained relying on both left and right attributes.

### 6.6.3 Definition of Attribute Grammar

It is time to formalize the concepts introduced by previous examples.

**Definition 6.33.** An *attribute grammar* $H$ is defined as follows.

1. A context-free syntax $G = (V, \Sigma, P, S)$, where $V$ and $\Sigma$ are the terminal and nonterminal sets, $P$ the production set, and $S$ the axiom. It is convenient to avoid the presence of the axiom in the right parts of productions.
2. A set of symbols, the (semantic) *attributes*, associated with nonterminal and terminal syntax symbols. The set of attributes associated with symbol $D$ is denoted $attr(D)$.
   The attribute set of a grammar is partitioned into two disjoint subsets, the *left attributes* and the *right attributes*.
3. Each attribute $\sigma$ has a *domain*, the set of values it may take.
4. A set of *semantic functions* (or rules). Each function is associated with a production
   $$p:\ D_0 \to D_1 D_2 \ldots D_r, \quad r \geqslant 0$$
   where $D_0$ is a nonterminal and the other symbols can be terminal or nonterminal. The production is the syntactic *support* of the function. In general, several functions may have the same support.
   Notation: the attribute $\sigma$ associated with a symbol $D_k$ is denoted by $\sigma_k$, or also by $\sigma_D$ if the syntactic symbol occurs exactly once in production $p$.
   A function has the form:
   $$\sigma_k := f\left(attr\left(\{D_0, D_1, \ldots, D_r\}\right) \setminus \{\sigma_k\}\right)$$
   where $0 \leqslant k \leqslant r$ ; the function assigns to attribute $\sigma$ of symbol $D_k$ the value computed by the function body; the arguments of $f$ can be any attributes of the same production $p$, excluding the result of the function.

Usually the semantic functions are total functions in their domains. They are written in a suitable notation, termed *semantic metalanguage*, such as a programming language or a higher level specification language, which can be formal, or informal as a pseudo-code.
A function $\sigma_0 := f(\ldots)$ defines an attribute, qualified as *left*, of the nonterminal $D_0$, which is the left part (or father) of the production.
A function $\sigma_k := f(\ldots)$ with $k \geqslant 1$, defines an attribute qualified as *right*, of a symbol (sibling) $D_k$ occurring in the right part.
It is forbidden (as stated in 2.) for the same attribute to be left in a function and right in another one.
Notice that since terminal characters never occur in the left part, their attributes cannot be of the left type.[16]
5. Consider the set $fun(p)$ of all the functions supported by production $p$. They must satisfy the following conditions:

   a. for each left attribute $\sigma_0$ of $D_0$, there exists in $fun(p)$ exactly one function defining the attribute;
   b. for each right attribute $\delta_0$ of $D_0$, no function exists in $fun(p)$ defining the attribute;
   c. for each left attribute $\sigma_i$, where $i \geqslant 1$, no function exists in $fun(p)$ defining the attribute;
   d. for each attribute $\delta_i$, where $i \geqslant 1$, there exists in $fun(p)$ exactly one function defining the attribute.

   The left attributes $\sigma_0$ and right ones $\delta_i$ with $i \geqslant 1$, are termed *internal* for production $p$, because they are defined by functions supported by $p$. The right attributes $\delta_0$ and left attributes $\sigma_i$ with $i \geqslant 1$, are termed *external* for production $p$, because they are defined by functions supported by other productions.
6. Some attributes can be initialized with constant values or with values computed by external functions. This is often the case for the so-called lexical attributes, those associated with terminal symbols. For such attributes the grammar does not specify a computation rule.

*Example 6.34.* We refer again to example 6.32 (p. 302) where attributes are classified as follows:

left attributes: *length, last*
right attributes: *prec*
internal/external: for production 2 the internal attributes are $prec_1, prec_2$, and $last_0$; the external ones are $prec_0, last_0$, and $last_2$ (attribute *length* is not pertinent to production 2).

[16] In practice, the attributes of terminal symbols are often not defined by semantic functions of the grammar, but are initialized with values computed during lexical analysis, which is the scanning process preceding parsing and semantic analysis.

Then we have

$$attr(T) = \{prec, last\} \qquad attr(V) = \{length\} \qquad attr(S) = \emptyset$$

A caution against misuse of not local attributes. Item 4. expresses a sort of *principle of locality* of semantic functions: it is an error to designate as argument or result of a semantic function supported by $p$, an attribute which is not pertinent to production $p$. An instance of such error occurs in the modified rule 2 below:

| *syntax* | *semantic function* |
|---|---|
| 1 $S_0 \to T_1$ | ... |
| 2 $T_0 \to T_1 \bot T_2$ | $prec_1 := prec_0 + \underbrace{length_0}_{\text{non- pertinent attr.}}$ |
| 3 ... | |

Here the principle of locality is violated because $length \notin attr(T)$: any attribute of a node, other than the father or a sibling, is out of scope.

The rationale of the condition that left and right attributes be disjoint sets is discussed next. Each attribute of a node of the syntax tree must be defined by exactly one assignment, otherwise it may take two or more different values depending on the order of evaluation, and the meaning of the tree would not be unique. To prevent this, the same attribute may not be left and right, because in that case there would be two assignments, as shown in the fragment:

| *support* | *function* |
|---|---|
| 1 $A \to BC$ | $\sigma_C := f_1(attr(A, B))$ |
| 2 $C \to DE$ | $\sigma_C := f_2(attr(D, E))$ |

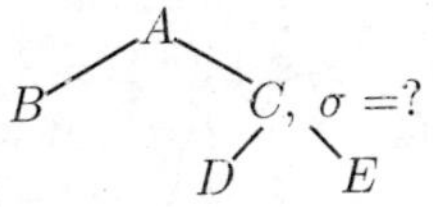


Clearly variable $\sigma_C$, internal for both productions, is a right attribute in the former, a left one in the latter. Therefore the final value it takes will depend on the order of function applications. Then the semantics loses the most desirable property of being independent of the implementation of the evaluator.

### 6.6.4 Dependence Graph and Attribute Evaluation

An advantage of a grammar as a specification of a translation is that it does not get involved with details of tree traversing procedures. In fact, the attribute evaluation program can be automatically constructed, starting from the functional dependencies between attributes, knowing of course the bodies of the semantic functions.

To prepare for that, we introduce the *dependence graph of a semantic function*: the nodes of this directed graph are the arguments and result and there is an arc from each argument to the result. Collecting the dependence graphs for all functions supported by the same production, we obtain the *dependence graph of a production*.

*Example 6.35.* Dependence graph of productions
We reproduce from p. 303 in Figure 6.12 the grammar of example 6.32. For clarity we lay each graph over the supporting production (dotted edges), to evidence the association between attributes and syntactic components. Production 2 is the most complex, with three semantic functions, each one

Grammar:

| *syntax* | *right attributes* | *left attributes* |
|---|---|---|
| 1 $S_0 \to T_1$ | $prec_1 := -1;$ | |
| 2 $T_0 \to T_1 \bot T_2$ | $prec_1 := prec_0$ | |
| | $prec_2 := last_1$ | $last_0 := last_2$ |
| 3 $T_0 \to V_1$ | | $last_0 :=$ if $(prec_0 + 1 + length_1) \leqslant W$ then $(prec_0 + 1 + length_1)$ else $length_1$ |
| 4 $V_0 \to cV_1$ | | $length_0 := length_1 + 1$ |
| 5 $V_0 \to c$ | | $length_0 := 1$ |

Dependence graph of production 2:

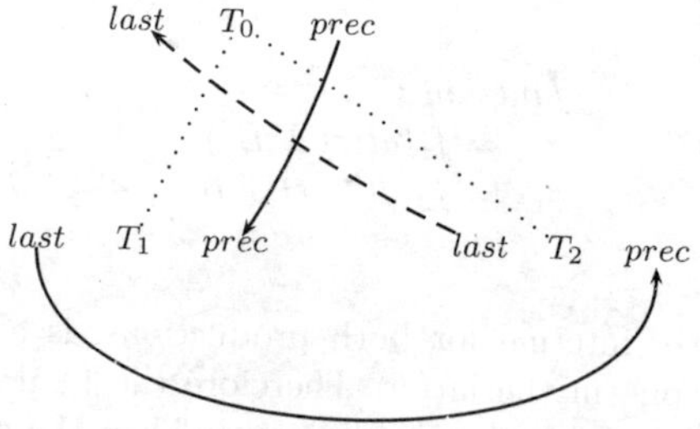


Dependence graphs of the remaining productions:

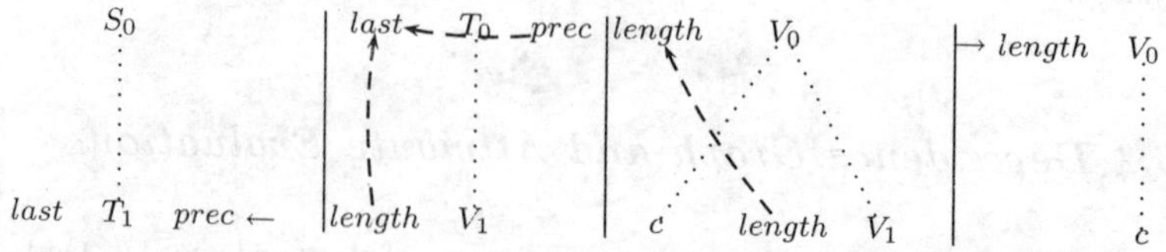


**Fig. 6.12** Grammar of example 6.32 and dependence graphs of productions.

with just one argument, hence one arc (visually differentiated by the style) of the graph.

Notice a node with (respectively without) incoming arcs is an attribute of type internal (respectively external).

The *dependence graph of a (decorated) syntax tree*, already introduced, is obtained by pasting together the graphs of the individual productions used in the tree nodes. For example, look back at Figure 6.11 on p. 304.

## Attribute Values as Solution of Equations

We expect each sentence of a technical language to have exactly one meaning, i.e., a unique set of values assigned to the semantic attributes; otherwise we would be faced with an undesirable case of semantic ambiguity.

We know the values are computed by assignments and there is exactly one assignment per instance of attribute in the tree. We may view the set of assignments as a system of simultaneous equations, where the unknowns are the attribute values. From this perspective, the system solution is the meaning of the sentence.

For a sentence, consider now the attribute dependence graph of the tree, and suppose it contains a directed path

$$\sigma_1 \rightarrow \sigma_2 \rightarrow \ldots \rightarrow \sigma_{j-1} \rightarrow \sigma_j, \quad \text{with } j > 1$$

where each $\sigma_k$ stands for some attribute instance. The attribute names of the instances can be the same or different. The corresponding equations are

$$\begin{aligned} \sigma_j &= f_j(\ldots, \sigma_{j-1}, \ldots) \\ \sigma_{j-1} &= f_{j-1}(\ldots, \sigma_{j-2}, \ldots) \\ &\ldots \\ \sigma_2 &= f_2(\ldots, \sigma_1, \ldots) \end{aligned}$$

since the result of a function is an argument of the next one.
For instance, in Figure 6.11 on p. 304 one such path is

$$prec(T_1) \rightarrow prec(T_2) \rightarrow last(T_2) \rightarrow prec(T_4) \rightarrow prec(T_5) \rightarrow \ldots$$

Revisiting the previous examples of decorated trees, it would be easy to verify that, for any sentence and syntax tree, no path of the dependence graph ever makes a circuit, to be formalized next.

A *grammar* is *acyclic* if, for each sentence, the dependence graph of the tree[17] is acyclic.

*Property 6.36.* Given an attribute grammar satisfying the conditions of definition 6.33, consider a syntax tree. If the attribute dependence graph of

17 We assume the parser returns exactly one syntax tree per sentence.

the tree is acyclic, the system of equations corresponding to the semantic functions has exactly one solution.

To prove the property, we show that, under the acyclicity condition, the equations can be ordered in such a way that any semantic function is applied after the functions which compute its arguments. This produces a value for the solution since the functions are total. The solution is clearly unique, as in a classical system of simultaneous linear equations.

Let $G = (V, E)$ be an acyclic directed graph, and identify the nodes by numbers $V = \{1, 2, \ldots, |V|\}$. The next algorithm computes a total order of nodes, called *topological*. The result, $ord[i]$, is the vector of sorted nodes: it gives the identifier of the node that has been assigned to the $i$-th position in the ordering.

*Algorithm.* Topological sorting.

```
begin
    m := 1; -- node counter
    while V ≠ ∅
    do
    n :=  any node of V having no incoming arc;
              -- node n exists because G is acyclic
    remove node n from V;
              ord[m] := n; m := m + 1;
              -- insert n in the ordering and increment counter
    E := E \ {outgoing arcs from node n};
    end do
end
```

In general many different topological orders are possible, because the dependence graph typically does not enforce a total order relation.

*Example 6.37.* Applying the algorithm to the graph of Figure 6.11 on p. 304, we obtain a topological order:

$$length_3, length_6, length_9, length_{11}, prec_1, prec_2, last_2, prec_4,$$
$$prec_5, last_5, prec_7, prec_8, last_8, prec_{10}, last_{10}, last_7, last_4, last_1.$$

Next we apply the semantic functions in topological order. Pick the first node, its equation is necessarily constant, i.e., it initializes the result attribute. Then proceed by applying the next equations in the order, which guarantees availability of all arguments. Since all functions are total, a result is always computed. The tree is thus progressively decorated with a unique set of values. Therefore for an acyclic grammar the meaning of a sentence is a single-valued function.

Actually the above evaluation algorithm is not very efficient, because on one hand it requires computing the topological sort, on the other hand, it may require multiple visits of the same node of the syntax tree. We are going to consider more efficient, although less general, algorithms, operating under the assumption of a fixed order of visit (scheduling) of the tree nodes.

Now consider what happens if the dependence graph of a tree contains a path that makes a circuit, implying that in

$$\sigma_1 \to \sigma_2 \to \ldots \to \sigma_{j-1} \to \sigma_j,\ j > 1$$

two elements $i$ and $k$ with $1 \leqslant i < k \leqslant j$, are identical, i.e., $\sigma_i = \sigma_k$. Then the system of equations may have more than one solution, i.e., the grammar may be semantically ambiguous.

A remaining problem is how to check whether a given grammar is acyclic: how can we be sure that no decorated syntax tree will ever present a closed dependence path? Since the source language is usually infinite, the acyclicity test cannot be performed by the exhaustive enumeration of the trees. An algorithm to decide if an attribute grammar is acyclic exists but is complex,[18] and not used in practice. It is more convenient to test certain sufficient conditions, which not only guarantee the acyclicity of a given grammar, but also permit constructing the attribute evaluation schedule, to be used by the semantic analyzer. Some simple yet practical conditions are described next.

### 6.6.5 One Sweep Semantic Evaluation

A fast evaluator should compute the attributes of each tree node with a single visit, or at worst, with a small number of visits of the nodes. A well-known order of visit of a tree, the *depth-first* traversal, permits in many cases evaluation of the attributes with just one sweep over the tree.

Let $N$ be a node of a tree and $N_1, \ldots, N_r$ its siblings; denote by $t_i$ the subtree rooted in node $N_i$.

A depth-first visit algorithm first visits the root of the tree. Then, in order to visit the generic subtree $t_N$, rooted in a node $N$, it recursively proceeds as follows. It performs a depth-first visit of the subtrees $t_1, \ldots, t_r$, in an order, not necessarily coincident with the natural one $1, 2, \ldots r$, i.e., according to some permutation of $1, 2, \ldots r$.

When a node is visited, the local attributes are computed. This semantic evaluation algorithm, termed *one-sweep*, computes attributes according to the following principles:

- before entering and evaluating subtree $t_N$, it computes the right attributes of node $N$ (the root of the subtree);
- at the end of visit of subtree $t_N$, it computes the left attributes of $N$.

---

18 See [30, 31]. The asymptotic time complexity is $NP$-complete with respect to the size of the attribute grammar.

We hasten to say that not all grammars are compatible with this algorithm, because more intricate functional dependencies may require several visits of the same node. The appeal of this method is that it is very fast, and that practical, sufficient conditions for one-sweep evaluation are simple to state and to check on the dependence graph $dip_p$ of each production $p$.

Experience with grammar design indicates it is often possible to satisfy the one-sweep conditions, sometimes with minor changes to the original semantic functions.

### One-Sweep Grammars

For each production

$$p: \; D_0 \to D_1 D_2 \ldots D_r, \quad r \geqslant 0$$

we need to define a binary relation between the syntactic symbols of the right part, to be represented in a directed graph, called the *sibling graph*, denoted $sibl_p$. The idea is to summarize the dependencies between the attributes of the semantic functions supported by the production. The nodes of the sibling graph are the symbols $\{D_1, D_2, \ldots, D_r\}$ of the production. The sibling graph has an arc

$$D_i \to D_j \text{ with } i \neq j \text{ and } i, j \geqslant 1$$

if in the dependence graph $dip_p$ there is an arc $\sigma_i \to \delta_j$ from an attribute of symbol $D_i$ to an attribute of symbol $D_j$.

We stress that the nodes of the sibling graph are not the same as the nodes of the dependence graph of the production: the former are syntactical symbols, the latter are attributes. Clearly all attributes of $dip_p$ having the same subscript $j$ are coalesced into a node $D_j$ of $sibl_p$: in mathematical terms, the sibling graph is related to the dependence graph by a node homomorphism.

**Definition 6.38.** One-sweep grammar.
A grammar satisfies the one-sweep condition if, for each production

$$p: \; D_0 \to D_1 D_2 \ldots D_r, \qquad r \geqslant 0$$

having dependence graph $dip_p$, the following clauses hold:

1. $dip_p$ contains no circuit;
2. $dip_p$ does not contain a path

$$\lambda_i \to \ldots \to \rho_i, \; i \geqslant 1$$

that goes from a left attribute $\lambda_i$ to a right attribute $\rho_i$ of the same symbol $D_i$, where $D_i$ is a sibling;
3. $dip_p$ contains no arc $\lambda_0 \to \rho_i, i \geqslant 1$, from a left attribute of the father node $D_0$ to a right attribute of a sibling $D_i$;

4. the sibling graph $sibl_p$ contains no circuit.

We orderly explain each item.

1. This condition is necessary for the grammar to be acyclic (a requirement for ensuring existence and uniqueness of meaning).
2. If we had a path $\lambda_i \to \ldots \to \rho_i, i \geqslant 1$, it would be impossible to compute the right attribute $\rho_i$ before visiting subtree $t_i$, because the value of the left attribute $\lambda_i$ is available only after the visit of the subtree. This contravenes the depth-first visit order we have opted for.
3. As in the preceding item, the value of attribute $\rho_i$ would not be available when we start visiting the subtree $t_i$.
4. This condition permits to topologically sort the siblings, i.e., the subtrees $t_1, \ldots, t_r$, and to schedule their visit in an order consistent with the precedences expressed by $dip_p$. If the sibling graph had a circuit, there would be conflicting precedence requirements on the order of visiting the sibling subtrees. In that case it would be impossible to find a schedule valid for all the attributes of the right part of $p$.

*Algorithm.* Construction of one-sweep evaluator.
We write a semantic procedure for each nonterminal symbol, having as arguments the subtree to be decorated and the right attributes of its root. The procedure visits the subtrees and computes and returns the left attributes of the root (of the subtree).

For each production

$$p: D_0 \to D_1 D_2 \ldots D_r, \qquad r \geqslant 0$$

1. Choose a topological order, denoted $TOS$, of the nonterminals $D_1$, $D_2$, $\ldots, D_r$ with respect to the sibling graph $sibl_p$.
2. For each symbol $D_i, 1 \leqslant i \leqslant r$, choose a topological order, denoted $TOR$, of the right attributes of symbol $D_i$ with respect to the dependence graph $dip_p$.
3. Choose a topological order, denoted $TOL$, of the left attributes of symbol $D_0$, with respect to the dependence graph $dip_p$.

The three orders $TOS, TOR$, and $TOL$ together prescribe how to arrange the instructions in the body of the semantic procedure, to be illustrated in the coming example.

*Example 6.39.* One-sweep semantic procedure
For brevity we consider a grammar fragment containing just one production and we leave the semantic functions unspecified. Production $D \to ABC$ has the dependence graph *dip* shown in Figure 6.13. It is straightforward to check the graph satisfies conditions 1., 2., and 3. of definition 6.38:

1. there are neither circuits,
2. nor any path from a left attribute $\lambda_A, \lambda_B$, or $\lambda_C$ to a right attribute, such as $\rho_B$, of the same node;

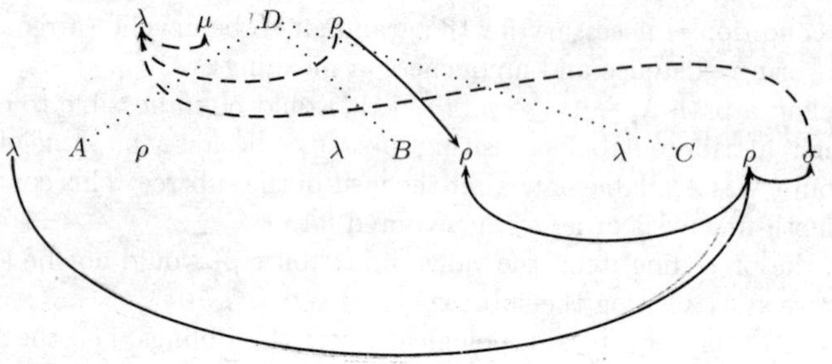


**Fig. 6.13** Dependence graph of the production of example 6.39.

3. nor any arc from a left attribute $\lambda_D$ or $\mu_D$ to a right attribute of $A, B$, or $C$;
4. the sibling graph *sibl*, below, is acyclic:

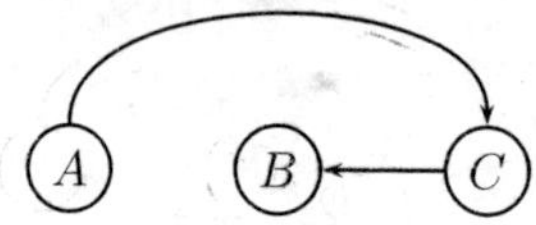


We explain where its arcs come from:

- $A \to C$ from dependence $\lambda_A \to \rho_C$;
- $C \to B$ from dependence $\rho_C \to \rho_B$.

Next we compute the topological orders.

- sibling graph: $TOS = A, C, B$;
- right attributes of each sibling: since $A$ and $B$ have only one right attribute, the topological sorting is trivial; for $C$ we have $TOR = \rho, \sigma$;
- left attributes of $D$: the topological order is $TOL = \lambda, \mu$.

To complete the design, it remains to list the instructions of the semantic procedure of this production, in an order compatible with the chosen topological orders.

More precisely, the order of left attribute assignments is $TOL$, the order of procedure invocations (to evaluate subtrees) is $TOS$, and the order of right attribute assignments is $TOR$.

*procedure* $D(in\ t, \rho_D; out\ \lambda_D, \mu_D)$
*begin*
-- $t$ root of subtree to be decorated
$\rho_A := f_1(\rho_D)$
-- abstract functions are denoted $f_1, f_2$, etc.;
$A(t_A, \rho_A; \lambda_A)$
-- invocation of $A$ to decorate subtree $t_A$;
$\rho_C := f_2(\lambda_A)$
$\sigma_C := f_3(\rho_C)$
$C(t_C, \rho_C, \sigma_C; \lambda_C)$
-- invocation of $C$ to decorate subtree $t_C$;
$\rho_B := f_4(\rho_D, \rho_C)$
$B(t_B, \rho_B; \lambda_B)$
-- invocation of $B$ to decorate subtree $t_C$;
$\lambda_D := f_5(\rho_D, \lambda_B, \lambda_C)$
$\mu_D := f_6(\lambda_D)$
*end*

To conclude, this simple method is very useful for designing an efficient recursive semantic evaluator, provided the grammar satisfies the one-sweep condition.

### 6.6.6 Other Evaluation Methods

One-sweep evaluation is practical, but some grammars have complicated dependencies which prevent its use. More general classes of evaluators and corresponding grammar conditions are available, which we do not discuss.[19]

To expand the scope of one-sweep evaluation methods, we develop a rather intuitive idea. The evaluation process is decomposed into a cascade of two or more phases, each one of the one-sweep type, operating on the same syntax tree.

We describe the method focussing on two phases, but generalization is straightforward. The attribute set *Attr* of the grammar is partitioned by the designer into two disjoint sets $Attr_1 \cup Attr_2 = Attr$, to be respectively evaluated in phase one and two. Each attribute set, together with the corresponding semantic functions, can be viewed as an attribute *subgrammar*.

Next we have to check that the first subgrammar satisfies the general conditions 6.33 (p. 305) as well as the one-sweep condition 6.38 (p. 312). In particular, the general condition imposes that every attribute is defined by some semantic function, as a consequence no attribute of set $Attr_1$ may

[19] Among them we mention the evaluators based on multiple visits, ordered attribute grammar (OAG) condition, and absolutely acyclicity condition. A survey of evaluation methods and grammar conditions is in Engelfriet [19].

depend on any attribute of set $Attr_2$; otherwise it would be impossible to evaluate the former attribute in phase one.

Then we construct the one-sweep semantic procedures for phase one, exactly as we would have done for a one-sweep grammar. After phase one execution, all the attributes in $Attr_1$ have a value, and it remains to evaluate the attributes of the second set.

For phase two we have again to check whether the second subgrammar meets the same conditions. Notice, however, that for the second evaluator, the attributes of set $Attr_1$ are considered as initialized constants. This means the dependencies between elements of $Attr_1$ and between an element of $Attr_1$ and an element of $Attr_2$ are disregarded, when checking the conditions. In other words, only the dependencies inside $Attr_2$ need to be considered. The phase two evaluator operates on a tree decorated with the attributes of the first set, and computes the remaining attributes in one-sweep.

The crucial point for multi-sweep evaluation to work, is to find a good partition of the attributes into two (or more) sets. Then the construction works exactly as in one-sweep. Notice not all attribute values computed in stage one have to be stored in the decorated tree produced by phase one, but only those used as arguments by semantic functions applied in the second sweep.

As a matter of fact, designing a semantic evaluator for a rich technical language is a complex task, and it is often desirable to modularize the project in order to master the difficulty. The partition of the global attribute set into subsets associated with evaluation phases offers a precious help for modularization. In practice, in many compilers the semantic analyzer is subdivided into phases of smaller complexity. For instance, the first stage analyzes the declarations of the various program entities (variables, types, classes, etc.) and the second stage processes the executable instructions of the programming language to be compiled.

### *6.6.7 Combined Syntax and Semantic Analysis*

For faster processing, it is sometimes possible and convenient to combine syntax tree construction and attribute computation, trusting the parser with the duty to invoke the semantic functions.

There are three typical situations for consideration, depending on the nature of the source language:

- the source language is regular: lexical analysis with lexical attributes;
- the source syntax is $LL(k)$ : recursive descent parser with attributes;
- the source syntax is $LR(k)$: shift-reduce parser with attributes.

Next we discuss the enabling conditions for such combined syntax-semantic processors.

## Lexical Analysis with Attribute Evaluation

The task of a *lexical analyzer* (or *scanner*) is to segment the source text into the lexical elements, called *lexemes* or tokens, such as identifiers, integer or real constants, comments, etc. Lexemes are the smallest substrings which can be invested with some semantic property. For instance, in many languages the keyword *begin* has the property of opening a compound statement, whereas its substring *egin* has no meaning.

Each technical language uses a finite collection of *lexical classes*, as the ones just mentioned. A lexical class is a regular formal language: a typical example is the class of identifiers (example 2.27) defined by the regular expression on p. 28. A lexeme of identifier class is a sentence belonging to the corresponding regular language.

In language reference manuals we find two levels of syntactic specifications: from lower to higher, the lexical and syntactic levels. The former defines the form of the lexemes. The latter assumes the lexemes are given in the text, and considers them to be the characters of its terminal alphabet. Moreover, the lexemes may carry a meaning, i.e., a semantic attribute, which is computed by the scanner.

### Lexical Classes

Focussing on typical lexicons, we notice that some lexical classes, viewed as formal languages, have finite cardinality. Thus, the reserved keywords of a programming language make a finite or *closed* class, including for instance

$$\{begin, end, if, then, else, do, \ldots, while\}$$

Similarly, the number of arithmetic, boolean, and relational operation signs is finite.
On the contrary, identifiers, integer constants, and comments are cases of *open* lexical classes, having unbounded cardinality.

A scanner is essentially a finite transducer ($IO$-automaton) that divides the source text into lexemes, assigning an encoding to each one. In the source text lexemes are separated, depending on their classes, by blank spaces or delimiters such as `new-line`. The transducer returns the encoding of each lexeme and removes the delimiters.

More precisely, the scanner transcribes into the target string each lexeme as a pair of elements: the name, i.e., the encoding of the lexical class, and a semantic attribute, termed *lexical*.

Lexical attributes change from a class to another and are altogether missing from certain classes. Some typical cases are:

- decimal constant: the attribute is the value of the constant in base ten;
- identifier: the attribute is a key, to be used by the compiler for quickly locating the identifier in a symbol table;
- comment: a comment has no attribute, if the compilation framework does not manage program documentation, and throws away source program comments; if the compiler keeps and classifies comments, their lexical attribute is instrumental to retrieve them;
- keyword: has no semantic attribute, just a code for identification.

### Unique Segmentation

In a well-designed technical language, lexical definitions should ensure that, for any source text, the segmentation into lexemes is unique. A word of caution is necessary, for the concatenation of two or more lexical classes may introduce ambiguity. For instance, string $beta237$ can be divided in many ways into valid lexemes: a lexeme $beta$ of class $identifier$ followed by 237 of class $integer$; or an identifier $beta2$ followed by the integer 37, and so on.

In practice, this sort of concatenation ambiguity (p. 52) is often cured by imposing to the scanner the *longest prefix rule*. The rule tells the scanner to segment a string $x = uv$ into the lexemes, say, $u \in identifier$ and $v \in integer$, in such a way that $u$ is the longest prefix of $x$ belonging to class $identifier$. In the example, the rule assigns the whole string $beta237$ to class $identifier$.
By this prescription the translation is made single-valued and can be computed by a finite deterministic transducer, augmented with the actions needed to evaluate the lexical semantic attributes.

### Lexical Attributes

We have observed that some lexical classes carry a semantic attribute and different classes usually have different attribute domains. Therefore, at first glance it would seem necessary to differentiate the semantic functions for each lexical class. However, it is often preferable to unify the treatment of lexical attributes as far as possible, in order to streamline the scanner organization: remember that a scanner has to be efficient because it is the innermost loop of the compiler. To this end, each lexical class is assigned the same attribute of type string, named $ss$, which contains the substring recognized as lexeme by the scanner.

For instance, attribute $ss$ of identifier $beta237$ is just string '$beta237$' (or a pointer thereto). Then the finite transducer returns the translation

$$\langle \text{class} = identifier,\ \text{ss} = 'beta237' \rangle$$

upon recognizing lexeme *beta*237. This pair clearly contains sufficient information, to pass as argument to a later invocation of an identifier-specific semantic function. The latter looks up string *ss* in the symbol table of the program under compilation; if it is not present, it inserts the string into the table and returns its position as a semantic attribute. Notice such identifier-specific semantic function is better viewed as a part of the attribute grammar of the syntax-directed translator, rather than of the scanner.

## Attributed Recursive Descent Translator

Assume the syntax is suitable for deterministic top-down parsing. Attribute evaluation can proceed in lockstep with parsing, if the functional dependencies of the grammar obey certain additional conditions beyond the one-sweep ones.

We recall a one-sweep algorithm (p. 312) visits in depth-first order the syntax tree, traversing the subtrees $t_1, \ldots, t_r$, for the current production $D_0 \to D_1 \ldots D_r$ in an order which may be different from the natural one. The order is a topological sorting, consistent with the dependencies between the attributes of nodes $1, \ldots, r$.

On the other hand, we know a parser constructs the tree in the natural order, i.e., subtree $t_j$ is constructed after subtrees $t_1, \ldots, t_{j-1}$. It follows that, to combine the two processes we must exclude any functional dependence that would enforce an attribute evaluation order other than the natural one, as stated next.

**Definition 6.40.** $L$ condition.
A grammar satisfies condition[20] $L$ if, for each production $p: \ D_0 \to D_1 \ldots D_r$:

1. the one-sweep condition 6.38 (p. 312) is satisfied; and
2. the sibling graph $sibl_p$ contains no arc $D_j \to D_i$ with $j > i \geqslant 1$.

Notice the second clause prevents a right attribute of node $D_i$ to depend on any (left or right) attribute of a node $D_j$ placed to its right in the production. As a consequence, the natural order $1, \ldots, r$ is a topological sort of the sibling graph and can be applied to visit the sibling subtrees.

*Property 6.41.* Let a grammar be such that

- the syntax satisfies the $LL(k)$ condition, and
- the semantic rules satisfy the $L$ condition.

Then it is possible to construct a top-down deterministic parser with attribute evaluation, to compute the attributes at parsing time.

The construction, presented in the coming example, is a straightforward combination of a recursive descent parser and a one-sweep recursive evaluator.

---

20 The letter $L$ stands for left-to-right.

*Example 6.42.* Recursive descent parser with attribute evaluation
Revising example 6.31 (p. 299), we write a grammar to convert a fractional number smaller than 1, from base two to base ten. The source language is defined by the regular expression

$$L = \bullet(0 \mid 1)^*$$

The meaning of a string such as •01 is decimal number 0.25. The grammar is listed in Table 6.4. Notice the value of a bit is weighted by a negative exponent, equal to its distance from the fractional point.
The syntax, as it can be checked, is deterministic $LL(2)$.

**Table 6.4** Grammar of example 6.42.

| *syntax* | *left attributes* | *right attributes* | |
|---|---|---|---|
| $N \to \bullet D$ | $v_0 := v_1$ | $l_1 := 1$ | |
| $D \to BD$ | $v_0 := v_1 + v_2$ | $l_1 := l_0$ | $l_2 := l_0 + 1$ |
| $D \to B$ | $v_0 := v_1$ | $l_1 := l_0$ | |
| $B \to 0$ | $v_0 := 0$ | | |
| $B \to 1$ | $v_0 := 2^{-l_0}$ | | |

Attributes:

| *attribute* | *type* | *associated nonterminal symbols* |
|---|---|---|
| $v$, value | left | $N, D, B$ |
| $l$, length | right | $D, B$ |

Next we verify condition $L$, production by production.

$N \to \bullet D$: The dependence graph has one arc $v_1 \to v_0$, hence:

- there are no circuits in the graph;
- there is no path from left attribute $v$ to right attribute $l$ of the same sibling;
- in the graph there is no arc from attribute $v$ of father to a right attribute $l$ of a sibling;
- the sibling graph *sibl* has no arcs.

$D \to BD$: The dependence graph

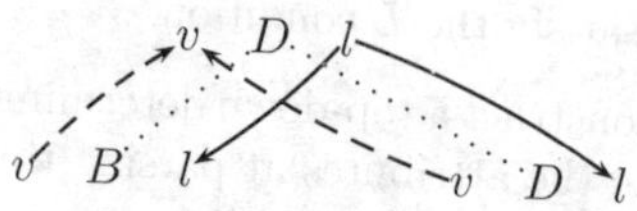


- has no circuit;
- has no path from left attribute $v$ to right attribute $l$ of the same sibling;

- has no arc from left attribute $v$ of father to right attribute $v$ of a sibling;
- the sibling graph has no arcs.

$D \to B$: same as above.
$B \to 0$: the dependence graph has no arcs.
$B \to 1$: the dependence graph has one arc $l_0 \to v_0$, which is compatible with one-sweep; there are no brothers.

Similar to a parser, the program comprises three procedures $N, D$, and $B$, having as their arguments the left attributes of the father. To implement parser look-ahead, a procedure uses two variables to store the current character $cc1$ and the next one $cc2$. Function "read" updates both variables. Variable $cc2$ determines the choice between the syntactic alternatives of $D$.

```
procedure N(in ∅; out v0)
begin
    if cc1 =' •' then read else error end if
    l1 := 1
            -- initialize a local var. with right attr. of D;
    D(l1; v0)
            -- call D to construct subtree and compute v0;
end
procedure D(in l0; out v0)
begin
    case cc2 of
    '0,1':      begin
                    -- case D → BD
                B(l0; v1)
                l2 := l0 + 1
                D(l2; v2)
                v0 := v1 + v2
                end
    '⊣':        begin
                    -- case D → B
                B(l0; v1)
                v0 := v1
                end
    otherwise   error
end
```

```
procedure B(in l0; out v0)
begin
    case cc1 of
    '0' :        v0 := 0
                 -- case B → 0
    '1':         v0 := 2^(-l0)
                 -- case B → 1
    otherwise    error
end
```

To activate the analyzer, the compiler invokes the axiom procedure.

Clearly a skilled programmer could improve in several ways the previous schematic implementation.

### Attributed Bottom-up Parser

Supposing the syntax meets the $LR(1)$ condition, we want to combine bottom-up syntax tree construction with attribute evaluation. Some problems have to be addressed: how to ensure that precedences on semantic function calls induced by attribute dependencies are consistent with the order of tree construction, when to compute the attributes, and where to store their values.

Considering first the problem of when semantic functions should be invoked, it turns out that right attributes cannot be evaluated during parsing, even assuming the grammar complies with the $L$ condition (that was sufficient for top-down evaluation in one sweep). The reason is a shift-reduce parser defers the choice of the production until it performs a reduction, when the parser is in a macro-state containing the marked production $D_0 \rightarrow D_1 \dots D_r \bullet$. This is the earliest time the parser can choose the semantic functions to be invoked.

The next problem comes from attribute dependencies. Just before reduction, the parser stack contains $r$ elements from top, which correspond to the syntactic symbols of the right part. Assuming the values of all the attributes of $D_1 \dots D_r$ are available, the algorithm can invoke the functions and return the values of the left attributes of $D_0$.

But a difficulty comes from evaluation of the right attributes of $D_1 \dots D_r$. Imagine the algorithm is about to construct and decorate the subtree of $D_1$. In accordance with one-sweep evaluation, every right attribute $\rho_{D_1}$ should be available before evaluating the subtree rooted in $D_1$. But $\rho_{D_1}$ may depend on some right attribute $\rho_0$ of the father $D_0$, which is not available, because the syntax tree does not yet contain the upper part, including the node associated with the father. The simplest way to circumvent this obstacle is to assume the grammar does not use right attributes. This ensures that the left attributes of a node will only depend on the left attributes of the siblings, which are available at reduction time.

Coming to the question of memorization, the attributes can be stored in the stack, next to the items (macro-states of the pilot machine) used by the parser. Thus each stack element is a record, made of a syntactic field and one or more semantic fields containing attribute values (or pointers to values stored elsewhere); see the next example.

*Example 6.43.* Calculating machine without right attributes
The syntax of example 5.16 (p. 222) for certain arithmetic expressions meets condition $LR(1)$. The following grammar computes the expression value $v$, or sets to true a predicate $o$ in case of overflow. Constant $maxint$ is the largest integer the calculator can represent. A character $a$ has an initialized attribute $v$ with the value of the integer constant $a$. Both attributes are left.

| *syntax* | *semantic functions* |
|---|---|
| $E \to E + T$ | $o_0 := o_1$ or $o_1$ or $(v_1 + v_2 > maxint)$<br>$v_0 :=$ if $o_0$ then $nil$ else $v_1 + v_2$ |
| $E \to T$ | $o_0 := o_1$<br>$v_0 := v_1$ |
| $T \to T \times a$ | $o_0 := o_1$ or $(v_1 \times v_2 > maxint)$<br>$v_0 :=$ if $o_0$ then $nil$ else $v_1 \times v_2$ |
| $T \to a$ | $o_0 := false$<br>$v_0 := value(a)$ |

We trace in Figure 6.14 a computation of the pushdown machine, extended with the semantic fields. The source sentence is $a_3 + a_5$, where the subscript of a constant is its value. When the parser terminates, the stack contains attributes $v$ and $o$ of the root of the tree.

### Right Attributes Independent of Father

Actually, prohibition to use right attributes may badly complicate the task of writing an attribute grammar. Attribute domains and semantic functions may turn less simple and natural, although in principle we know any translation can be specified without using right attributes.

Grammar expressivity improves if right attributes are readmitted, although with the following limitation on their dependencies.

**Definition 6.44.** Condition $A$[21] for bottom-up evaluation.
For each production $p : D_0 \to D_1 \dots D_r$

1. the $L$ condition (p. 319) for top-down evaluation is satisfied, and
2. no right attribute $\rho_{D_k}$, $1 \leqslant k \leqslant r$, of a sibling depends on a right attribute $\sigma_{D_0}$ of the father.

21 The letter $A$ stands for ascending order.

| Stack | String |
|---|---|
| $I_0$ | $a_3 + a_5 \dashv$ |
| $I_0 \; a_3 \; I_4$ | $+ \; a_5 \dashv$ |
| $I_0 \; T \; (v=3, \; o=\mathit{false}) \; I_5$ | $+ \; a_5 \dashv$ |
| $I_0 \; E \; (v=3, \; o=\mathit{false}) \; I_1$ | $+ \; a_5 \dashv$ |
| $I_0 \; E \; (v=3, \; o=\mathit{false}) \; I_1 + I_2$ | $a_5 \dashv$ |
| $I_0 \; E \; (v=3, \; o=\mathit{false}) \; I_1 + I_2 \; a_5 \; I_4$ | $\dashv$ |
| $I_0 \; E \; (v=3, \; o=\mathit{false}) \; I_1 + I_2 \; T \; (v=5, \; o=\mathit{false}) \; I_3$ | $\dashv$ |
| $I_0 \; E \; (v=3+5=8, \; o=\mathit{false})$ | $\dashv$ |

**Fig. 6.14** Shift-reduce parsing with attribute evaluation for example 6.43.

Positively stated, the same condition becomes: a right attribute $\rho_{D_k}$ with $1 \leqslant k \leqslant r$, may only depend on the right or left attributes of symbols $D_1 \dots D_{k-1}$.

If a grammar meets the $A$ condition, the left attributes of nonterminal symbols $D_1, \dots, D_r$ are available when a reduction is executed. Thus the remaining attributes can be computed in the order:

1. right attributes of the same nonterminal symbols, in the order $1, 2, \dots, r$;
2. left attributes of father $D_0$.

Notice this order differs from the scheduling of top-down evaluation, in that right attributes are computed later, during reduction.

Finally we observe that this delayed evaluation gives more freedom to compute the right attributes in an order other than the natural left-to-right order necessarily applied by top-down parsers. This would allow to deal with more involved dependencies between the nodes of the sibling graph (p. 312), similarly to one-sweep evaluators.

### 6.6.8 Typical Applications of Attribute Grammars

Syntax-directed translation is widely applied in compiler design. Attribute grammars provide a convenient and modular notation for specifying the large number of local operations, without actually getting into compiler implementation. Since it would be too long to describe with some degree of completeness the semantic analysis operations for a programming language, we simply present in a schematic manner some typical interesting parts. Actually, it is the case that the semantic analysis of programming languages comprises rather repetitive parts, and it would not add to a conceptual understanding of compilation to spell out them in detail.

We selected for presentation the following: semantic checks, code generation, and the use of semantic information for making parsing deterministic.

### Semantic Checks

The formal language $L_F$ defined by the syntax is just a gross approximation by excess to the actual programming (or technical) language $L_T$ to be compiled, that is, the set inclusion holds $L_F \supset L_T$. The left member is a context-free language, while the right one is informally defined by the language reference manual. Formally speaking, $L_T$ belongs to a more complex language family, the context-sensitive. Without repeating the reasons presented at the end of Chapter 3, a context-sensitive syntax cannot be used in practice and formalization must be contented with the context-free approximation.

To touch the nature of such approximations, imagine a programming language $L_T$. The sentences of $L_F$ are syntactically correct, yet they may violate many prescriptions of the language manual, such as type compatibility between the operands of an expression, agreement between actual and formal parameters of a procedure, and consistence between a variable declaration and its use in an instruction.

A good way to check such prescriptions is by means of semantic rules returning boolean attributes called *semantic predicates*. A given source text violates a semantic prescription, if the corresponding semantic predicate turns out false after attribute evaluation. Then the compiler reports a corresponding error, referred to as a *static semantic error*.

In general, semantic predicates functionally depend on other attributes representing various program properties. For an example, consider the agreement between a variable declaration and its use in an assignment statement. In the program, declaration and use are arbitrarily distant substrings, therefore the compiler must store the type of the declared variable in an attribute, called *symbol table* or *environment*. This attribute will be propagated along the syntax tree, to reach any node where the variable is used, in an assignment or another statement. Such propagation is, however, just fiction, because, if performed by copying the table, it would be too inefficient. In practice, the environment is implemented by a global data structure (or object), which is in the scope of all concerned semantic functions.

The next attribute grammar schematizes the creation of a symbol table and its use for checking the variables used in assignment statements.

*Example 6.45.* Symbol table and type checking
The example covers declarations of scalar and vectorial variables to be used in assignments. For the sake of the example, we assume the following semantic prescriptions have to be enforced:

1. a variable may not be multiply declared;
2. a variable may not be used before declaration;
3. the only valid assignments are between scalar variables and between vectors of identical dimension.

The attribute grammar is in Table 6.5. The syntax, in rather abstract form, distinguishes variable declarations from uses.

The symbol table is searched using as key the name $n$ of a variable. For each declared variable the table contains a descriptor $descr$ with the type (scalar or vector) and, if relevant, the dimension of the vector. During construction, the table is hosted by attribute $t$. Predicate $dd$ denounces a double declaration; predicate $ai$ type incompatibility between the left and right parts of an assignment.

Attribute $t$ is propagated to the whole tree for local controls to take place. A summary of attributes follows:

| *attribute* | *type* | *associated symbols* |
|---|---|---|
| $n$, variable name | left | $id$ |
| $v$, constant value | left | $const$ |
| $dd$, bool., double declaration | left | $D$ |
| $ai$, bool., incompatibility | left | $D$ |
| $descr$, descriptor | left | $D, L, R$ |
| $t$, symbol table | right | $A, P$ |

The semantic analyzer processes a declaration $D$ and sets to true predicate $dd$, if the declared variable is already present in the symbol table. Otherwise the variable descriptor is constructed and passed to the father node, together with the variable name.

The left and right part $L$ and $R$ of an assignment $A$ have attribute $descr$ (descriptor) that specifies the type of each part: variable (subscripted or not) or constant. If a name does not exist in the symbol table, the descriptor is assigned an error code.

For an assignment, the semantic rules control type compatibility and return predicate $ai$. The control that left and right parts of an assignment are compatible is specified in pseudo-code: the error conditions listed in items 2. and 3. make the predicate true.

For instance, in the syntactically correct text

$$\overbrace{a[10]}^{D_1}\quad \overbrace{i}^{D_2}\quad \overbrace{b}^{D_3}\quad \overbrace{i := 4}^{A_4}\quad \overbrace{c := a[i]}^{A_5:ai=true}\quad \overbrace{c[30]}^{D_6}\quad \overbrace{i}^{D_7:dd=true}\quad \overbrace{a := c}^{A_8:ai=true}$$

**Table 6.5** Grammar for checking variable declaration versus use in assignments (example 6.45).

| *syntax* | *semantic functions* |
|---|---|
| $S \to P$ | $t_1 := \emptyset$ -- initially empty table |
| $P \to DP$ | $t_1 := t_0$ -- propagate table<br>$t_2 := insert(t_0, n_1, descr_1)$<br>-- add name and descr. to table |
| $P \to AP$ | $t_1 := t_0$<br>$t_2 := t_0$<br>-- propagate table to both subtrees |
| $P \to \varepsilon$ | |
| $D \to id$ | -- scalar variable declaration<br>$dd_0 := present(t_0, n_{id})$<br>if $\neg dd_0$ then $descr_0 := 'sca'$<br>$n_0 := n_{id}$ |
| $D \to id[const]$ | -- vector variable declaration<br>$dd_0 := present(t_0, n_{id})$<br>if $\neg dd_0$ then $descr_0 := ('vect', v_{const})$<br>$n_0 := n_{id}$ |
| $A \to L := R$ | $t_1 := t_0$<br>$t_2 := t_0$<br>-- propagate table to both subtrees<br>$ai_0 := \neg\langle descr_1$ is compatible with $descr_2\rangle$ |
| $L \to id$ | $descr_0 :=<$ type of $n_{id}$ in $t_0 >$ |
| $L \to id[id]$ | if $\langle$ type of $n_{id_1}$ in $t_0\rangle =' vect' \wedge \langle$ type of $n_{id_2}$ in $t_0\rangle =' sca'$ then<br>$descr_0 := \langle$ descr. of $n_{id_1}$ in $t_0\rangle$ else *error* |
| $R \to id$ | -- use of scalar/vector variable<br>$descr_0 := \langle$type of $n_{id}$ in $t_0\rangle$ |
| $R \to const$ | -- use of constant<br>$descr_0 :=' sca'$ |
| $R \to id[id]$ | -- use of subscripted variable<br>if $\langle$ type of $n_{id_1}$ in $t_0\rangle =' vect' \wedge \langle$ type of $n_{id_2}$ in $t_0\rangle =' sca'$ then<br>$descr_0 := \langle$ descr. of $n_{id_1}$ in $t_0\rangle$ else *error* |

semantic errors have been detected in assignments $A_5$, $A_8$ and in declaration $D_7$.

Many improvements and addition would be needed for a real compiler; we mention a few.

To make diagnostic more accurate, it is preferable to separate various error classes (undefined variable, incompatible type, wrong dimension, ...).

The compiler must tell the programmer the position (line number) of each error occurrence. By enriching the grammar with other attributes and functions it is not difficult to improve on diagnostic and error identification. In particular, any semantic predicate, when it returns true in some tree position, can be propagated towards the tree root, together with a node coordinate.

Then in the root another semantic function will be in charge of writing comprehensive and readable error messages.

Other semantic errors are not covered by this example: for instance the check that each variable is initialized before its first use in an expression; or that, if it is assigned a value, it is used in some other statement. For such controls, compilers adopt a more convenient method instead of attribute grammars, called *static program analysis*, to be described at the end of this chapter.

Finally, a program having passed all semantic controls in compilation may still produce *dynamic or run-time errors* when executed. See for instance the fragment

$$\text{array } a[10];\ \dots\ read(i);\ a[i] := \dots$$

The read instruction may assign to variable $i$ a value which falls out of interval $1 \dots 10$, a condition clearly not detectable in compilation.

### Code Generation

Since the final product of compilation is to translate a source program to a sequence of target instructions, their selection is an essential part of the process. The problem occurs in different settings and connotations, depending on the nature of the source and target languages, and on the distance between them. If the differences between the two languages are small, the translation can be directly produced by the parser, as we have seen in Section 6.5.1 (p. 277) for the conversion from infix to polish notation of arithmetic expressions.

On the other hand, it is much harder to translate a high-level language, say *Java*, to a machine language, and the large distance between the two makes it convenient to subdivide the translation process into a cascade of simpler phases. Each phase translates an *intermediate language* or *representation* to another one. The first stage takes *Java* as source language, the last phase produces machine code as target language. Compilers have used quite a variety of intermediate representations: textual representations in polish form, trees or graphs, representations similar to assembly language, etc.

An equally important goal of decomposition is to achieve *portability* with respect to the target and source language. In the first case, portability (also called *retargeting*) means the ease of modifying an existing compiler, when it is required to generate code for a different machine. In the second case, the modification comes from a change in the source language, say, from *Java* to *FORTRAN*. In both cases some phases of a multi-phase compiler are independent of the source or target languages, and can be reused at no cost.

The first phase is a syntax-directed translator, guided by the syntax of say *Java*. The following phases select machine instructions and transform the program, in order to maximize speed of target program execution, to minimize memory occupation, or, in some cases, to reduce electric energy consumption.[22] Notice the first phase or phases of a compiler are essentially independent of the characteristic of the target machine; they comprise the so-called *front-end*.

The last phases are machine dependent and are called the *back-end* compiler. The back-end actually contains several subsystems, including at least a machine code selection module and a machine register allocation one. The same front-end compiler is usually interfaced to several back-end compilers, each one oriented towards a specific target machine.

The next examples offer a taste of the techniques involved in translating from high-level to machine level instructions, in the very simple case of control instructions. In a programming language, control statements prescribe the order and choice of instructions to be executed. Constructs like *if then else* and *while do* are translated by the compiler to conditional and unconditional jumps. We assume the target language offers a conditional instruction 'jump-if-false' with two arguments: a register $rc$ containing the test condition, and the label of the instruction to jump to.

In the syntax, the nonterminal $L$ stands for a list of instructions. Clearly each jump instruction requires a fresh label that differs from already used labels: the translator needs an unbounded supply of labels. To create such new labels when needed, the compiler invokes a function $fresh$ that assigns a new label to attribute $n$ at each invocation.

The translation of a construct is accumulated in attribute $tr$, by concatenating (sign $\bullet$) the translations of constituents, and inserting jump instructions with newly created labels. Labels have the form $e397, f397, i23, \ldots$, where the integer suffix is the number returned by function $fresh$.

Register $rc$ is designated by the homonymous attribute of nonterminal *cond*.

We illustrate with conditional and iterative instructions.

*Example 6.46.* Conditional instruction
The grammar of conditional instructions $I$ is in Table 6.6. For brevity we omit the translation of a boolean condition *cond*, and of other language constructs. A complete compiler should include grammar rules for all of them.

We exhibit the translation of a program fragment, assuming the label counter is set to $n = 7$:

| | |
|---|---|
| if $a > b$ | $tr(a > b)$; |
| then $a := a - 1$; | jump-if-false rc, e7 ; $tr(a := a - 1)$; jump f7 ; |
| else $a := b$; | e7 : $tr(a := b)$; |
| | f7 : -- rest of program |

[22] Code selecting phases are often designed using specialized algorithms based on the recognition of patterns on an intermediate tree representation. For an introduction to such methods see, e.g.,[1] or [4].

**Table 6.6** Grammar for translating conditional instructions to jumps (example 6.46).

| *syntax* | *semantic functions* |
|---|---|
| $F \to I$ | $n_1 := fresh$ |
| $I \to$ if *cond* then $L_1$ else $L_2$ | $tr_0 := tr_{cond}$ • jump-if-false $rc_{cond}$, e • $n_0$• $tr_{L_1}$ • jump f • $n_0$• e • $n_0$• : $tr_{L_2}$• f • $n_0$• : |

Remember that $tr(\ldots)$ is the machine language translation of a construct. Register $rc$ is not chosen here, but when the compiler translates expression $a > b$.

Next we show the translation of a loop.

*Example 6.47.* Iterative instructions
The grammar for a *while do* statement, shown in Table 6.47, is quite similar and does not need comments. It suffices to display the translation of a program fragment (assuming function $fresh$ returns value 8):

| | |
|---|---|
| while $(a > b)$ do | i8: $tr(a > b)$; |
| | jump-if-false rc, f8; |
| $a := a - 1$; | $tr(a := a - 1)$ ; |
| | jump i8; |
| end while | f8: -- rest of program |

**Table 6.7** Grammar for translating *while do* instructions to jumps (example 6.47).

| *syntax* | *semantic functions* |
|---|---|
| $F \to W$ | $n_1 := fresh$ |
| $W \to$ while *cond* do $L$ end | $tr_0 :=$ i • $n_0$• : •$tr_{cond}$• jump-if-false $rc_{cond}$, f • $n_0$• $tr_L$ • jump i • $n_0$; f • $n_0$• : |

Other iterative and conditional statements require a similar set of compiler rules.

However, the straightforward translations obtained are often inefficient and need improvement, which is done by the optimizing phases of the compiler.[23]

[23] The optimizer is by far the most complex and expensive part of a modern compiler; the reader is referred to, e.g.,[4, 38, 1].

A trivial example is the condensation of a chain of unconditional jumps into a single jump instruction.

### Semantics-Directed Parsing

In a standard compilation process, we know parsing comes before semantic analysis; the latter operates on the syntax tree constructed by the former. But in some circumstances, syntax is ambiguous and parsing cannot be successfully executed on its own, because it would produce too many trees thus puzzling the semantic evaluator. Actually this danger concerns just a few technical languages, because the majority are designed so that their syntax is deterministic. But in natural language processing the change of perspective is dramatic, because the syntax of human languages by itself is very ambiguous.

We are here considering the case when the reference syntax of the source language is indeterministic or altogether ambiguous, so that a deterministic look-ahead parser cannot produce a unique parse of the given text. A synergic organization of syntax and semantic analysis permits overcoming this difficulty, as explained next.

Focusing on artificial rather than natural languages, a reasonable assumption is that no sentence is semantically ambiguous, i.e., that every valid sentence has a unique meaning. Of course this does not exclude a sentence from being syntactically ambiguous. But then the uncertainty between different syntax trees can be solved at parsing time, by collecting and using semantic information as soon as it is available.

For top-down parsing, we recall the critical decision is the choice between alternative productions, when their $LL(k)$ guide sets (p. 182) overlap on the current input character. Now we propose to help the parser to solve the dilemma by testing a semantic attribute termed a *guide predicate*, which supplements the insufficient syntactic information. Such predicate has to be computed by the parser, which is enhanced with the capability to evaluate the relevant attributes.

Notice this organization resembles the multi-sweep attribute evaluation method described on p. 315. The whole set of semantic attributes is divided in two parts assigned for evaluation to cascaded phases. The first set includes the guide predicates and the attributes they depend on; this set must be evaluated in the first phase, during parsing. The remaining attributes may be evaluated in the second phase, after the, by now unique, syntax tree has been passed to the phase two evaluator.

We recall the requirements for the first set of attributes to be computable at parsing time: the attributes must satisfy the $L$ condition (p. 319). Consequently the guide predicate will be available, when it is needed for selecting one of the alternative productions, for expanding a nonterminal $D_i$, $1 \leqslant i \leqslant r$, in production $D_0 \to D_1 \ldots D_i \ldots D_r$. Since the parser works depth-first from left to right, the part of the syntax tree from the root down to the subtrees $D_1 \ldots D_{i-1}$ is then available.

Following condition $L$, the guide predicate may only depend on the right attributes of $D_0$, and on other (left or right) attributes of any symbol, which in the right part of the production precedes the root of the subtree $D_i$ under construction.

The next example illustrates the use of guide predicates.

*Example 6.48.* A language without punctuation marks
The syntax of the historical Pascal-like language PLZ-SYS[24] did without commas and any punctuation marks, thus causing many syntactic ambiguities, in particular, in the parameter list of a procedure. In this language a parameter is declared with a type, and more parameters may be grouped together by type.

Procedure $P$ contains five identifiers in its parameter list, which can be interpreted in three ways:

$$P \text{ proc } (X\ Y\ T1\ Z\ T2) \begin{cases} 1.\ X \text{ has type } Y; T1, Z \text{ have type } T2; \\ 2.\ X, Y \text{ have type } T1; Z \text{ has type } T2; \\ 3.\ X, Y, T1, Z \text{ have type } T2. \end{cases}$$

Insightfully, the language designers prescribed that type declarations must come before procedure declarations. If, for instance, the type declarations occurring before the declaration of procedure $P$ are

$$\text{type } T1 \text{ record } \ldots \text{ end} \quad \text{type } T2 = \text{ record } \ldots \text{ end}$$

then case 1. is excluded, because $Y$ is not a type, and $T1$ is not a variable. Similarly case 3. is excluded, and the ambiguity is solved.

It remains to be seen how the knowledge of preceding type declarations can be incorporated into the parser, to direct the choice between the several possible cases.

Within the declarative section $D$ of language PLZ-SYS, we need to consider just two parts of the syntax: the type declarations $T$, and the procedure heading $I$ (we need not concern us here with procedure bodies). Semantic rules for type declarations will insert type descriptors into a symbol table $t$, managed as a left attribute. As in earlier examples, $n$ is the name or key of an identifier.

Upon termination of type declaration analysis, the symbol table is distributed toward the subsequent parts of the program, and, in particular, to procedure heading declarations. For downward and rightward propagation, the left attribute $t$ is (conceptually) copied into a right attribute $td$. Then the descriptor $descr$ of each identifier allows the parser to choose the correct production.

---

[24] Designed in the 1970s for an 8-bit microprocessor with minimal memory resources.

To keep the example small, we make drastic simplifications: the scope (or visibility) of declared entities is global to the entire program; every type is declared as a record not further specified; we omit control of double declarations; we do not insert in the symbol table the descriptors for declared procedures and their arguments.

The grammar fragment is listed in Table 6.48.

Nonterminal $V$ has two alternatives that violate the $LL(2)$ condition, because

**Table 6.8** Grammar for using type declaration for disambiguation (example 6.48).

| *syntax* | *semantic functions* |
|---|---|
| -- declarative part<br>$D \to TI$ | $td_I := t_T$<br>-- symbol table is copied |
| -- type declaration<br>$T \to$ type $id$ = record... end $T$ | $t_0 := insert(t_2, n_{id}, 'type')$<br>-- descr. inserted in table |
| $T \to \varepsilon$ | $t_0 := \emptyset$ |
| -- proc. heading<br>$I \to id$ proc $(L)$ $I$ | $td_L := td_0$<br>$td_3 := td_0$<br>--table is passed to $L$ and to $I \equiv 3$ |
| $I \to \varepsilon$ | |
| -- parameter list<br>$L \to V$ *type_id* $L$ | $td_V := td_0$<br>$td_3 := td_0$ |
| $L \to \varepsilon$ | |
| --var. list (having same type)<br>$V \to$ *var_id* $V$ | $td_1 := td_0$<br>$td_2 := td_0$ |
| $V \to$ *var_id* | $td_1 := td_0$ |
| *type_id* $\to id$ | |
| *var_id* $\to id$ | |

type and variable identifiers are syntactically undistinguishable:

$V \to$ *var_id* $V$ : starts with *var_id var_id*, i.e., with *id id*

$V \to$ *var_id* : starts with *var_id*, that is, *id* followed by *type_id*, i.e., *id*

Next the parser is enhanced with a semantic test, allowing it to choose the correct alternative. Let $cc_1, cc_2$ respectively be the current terminal character (or rather lexeme) and the next one.

The guide predicates for each alternative are listed:

| | *production* | *guide predicate* |
|---|---|---|
| 1 | $V \to$ *var_id* $V$ | $\langle$ the descr. of $cc_2$ in table $td_0\rangle \neq$ 'type' $\wedge$ |
| 1' | | $\langle$ the descr. of $cc_1$ in table $td_0\rangle \neq$ 'type' |
| 2 | $V \to$ *var_id* | $\langle$ the descr. of $cc_2$ in table $td_0\rangle =$ 'type' $\wedge$ |
| 2' | | $\langle$ the descr. of $cc_1$ in table $td_0\rangle \neq$ 'type' |

The mutually exclusive clauses 1 and 2 act as guide predicates, to select one alternative out of 1 and 2. Clauses 1' and 2' are a semantic predicate controlling that the identifier associated with *var_id* is not a type identifier.

Furthermore, we may add a semantic predicate to production $L \rightarrow V\ type\_id\ L$, in order to check whether the sort of $type\_id \equiv cc_2$ in the table is equal to $'type'$.

In this manner the top-down parser gets help from the values of available semantic attributes and deterministically constructs the tree.

## 6.7 Static Program Analysis

In this last part of the book we describe a technique for program analysis and optimization, used by all compilers translating a programming language, and also by many software engineering tools.

Imagine the front-end compiler has translated a program to an intermediate representation closer to machine or assembly language. The intermediate program is then analyzed by other compiler phases, whose purpose and functionality differ depending on circumstances:

*verification*, to further examine program correctness;
*optimization*, to transform the program into a more efficient version, for instance by optimally assigning machine registers to program variables;
*scheduling*, to change instruction order, for a better exploitation of processor pipelines and functional units, avoiding that such resources be at times idle and at times overcommitted.

Although very different, such cases use a common representation of the program, called a *control flow graph*, similar to a program flowchart. It is convenient to view this graph as describing the state transition function of a finite automaton. Here our standpoint is entirely different from syntax-directed translation, because the automaton is not used to formally specify a programming language, but just a particular program, on which attention is focussed. A string recognized by the control flow automaton denotes a trace of execution of that program, i.e., a sequence of machine operations.

Static analysis consists of the study of certain properties of control flow graphs using various methods coming from logic, automata theory, and statistic. In our concise presentation we mainly consider the logical approach.

### 6.7.1 A Program as an Automaton

In a program control flow graph each node is an instruction. At this level instructions are usually simpler than in a high-level programming language, since they are a convenient intermediate representation produced by the front-end compiler. Further simplifying matters, we assume instruction operands are simple variables and constants (there are no aggregate data types). Typical instructions are assignments to variables, and elementary arithmetic, relational, and boolean expressions, usually with at most one operator.

In this book we only consider *intraprocedural* analysis, meaning the control flow graph describes one subprogram a time. More advanced studies are *interprocedural*: they analyze the properties of a full program involving multiple procedures and their invocations.

If execution of instruction $p$ can be immediately followed by execution of instruction $q$, the graph has an arc directed from $p$ to $q$. Thus an arc represents the immediate precedence relation between instructions: $p$ is the *predecessor* and $q$ the *successor*.

The first instruction a program executes is the *entry* point, represented by the *initial node* of the graph; for convenience we assume the initial instruction has no predecessor. On the other hand, an instruction having no successors is a program *exit* point, or *final node* of the graph.
Unconditional instructions have at most one successor. Conditional instructions have two successors (more than two for instructions such as *C* language switches). An instruction with two or more predecessors is a *confluence* of so many arcs of the graph.

A control flow graph is not a faithful program representation, but just an abstraction: it suffices for extracting the properties of interest, but some information is missing, as explained next.

- The true/false value determining the successor of a conditional instruction such as *if then else* is not represented.
- An unconditional *go to* instruction is not represented as a node, but simply as the arc to the successor instruction,
- An operation (arithmetic, reading, writing, etc.) performed by an instruction is replaced by the following abstraction:
  - a value assignment to a variable, by means of a statement such as an assignment or a reading instruction, is said to *define* that variable;
  - if a variable occurs in an expression, namely, in the right part of an assignment statement or in a boolean expression of a conditional, or in the argument list of a writing instruction, we say the statement *uses* (or makes reference to) that variable;
  - thus, in the graph, a node representing a statement $p$ is associated with two sets: the set $def(p)$ of defined variables and the set $use(p)$ of used variables.

Notice in this model the actual operation performed by a statement may be often overlooked.

Consider for instance a statement $p:\ a := a \oplus b$, where $\oplus$ is an unspecified binary operator; the instruction is represented in the control flow graph by a node carrying the information:

$$def(p) = \{a\}, \qquad use(p) = \{a, b\}$$

In this abstract model the statements $read(a)$ and $a := 7$ are undistinguishable, as they carry the same associate information: $def = \{a\}$ and $use = \emptyset$.

In order to clarify the concepts and to describe some applications of the method, we present a more complete example.

*Example 6.49.* Flowchart and control flow graph
We see in Figure 6.15 a subprogram, its flowchart, and control flow graph. In the abstract control flow graph we need not list the actual instructions, but just the sets of defined and used variables.

*program*:
$a := 1$
e1: $b := a + 2$
$c := b + c$
$a := b \times 3$
if $a < m$ goto e1
return $c$

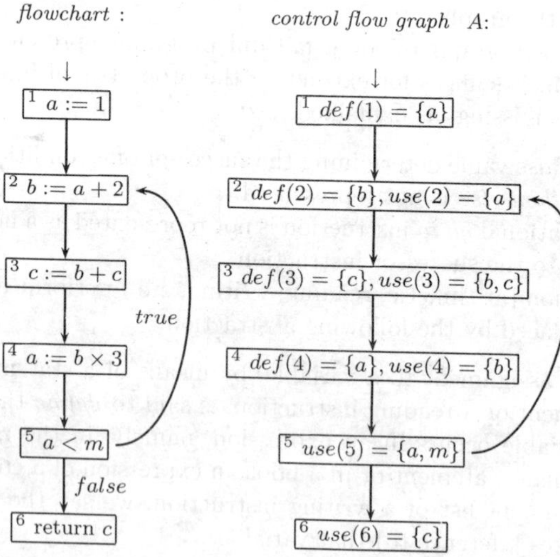


**Fig. 6.15** Program, flowchart, and abstract control flow graph of example 6.49.

Instruction 1 has no predecessors and is the subprogram entry or initial node. Instruction 6 has no successors and is the program exit or final node.

Node 5 has two successors, whereas node 2 is at the confluence of two predecessors. The sets $use(1)$ and $def(5)$ are empty.

## Language of Control Flow Graph

We consider the finite automaton $A$, represented by a control flow graph. Its terminal alphabet is the set $I$ of program instructions, each one schematized by a triple $\langle$ label, defined variables, used variables$\rangle$ such as $\langle 2, def(2) = \{b\}, use(2) = \{a\}\rangle$; for brevity sake, we often denote such instruction by the first component, i.e., the instruction *label* or number.

Notice the terminal characters are not written on the arcs but inside the nodes, as we did with the local automata studied on p. 128. Clearly all arcs entering the same node "read" the same character. The states of the automaton (as in syntax charts on p. 174) are not given an explicit name, since they are anyhow identified by the terminal character of entering arcs. The initial state is marked by an entering arrow. The final states are those without successor.

The formal language $L(A)$ recognized by the automaton contains the strings over alphabet $I$, that label a path from the entry node to an exit node. Such path denotes a sequence of instructions which may be executed when the program is run.

Clearly each node number is distinct since it corresponds to a different instruction label. This confirms that the formal language $L(A)$ belongs to the family of local languages, which are a rather restricted subset of the regular language family $REG$.

In the previous example, the alphabet is $I = \{1, 2, 3, 4, 5, 6\}$. A recognized path is

$$1 \to 2 \to 3 \to 4 \to 5 \to 2 \to 3 \to 4 \to 5 \to 6 \equiv 1234523456$$

The set of such recognized paths is the language $L(A) = 1(2345)^+6$.

## Conservative Approximations

Actually the automaton specifies only an approximation of the valid execution paths of a program. Not all recognized paths are really executable by the program, because our model disregards the boolean condition that selects a successor node of a conditional statement. A trivial example is the program

$$1: \text{ if } a ** 2 \geqslant 0 \text{ then } istr_2 \text{ else } istr_3$$

where the formal language accepted by the automaton contains two paths $\{12, 13\}$, but path 13 is not executable, because a square is never negative.

As a consequence of such approximation,static analysis may sometimes reach pessimistic conclusions: in particular, it may discover errors in a never executed path.

Of course it is in general undecidable whether a path of a control flow graph will ever be executed, because this would be equivalent to deciding whether there exists a value assignment to input variables that cause the execution of that path. The latter problem can be reduced to the halting problem of a Turing machine, which is undecidable.

As it is generally impossible to know which paths are executable or not, it would be much worse if the static analysis erred by disregarding some path that turns out to be executable, because then it may fail to detect some real errors.

In conclusion, the decision to examine all recognized paths (from the initial to a final node) is a *conservative approximation* to program analysis, which may cause the diagnosis of nonexisting errors, or the prudential assignment of unnecessary resources, but it never misses real error conditions or real resource requirements.

A usual hypothesis in static analysis is that the automaton is clean (p. 102), i.e., each instruction is on a path from the initial to a final node. Otherwise one or more of the following anomalies may occur in the program: some executions never terminate, or some instructions are never executed (the program contains so-called *unreachable code*).

### 6.7.2 Liveness Intervals of Variables

A professional compiler performs several passes of analysis over the intermediate representations of a program in order to improve it. A very interesting analysis, allowing a variety of profitable optimizations, is the study of the liveness intervals of program variables.

**Definition 6.50.** A variable $a$ is *live* on the exit from a program node $p$ if, in the control flow graph, there exists a path from $p$ to a node $q$ (not necessarily distinct from $p$) such that

- the path does not traverse an instruction $r$ with $r \neq q$ that defines $a$, i.e., such that $a \in def(r)$ $\wedge$
- instruction $q$ uses $a$, i.e., $a \in use(q)$.

For brevity we say the variable is *live out* of node $p$. In other words, a variable is live out of a certain node if some instruction, which may be successively executed, makes use of the value the variable has in the former node.

To grasp the purpose of this definition, imagine that instruction $p$ is the assignment $a := b \oplus c$ and suppose we want to know if some instruction makes use of the value assigned to $a$ in $p$. The question can be rephrased as: is $a$ live out of node $p$? If not, the assignment is *useless* and can be deleted without affecting program semantics. Furthermore, if none of the variables used by $p$ is used in some other instruction, all the instructions assigning a value to such variables may become useless, after $p$ has been deleted.

*Example 6.51.* Example 6.49 continued
For the example of Figure 6.15 on p. 336, we reproduce in Figure 6.16 the control flow graph, with the live variable sets for each arc, also referred to as a *program point*. Observe in the picture the variables which are live in each

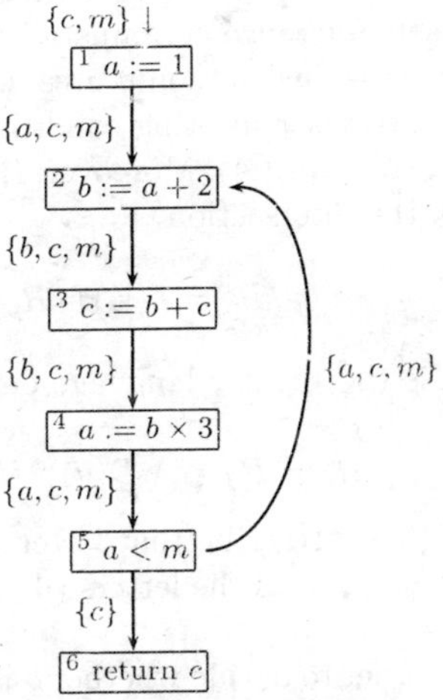


**Fig. 6.16** Control-flow graph with sets of variables live out of nodes (example 6.49).

program point. Thus variable $c$ is live on entrance to node 1 because there exists path 123, such that $c \in use(3)$, and neither 1 nor 2 defines $c$.
It is customary to say variable $a$ is live in the *intervals* (i.e., paths) 12 and 452; it is not live in the intervals 234 and 56, and so on.

More precisely we say a variable is *live-out for a node*, if it is live on any arc outgoing from the node. Similarly a variable is *live-in for a node*, if it is live on some arc entering the node. For instance, variables $\{a, c, m\} \cup \{c\}$ are live-out for node 5.

### Computing Liveness Intervals

Let $I$ be the instruction set. Let $\subseteq I$ and $U(a) \subseteq I$ respectively be the sets of instructions defining and using some variable $a$. For instance, in the running example it is $D(b) = \{2\}$ and $U(b) = \{3, 4\}$.

The liveness condition will be first expressed in terms of formal language operations, then using a more expressive set theoretical notation.

It is not difficult to see that $a$ is live-out for node $p$ if, and only if, for the language $L(A)$ accepted by the automaton, the following condition holds: $L(A)$ contains a sentence $x = upvqw$, where $u$ and $w$ are (possibly empty) arbitrary instruction sequences, $p$ is any instruction, $v$ is a possibly empty instruction sequence not containing a definition of $a$, and instruction $q$ uses $a$. The above conditions are formalized as:

$$u, w \in I^* \ \wedge \ p \in I \ \wedge \ v \in (I \setminus D(a))^* \ \wedge \ q \in U(a) \tag{6.1}$$

Observe again the set difference contains all the instructions which do not define variable $a$, whereas instruction $q$ uses $a$.

The set of all the strings $x$ meeting condition (6.1), denoted $L_p$, is a sub-language of $L(A)$, i.e., $L_p \subseteq L(A)$. Moreover, the language is regular, because it can be defined by the intersection

$$L_p = L(A) \cap R_p \tag{6.2}$$

where language $R_p$ is the regular language defined by the extended regular expression:

$$R_p = I^* p \, (I \setminus D(a))^* \, U(a) I^* \tag{6.3}$$

Formulas (6.2) and (6.3) prescribe that letter $p$ must be followed by a letter $q$ taken from $U(a)$, and that all the letters (if any) intervening between $p$ and $q$ must not belong to set $D(a)$.

It follows that, in order to decide whether $a$ is live out of $p$, one has to check that language $L_p$ is not empty. We know one way of doing it: we construct the recognizer of language $L_p$, that is, the product machine for intersection (6.2), as explained in Chapter 3 on p. 138. If this machine does not contain a path from the initial to a final state, then language $L_p$ is empty.

This procedure is not practical, when taking into account the large dimension of the real programs to be analyzed. Therefore we introduce another specialized method, which not only performs more efficiently, but it permits computing at once all live variables in all program points. The new method systematically examines all the paths from the current program point to some instruction using some variable.

The computation of liveness will be expressed by a system of *data-flow equations*. Consider a node $p$ of control-flow graph or program $A$. A first equation expresses the relation between the variables live-out $live_{out}(p)$ and those live-in $live_{in}(p)$. A second equation expresses the relation between variables live-out of a node and those live-in for its successors.

We denote by $succ(p)$ the set of the (immediate) successors of node $p$, and with $var(A)$ the set of all the variables of program $A$.

Data-flow equations:

for each final node (program exit) $p$:

$$live_{out}(p) = \emptyset \tag{6.4}$$

for any other node $p$ :

$$live_{in}(p) = use(p) \cup (live_{out}(p) \setminus def(p)) \tag{6.5}$$

$$live_{out}(p) = \bigsqcup_{\forall q \in succ(p)} live_{in}(q) \tag{6.6}$$

Comments:

- In equation (6.4) no variable is live out of the (sub)program graph. Here we have disregarded the output parameters (if any) of the subprogram, which are typically used after exit from the subprogram, and therefore may be considered to be live out of the final node, though in another subprogram.
- For equation (6.5), a variable is live-in for $p$ if it is used in $p$; or if it is live-out for $p$ but not defined by $p$.
  Consider instruction $4 : a := b \times 3$ (Figure 6.15 on p. 336). Out of 4, variables $a, m$, and $c$ are live, because for each one there exists a path that reaches a use of that variable, without traversing a node which defines the same variable. On entrance to 4, the following variables are live: $b$ because it is used in 4; $c$ and $m$ because they are live-out for 4 and not defined in 4. On the contrary, variable $a$, though live-out for 4, is not live-in for 4, because it is defined in 4.
- For equation (6.6), node 5 has successors 2 and 6; then the variables live-out for 5 are those $(a, c,$ and $m)$ live-in for 2 and the one $(c)$ live-in for 6.

## Solution of Data-Flow Equations

Given a control flow graph, it is straightforward to write the two equations for each instruction. For a graph with $|I| = n$ nodes the resulting system has $2 \times n$ equations with $2 \times n$ unknowns, $live_{in}(p)$ and $live_{out}(p)$, for every instruction $p \in I$. Each unknown is a set of variables, and the solution to be computed is a pair of vectors, each one containing $n$ sets.

To solve the systems we use iteration, taking the empty set as the initial approximation, $i = 0$, for every unknown:

$$\forall p \in I : live_{in}(p) = \emptyset; \qquad live_{out}(p) = \emptyset$$

Let $i$ be the current iteration. In each equation of system (6.5), (6.6), we replace the unknowns occurring in the right hand sides with the values of the current iteration, and thus we obtain the values of next iteration $i+1$. If at least one unknown differs from the previous iteration, we execute another iteration, otherwise we terminate, and the last vector pair computed is a solution of the system of equations.

This solution is termed the *least fixed point* of the transformation that computes a new vector from the vector of the preceding iteration.

To see why a finite number of iterations always suffices to converge to the least fixed point solution, observe the following:

- the cardinality of each set $live_{in}(p)$ and $live_{out}(p)$ is bounded by the number of program variables;
- each iteration may only add some variables to some sets or leave them unchanged, but it never removes any variable from a set; in other words, the transformation is monotonic nondecreasing with respect to set inclusion;
- if an iteration does not change any set, the algorithm terminates.

We illustrate the algorithm on the sunning example.

*Example 6.52.* Example 6.49 continued: iterative computation of live variables

First we compute by inspection the sets of instructions defining ($D$) and using ($U$) program variables:

| | $D$ | $U$ |
|---|---|---|
| $a$ | 1, 4 | 2, 5 |
| $b$ | 2 | 3, 4 |
| $c$ | 3 | 3, 6 |
| $m$ | $\emptyset$ | 5 |

Next the equations for the program (Figure 6.15 on p. 336) are written in Table 6.52.

Unknown names are shortened to $in(p)$ and $out(p)$ instead of $live_{in}(p)$and $live_{out}(p)$.

**Table 6.9** Liveness equations of the program in Figure 6.15 (example 6.52).

Equations:

| | | |
|---|---|---|
| 1 | $in(1) = out(1) \setminus \{a\}$ | $out(1) = in(2)$ |
| 2 | $in(2) = \{a\} \cup (out(2) \setminus \{b\})$ | $out(2) = in(3)$ |
| 3 | $in(3) = \{b, c\} \cup (out(3) \setminus \{c\})$ | $out(3) = in(4)$ |
| 4 | $in(4) = \{b\} \cup (out(4) \setminus \{a\})$ | $out(4) = in(5)$ |
| 5 | $in(5) = \{a, m\} \cup out(5)$ | $out(5) = in(2) \cup in(6)$ |
| 6 | $in(6) = \{c\}$ | $out(6) = \emptyset$ |

Unknowns computed at each iteration:

| | $in = out$ | $in$ | $out$ | $in$ | $out$ | $in$ | $out$ | $in$ | $out$ | $in$ | $out$ |
|---|---|---|---|---|---|---|---|---|---|---|---|
| 1 | $\emptyset$ | $\emptyset$ | $a$ | $\emptyset$ | $a, c$ | $c$ | $a, c$ | $c$ | $a, c, m$ | $c, m$ | $a, c, m$ |
| 2 | $\emptyset$ | $a$ | $b, c$ | $a, c$ | $b, c$ | $a, c$ | $b, c, m$ | $a, c, m$ | $b, c, m$ | $a, c, m$ | $b, c, m$ |
| 3 | $\emptyset$ | $b, c$ | $b$ | $b, c$ | $b, m$ | $b, c, m$ | $b, c, m$ | $b, c, m$ | $b, c, m$ | $b, c, m$ | $b, c, m$ |
| 4 | $\emptyset$ | $b$ | $a, m$ | $b, m$ | $a, c, m$ | $b, c, m$ | $a, c, m$ | $b, c, m$ | $a, c, m$ | $b, c, m$ | $a, c, m$ |
| 5 | $\emptyset$ | $a, m$ | $a, c$ | $a, c, m$ | $a, c$ | $a, c, m$ | $a, c$ | $a, c, m$ | $a, c, m$ | $a, c, m$ | $a, c, m$ |
| 6 | $\emptyset$ | $c$ | $\emptyset$ | $c$ | $\emptyset$ | $c$ | $\emptyset$ | $c$ | $\emptyset$ | $c$ | $\emptyset$ |

Then we compute and tabulate the successive approximations, starting from the empty sets; at each iteration we first compute the *in* values and then the *out* values. The least fixed point is reached after five iterations: it would be easy to verify that a further iteration would not change the last result.

It is important to note that, although the solution does not depend on the processing order of nodes, the speed of convergence to the fixed point is very sensitive to the order.

We mention the time complexity of the iterative algorithm.[25] The worst case complexity is $\mathcal{O}(n^4)$, where $n$ is the number of nodes i.e., of instructions of the subprogram. In practice, for many realistic programs the computational complexity is close to linear in time.

## Application of Liveness Analysis

We show two classical widespread applications of the previous analysis: memory allocation to variables and detection of useless instructions.

### Memory Allocation

Liveness analysis is best applied to decide if two variables can reside in the same memory cell (or in the same machine register). It is evident that if two variables are live in the same program point, both values must be present in memory when execution reaches that point, because they may have future uses. Therefore the values cannot reside in the same cell: we then say the two variables *interfere.*

Conversely, if two variables do not interfere, that is, they are never live in the same program point, the same memory cell or register can be used to keep their values.

*Example 6.53.* Interference and register assignment
In the control flow graph of Figure 6.16 on p. 339 we see variables $a, c$, and $m$ occur in the same set $live_{in}(2)$, therefore the three variables pairwise interfere. Similarly, the pairs $(b, c)$, $(b, m)$, and $(c, m)$ interfere in the set $live_{in}(3)$. On the other hand, no set contains variables $a$ and $b$, which therefore do not interfere.

As stated before, two interfering variables must reside in different memory cells. It follows each of variables $c$ and $m$ needs a separate cell, while both variables $a$ and $b$ may reside in the same cell, that must be different from the previous two cells, because $a$ interferes with $c$ and $m$. In conclusion we have found that three cells suffice to store the values of four program variables.

Current compilers optimally assign registers to program variables by heuristic methods relying on the interference relation.

---

25 For a proof refer for instance to any of [1, 4, 38].

Useless Definitions

An instruction defining a variable is *useless*, if the value assigned to the variable is never used by any instruction. This is tantamount to saying the value is not live-out for the defining instruction. Therefore, to verify that a definition of variable $a$ by an instruction $p$ is not useless, we have to check whether $a$ is present in the set $live_{out}(p)$.

The program of Figure 6.15 on p. 336 has no useless definitions, in contrast with the next example.

*Example 6.54.* Useless variable definition
Consider the program in Figure 6.17. The picture lists the live variables in and out of each instruction. Variable $c$ is not live-out for 3, hence instruction 3 is useless. Useless instructions can be erased by the compiler. The elimination of instruction 3 brings two benefits: the program is shorter and faster to execute, and variable $c$ disappears from the sets $in(1), in(2), in(3), out(5)$. This reduces interferences between variables and may bring a reduction in the number of registers needed, which is often a bottleneck for program performance.

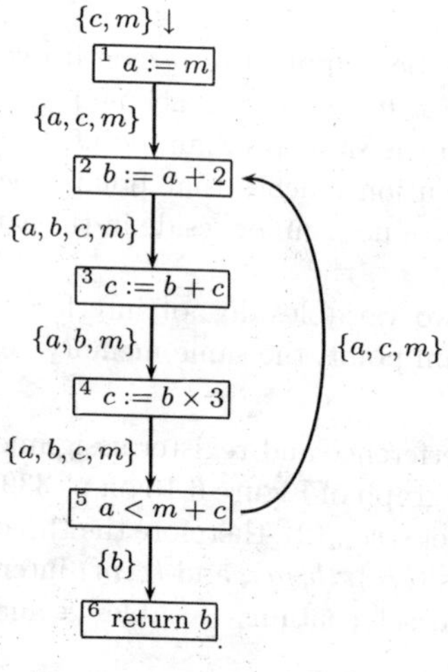


**Fig. 6.17** Control flow graph with live sets applied to detect useless definition (example 6.54).

This is an example of the frequently occurring phenomenon of chain reaction optimizations triggered by a simple program transformation.

### 6.7.3 Reaching Definitions

Another basic and widely applied type of static analysis is the search for variable definitions which reach some program point.

To introduce the idea by an application, consider an instruction assigning a constant value to variable $a$. The compiler examines the program to see if the same constant can be replaced for the variable, in the instructions using $a$. The benefit of the replacement is manyfold. First, a machine instruction having a constant as operand (so-called "immediate" operand) is often faster. Second, the substitution of a variable occurring in an expression with a constant may produce an expression where all operands are constant; the expression value can be computed at compile time, with no need to generate code for it. Lastly, since the replacement eliminates one or more uses of $a$, it shortens the liveness intervals and reduces interferences between variables; the pressure on registers is consequently reduced.

The above transformation is termed *constant propagation*. In order to develop it, we need a few conceptual definitions, which are also useful for other program optimizations and verifications.

Consider an instruction $p: \ a := b \oplus c$ that defines variable $a$. For brevity, we denote such variable definition as $a_p$, while $D(a)$ denotes the set of all the definitions of the same variable $a$ in the subprogram under analysis.

**Definition 6.55.** We say the *definition* of variable $a$ in instruction $q$, $a_q$, *reaches the entrance* of an instruction $p$, if there exists a path from $q$ to $p$, such that it does not traverse a node, distinct from $q$, which defines $a$.

When this happens, instruction $p$ may use the value of $a$ computed in $q$.

Referring to automaton $A$, i.e., to the control flow graph of the subprogram, the condition can be restated more precisely as follows. Definition $a_q$ reaches instruction $p$, if language $L(A)$ contains a sentence of the form $x = uqvpw$, where $u$ and $w$ are (possibly empty) arbitrary instruction sequences, $p$ is any instruction, $v$ is a possibly empty instruction sequence not containing a definition of $a$, and instruction $q$ defines variable $a$. The above conditions are formalized as

$$u, w \in I^* \ \wedge \ q \in D(a) \ \wedge \ v \in (I \setminus D(a))^* \ \wedge \ p \in I \tag{6.7}$$

Notice that $p$ and $q$ may coincide.

Looking again at the program reproduced in Figure 6.18 (identical to the one on p. 336), we find that definition $a_1$ reaches the entrance of instructions 2, 3, and 4 but not the entrance of instruction 5. Definition $a_4$ reaches the entrance of instructions 5, 6, 2, 3, and 4.

## Data-flow Equations for Reaching Definitions

To compute reaching definitions in all program points, we set up a system of equations similar to those for liveness analysis.

If node $p$ defines variable $a$, we say any other definition $a_q$ of the same variable in another node $q$, with $q \neq p$, is *suppressed* by $p$. Formally, the set of definitions suppressed by instruction $p$ is:

$$\begin{cases} sup(p) = \{a_q \mid q \in I \wedge q \neq p \wedge a \in def(q) \wedge a \in def(p)\}, & \text{if } def(p) \neq \emptyset \\ sup(p) = \emptyset, & \text{if } def(p) = \emptyset \end{cases}$$

Notice the set $def(p)$ may contain more than one name, in case of multiple variable defining instructions, such as the read statement "read(a,b,c)".

The sets of definitions reaching the entrance to and exit from a node $p$ are, respectively, denoted $in(p)$ and $out(p)$. The set of (immediate) predecessor nodes of $p$ is denoted $pred(p)$.

Data-flow equations:

For the initial node 1:

$$in(1) = \emptyset \tag{6.8}$$

For any other node $p \in I$ :

$$out(p) = def(p) \cup (in(p) \setminus sup(p)) \tag{6.9}$$

$$in(p) = \bigsqcup_{\forall q \in pred(p)} out(q) \tag{6.10}$$

Comments:
Equation (6.8) assumes for simplicity that no variables are passed as input parameters to the subprogram. Otherwise, more accurately, $in(1)$ should contain all the definitions, external to the subprogram, of the input parameters.
Equation (6.9) inserts into the exit from $p$ all local definitions of $p$ and the definitions reaching the entrance to $p$, provided the latter are not suppressed by $p$.
Equation (6.10) states that any definition reaching the exit of some predecessor node reaches also the entrance to $p$.

Similar to the liveness equations, the system can be solved by iteration, until the computed solution converges to the first fixed point. In the starting iteration all unknown sets are empty.

We illustrate with a program containing a loop.

*Example 6.56.* Reaching definitions
Observe in Figure 6.18 the same control flow graph of p. 336 with the reaching definition sets, computed by solving the system of equations listed below in Table 6.10.

Variables $c$ and $m$ are input parameters of the subprogram, and we may assume they are externally defined in the calling subprogram, at some unknown

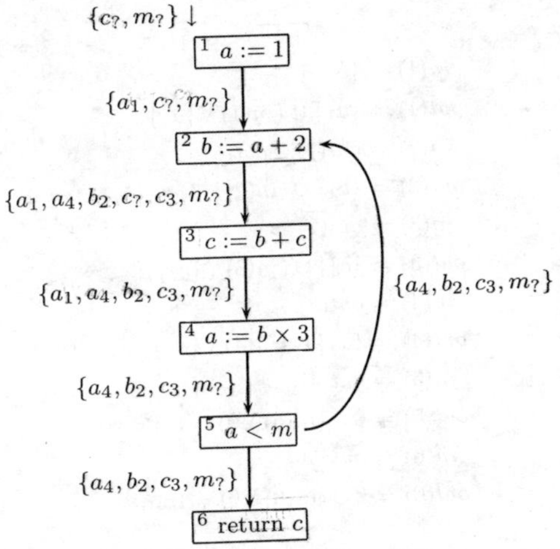


**Fig. 6.18** Control-flow graph with reaching definitions (example 6.56).

points denoted $c_?$ and $m_?$. Notice, for instance, that the external definition $c_?$ of variable $c$ does not reach the entrance of instruction 4, since it is suppressed by instruction 3.

We list the constant terms occurring in the equations:

| *node* | | *def* | *sup* |
|---|---|---|---|
| 1 | $a := 1$ | $a_1$ | $a_4$ |
| 2 | $b := a + 2$ | $b_2$ | $\emptyset$ |
| 3 | $c := b + c$ | $c_3$ | $c_?$ |
| 4 | $a := b \times 3$ | $a_4$ | $a_1$ |
| 5 | $a < m$ | $\emptyset$ | $\emptyset$ |
| 6 | return $c$ | $\emptyset$ | $\emptyset$ |

At iteration 0 all sets are empty. After a few iterations, the unknown values converge to the sets shown in Table 6.10.

### Constant Propagation

Carrying further the previous example (Figure 6.18), we look for opportunities to replace a variable by a constant value. An instance of the problem is the question: can we replace variable $a$ in instruction 2 with constant 1, assigned by instruction 1 (i.e., definition $a_1$)? The answer is negative because set $in(2)$ of reaching definitions contains another definition of $a$, namely, $a_4$, which implies that some computation may use for $a$ the value defined in instruction 4. Therefore the program containing instruction $b := 1 + 2$ instead

**Table 6.10** Data-flow equations for reaching definitions (example 6.56 in Figure 6.18).

$$
\begin{aligned}
in(1) &= \{c_?, m_?\} \\
out(1) &= \{a_1\} \cup (in(1) \setminus \{a_4\}) \\
in(2) &= out(1) \cup out(5) \\
out(2) &= \{b_2\} \cup (in(2) \setminus \emptyset) = \{b_2\} \cup in(2) \\
in(3) &= out(2) \\
out(3) &= \{c_3\} \cup (in(3) \setminus \{c_?\}) \\
in(4) &= out(3) \\
out(4) &= \{a_4\} \cup (in(4) \setminus \{a_1\}) \\
in(5) &= out(4) \\
out(5) &= \emptyset \cup (in(5) \setminus \emptyset) = in(5) \\
in(6) &= out(5) \\
out(6) &= \emptyset \cup (in(6) \setminus \emptyset) = in(6)
\end{aligned}
$$

of $b := a + 2$ would not be equivalent to the original, which is quite evident since a run can execute the loop body.

Generalizing this reasoning, it is easy to state a condition: it is legal to replace in instruction $p$, a variable $a$ used in $p$, with a constant $k$ if

1. there exists an instruction $q : a := k$, assigning constant $k$ to $a$, such that definition $a_q$ reaches the entrance of $p$ and
2. no other definition $a_r$ of variable $a$, with $r \neq q$, reaches the entrance of $p$.

We show some program improvements produced by constant propagation and by induced simplifications.

*Example 6.57.* Optimization following constant propagation
Figure 6.19 shows a simple control flow graph, and lists the reaching definition sets and the live variable sets in relevant program points. Observe the only definition of $v$ reaching the entrance of 2 is $v_1$. By the previous condition, it is legal to replace variable $v$ with constant 4 in the conditional instruction 2, which afterwards becomes the constant boolean expression $4 \times 8 \geqslant 0$. Now variable $v$ ceases to be live-out for assignment 1, which becomes useless and can be deleted.

But program simplification does not end here. The compiler can compute the value of the constant expression[26] $32 \geqslant 0 = true$, thus determining which one of the successor legs of statement 2 will be taken, say the one to the left. Then the right leg will never be taken, and can be deleted. We say instruction 4 becomes *unreachable* or *dead code*, since no computation starting in

---

[26] Anticipating to compiler time a computation is termed *constant folding*.

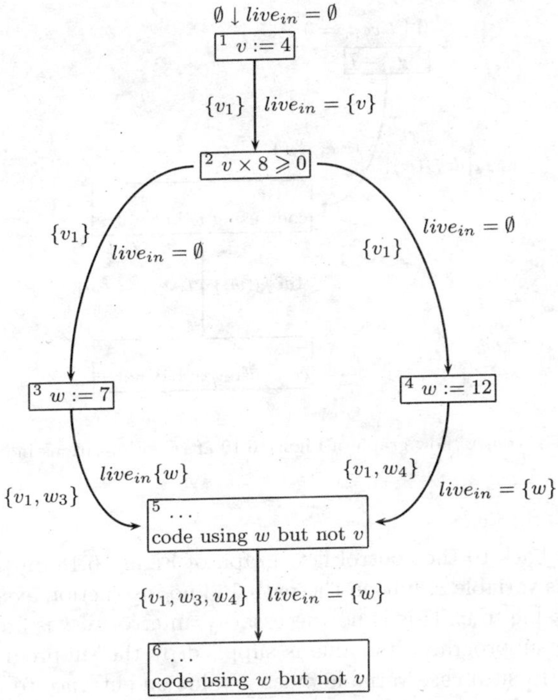


**Fig. 6.19** A control flow graph, with reaching definitions and live variables, before constant propagation (example 6.57).

the program entry will ever reach it. Now the conditional instruction 2 is redundant, and can be eliminated.

After the transformations, the simplified program is shown in Figure 6.20. Now analysis could proceed to determine if constant $w = 7$ can be legally propagated to the rest of the program.

### Availability of Variables and Initializations

A basic correctness check a compiler should perform is to control that variables are initialized before their first use. More generally, a variable used in some instruction must have on entrance to the instruction a value computed by means of a valid assignment (or by another variable defining statement). Otherwise we say the variable is not *available*, and a compiler-time error occurs.

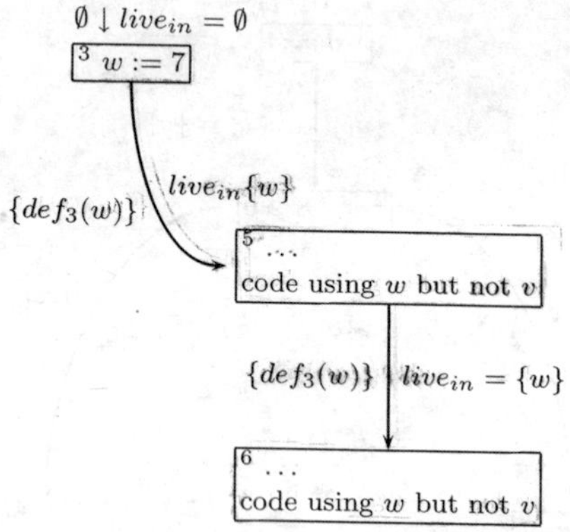


**Fig. 6.20** The control flow graph of Figure 6.19 after optimizations induced by constant propagation.

Coming back to the control flow graph of Figure 6.18 on p. 347, observe node 3 uses variable $c$, but on the path 123 no instruction executed before 3 assigns a value to $c$. This is not necessarily an error: if $c$ is an input parameter of the subprogram, its value is supplied by the subprogram invocation statement. In such case variable $c$ has a value on entrance to node 3 and no error occurs. The same discussion applies to variable $m$.

Variable $b$ is available on entrance to 3 because its value was defined in 2 by an assignment, which uses variable $a$; the latter is in turn available on entrance to 2, following initialization in 1.

This sort of reasoning becomes intricate, and we need to clarify the concept of availability. For simplicity we assume the subprogram has no input parameters.

**Definition 6.58.** A variable $a$ is *available on entrance to node* $p$, i.e., just before execution of instruction $p$, if in the control flow graph every path from the initial node 1 to the entrance of $p$, contains a statement that defines variable $a$.

Comparing this notion with the concept of reaching definitions introduced on p. 345, we notice a difference in the quantification over paths. If definition $a_q$ of variable $a$ reaches the entrance of node $p$, there exists necessarily a path from node 1 to node $p$ traversing the defining instruction $q$. But this does not guarantee that $a$ is available on entrance to $p$, because we cannot exclude that there exists another path from 1 to $p$, that avoids $q$ as well as any other node which defines variable $a$.

It follows that the condition of a variable definition being available on a node entrance is more constraining than that of the variable definition reaching the same node.

To compute the variables available on entrance to node $p$, let us examine more closely the set of definitions reaching the exits of $p$ predecessors. If, for every predecessor node $q$ of $p$, the set of reaching definitions $out(q)$ on the exit from $q$ contains (at least) one definition of variable $a$, then $a$ is available on entrance to $p$. In that case we also say that *some definition* of $a$ *always reaches* node $p$.

It is simple to convert the latter condition into an effective test that variables are correctly initialized. For an instruction $q$, the new notation $out'(q)$ denotes, as $out(q)$, the set of variable definitions reaching the exit from $q$, but with their subscripts deleted. For instance, for $out(q) = \{a_1, a_4, b_3, c_6\}$, we have $out'(q) = \{a, b, c\}$.

### Badly Initialized Variables

An instruction $p$ *is not well initialized* if the predicate holds:

$$\exists q \in pred(p) \text{ such that } \ use(p) \not\subseteq out'(q) \tag{6.11}$$

The condition says there exists a predecessor node $q$ of $p$, such that the set of definitions reaching its exit does not include all the variables used in $p$. Therefore, when program execution runs on a path through $q$, one or more variables used in $p$ do not have a value.

*Example 6.59.* Detecting uninitialized variables
Observe the control flow graph in Figure 6.21, completed with the sets of reaching definitions. Condition (6.11) is false for node 2, since for every predecessor (1 and 4) the set $out'$ contains a definition of $a$, which is the only variable used in 2.

On the other hand, the condition is true in node 3, because no definition of $c$ reaches the exit from 2. Our analysis has thus detected a program error: instruction 3 uses an uninitialized variable, $c$.

To find all the remaining initialization errors, we may proceed as follows. We replace by a dummy no-operation instruction any so far discovered erroneous instructions, such as node 3. Then we update the computation of reaching definition sets, and we reevaluate condition (6.11). By so doing, we would discover that instruction 4 is not well initialized, because definition $b_3$ although present in $out(3)$ is not really available, since instruction 3 has already been marked as ineffective. Then also instruction 4 becomes ineffective. Continuing in the same manner, no other errors would be discovered.

The previous analysis allows to catch at compile time many errors that had gone unnoticed during the preceding phases of parsing and semantic analysis,

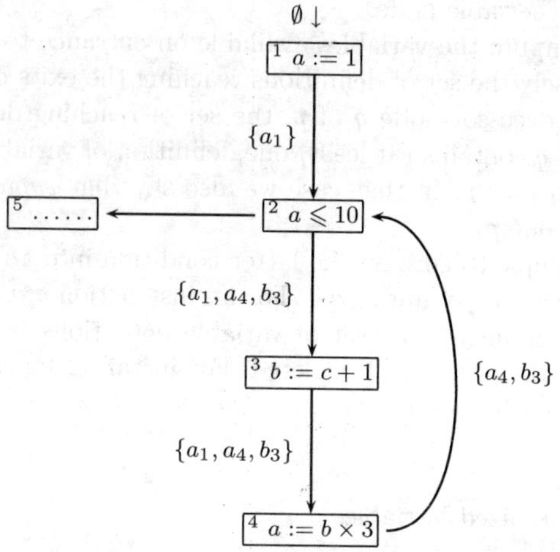


**Fig. 6.21** Control-flow graph with available variables for example 6.59.

with the benefit that they will not cause hard-to-understand runtime errors, or raise exceptions during program execution.

To conclude, static analysis[27] encompasses many more conditions and properties than the cases of liveness and reaching definitions we have been able to present. It is a powerful general method for analyzing programs before execution, in order to optimize them or to verify their correctness.

---

27 A book on the theory of static program analysis is [40]. For a survey of applications in compilation see e.g.,[1, 4, 38].

# References


1. A. Aho, M. Lam, R. Sethi, and J. Ullman, *Compilers: principles, techniques and tools*, Prentice-Hall, Englewoof Cliffs, NJ, 2006.
2. A. Aho and J. Ullman, *The theory of parsing, translation, and compiling, volume 1: parsing*, Prentice-Hall, Englewoof Cliffs, NJ, 1972.
3. ———, *The theory of parsing, translation and compiling, volume 2: compiling*, Prentice-Hall, Englewoof Cliffs, NJ, 1973.
4. A. Appel, *Modern compiler implementation in Java*, Cambridge University Press, Cambridge, UK, 2002.
5. J. Aycock and R. Horspool, *Practical Earley parsing*, Comput. J. **45** (2002), no. 6, 620–630.
6. J. Beatty, *Two iteration theorems for the LL(k) languages*, Theor. Comput. Sci. **12** (1980), 193–228.
7. G. Berry and R. Sethi, *From regular expressions to deterministic automata*, Theor. Comput. Sci. **48** (1986), no. 1, 117–126.
8. J. Berstel, *Transductions and context-free languages*, Teubner, Stuttgart, 1979.
9. J. Berstel and L. Boasson, *Formal properties of XML grammars and languages*, Acta Inform. **38** (2002), 115–125.
10. J. Berstel and J.E. Pin, *Local languages and the Berry-Sethi algorithm*, Theor. Comput. Sci. **155** (1996), no. 2, 439–446.
11. D. Bovet and P. Crescenzi, *Introduction to the theory of complexity*, Prentice-Hall, Englewood Cliffs, NJ.
12. N. P. Chapman, *LR parsing: theory and practice*, Cambridge University Press, Cambridge, UK, 1987.
13. J. Cleaveland and R. Uzgalis, *Grammars for programming languages*, North-Holland, Amsterdam, 1977.
14. S. Crespi Reghizzi, P. Della Vigna, and C. Ghezzi, *Linguaggi formali e compilatori*, ISEDI, Milano, 1976.
15. S. Crespi Reghizzi and M. Pradella, *Tile rewriting grammars and picture languages*, Theor. Comput. Sci. **340** (2005), no. 2, 257–272.
16. R. De Nicola and A. Piperno, *Semantica operazionale e denotazionale dei linguaggi di programmazione*, Utet Città Studi, Milano, 1999.
17. F. DeRemer and T. Pennello, *Efficient computation of LALR(1) look-ahead sets*, ACM Trans. Progr. Lang. and Syst. **4** (1982), no. 4, 615–649.
18. J. Earley, *An efficient context-free parsing algorithm*, Commun. ACM **13** (1970), 94–102.
19. J. Engelfriet, *Attribute grammars: Attribute evaluation methods*, Methods and tools for compiler construction (B. Lorho, ed.), Cambridge University Press, Cambridge, UK, 1984, pp. 103–138.

20. R. Floyd and R. Beigel, *The language of machines: an introduction to computability and formal languages*, Computer Science Press, New York, 1994.
21. F. Gecseg and M. Steinby, *Tree languages*, Handbook of formal languages, vol. 3: beyond words (G. Rozenberg and A. Salomaa, eds.), Springer-Verlag, New York, 1997, pp. 1–68.
22. C. Ghezzi and D. Mandrioli, *Incremental parsing*, ACM Trans. on Progr. Lang. Syst. **1** (1979), no. 1, 58–70.
23. D. Giammarresi and A. Restivo, *Two-dimensional languages*, Handbook of formal languages, vol. 3: beyond words (G. Rozenberg and A. Salomaa, eds.), Springer-Verlag, New York, 1997, pp. 215–267.
24. D. Grune and C. Jacobs, *Parsing techniques: a practical guide*, Vrije Universiteit, Amsterdam, 2004.
25. M. Harrison, *Introduction to formal language theory*, Addison Wesley, Reading, MA, 1978.
26. J. Heering, P. Klint, and J. Rekers, *Incremental generation of parsers*, IEEE Trans. Software Eng. **16** (1990), no. 12, 1344–1351.
27. S. Heilbrunner, *A direct complement construction for LR(1) grammars*, Acta Inform. **33** (1996), no. 8, 781–797.
28. J. Hopcroft and J. Ullman, *Formal languages and their relation to automata*, Addison-Wesley, Reading, MA, 1969.
29. ______, *Introduction to automata theory, languages, and computation*, Addison-Wesley, Reading, MA, 1979.
30. D. Knuth, *Semantics of context-free languages*, Math. Syst. Theory **2** (1968), no. 2, 127–145.
31. ______, *Semantics of context-free languages, errata corrige*, Math. Syst. Theory **5** (1971), no. 2, 95–99.
32. Dexter Kozen, *Theory of computation*, Springer, London, 2007.
33. J. Larchevêque, *Optimal incremental parsing*, ACM Trans. Progr. Lang. Syst. **17** (1995), no. 1, 1–15.
34. D. Mandrioli and C. Ghezzi, *Theoretical foundations of computer science*, Wiley, New York, 1987.
35. R. McNaughton, *Elementary computability, formal languages and automata*, Prentice-Hall, Englewood Cliffs, NJ, 1982.
36. R. McNaughton and S. Papert, *Counter-free automata*, MIT Press, Cambridge, MA, 1971.
37. S. Morimoto and M. Sassa, *Yet another generation of LALR parsers for regular right part grammars*, Acta Inform. **37** (2001), 671–697.
38. S. Muchnick, *Advanced compiler design and implementation*, Morgan Kaufmann, 1997.
39. P. Naur, *Revised report on the algorithmic language ALGOL 60*, Commun. ACM **6** (1963), 1–33.
40. F. Nielson, H. Nielson, and C. Hankin, *Principles of program analysis*, Springer-Verlag, New York, 2005.
41. D. Perrin and J.E. Pin, *Infinite words*, Elsevier, New York, 2004.
42. R. Quong and T. Parr, *ANTLR: A predicated-LL(k) parser generator*, Software Pract. Exp. **25** (1995), 789–810.
43. G. Révész, *Introduction to formal languages*, Dover, New York, 1991.
44. S. Rodger and T. W. Finley, *JFLAP: An interactive formal language and automata package*, Jones and Bartlett, Sudbury, MA, 2006.
45. G. Rozenberg and A. Salomaa (eds.), *Handbook of formal languages, vol. 1: word, language, grammar*, Springer-Verlag, New York, 1997.
46. J. Sakarovitch, *Éléments de théorie des automates*, Vuibert Informatique, Paris, 2003.
47. A. Salomaa, *Formal languages*, Academic Press, New York, 1973.
48. G. Senizergues, *L(A)=L(B)? A simplified decidability proof*, Theor. Comput. Sci. **281** (2002), 555–608.